Algebra:
Functions and Theory
of Equations

Algebra and Trigonometry
in four programmed volumes

I   REAL NUMBERS AND ELEMENTARY ALGEBRA

II SETS AND FUNCTIONS

III TRIGONOMETRY

IV ALGEBRA: FUNCTIONS AND THEORY OF EQUATIONS

Algebra and Trigonometry
is also available as a regular one-volume textbook

Algebra: Functions and Theory of Equations

**ALGEBRA AND TRIGONOMETRY
IN FOUR PROGRAMMED VOLUMES**

THOMAS A. DAVIS

De Pauw University

HARCOURT BRACE JOVANOVICH, INC.

New York Chicago San Francisco Atlanta

ISBN: 0-15-502154-0

Library of Congress Catalog Card Number: 73-184416

Printed in the United States of America

Preface

Algebra: *Functions and Theory of Equations* deals, in programmed form, with exponential and logarithmic functions and with polynomial functions and their zeros. This book and its three companion programmed volumes are designed for use in a variety of ways. Together, the four books constitute a basic college textbook in algebra and trigonometry. Individually, they may be used to cover a portion of the course; to supplement and reinforce another basic textbook; or to enable students, on their own, to acquire the necessary background for more advanced courses, such as calculus.

The virtues of programmed material are well known. A programmed text allows the student to proceed at his own rate, with the assurance that he has understood what he has learned. As, in part, a "self-teaching" and "self-testing" device, programming can free the instructor to use valuable class time for more advanced topics and for fuller explanation of particularly difficult concepts. Programming can also help compensate for the varying academic backgrounds students bring to their courses; each student can independently learn or review the concepts he needs to achieve the necessary level of preparation. Furthermore, I have found in my many classes at DePauw University that students enjoy working with programmed materials and profit from their use.

For instructors who like the content of the four programmed volumes but prefer a non-programmed approach, the identical material is also available as a single volume, non-programmed text, *Algebra and Trigonometry*. Some instructors will want to assign both versions, with the programmed volumes reinforcing what the student has learned from the non-programmed text. To make this dual use most effective, I have coordinated the two versions precisely: every exercise and every example in the two versions are numbered or lettered identically. But this coordination is merely a convenience and does not, of course, affect the use of the programmed volumes with any other textbook.

This book would not have been possible without the help of my wife Pat who read the material at each stage of its development. Her suggestions led to many improvements.

I also thank Dr. Michael Eraut, University of Sussex, who suggested many programming improvements, and Mrs. Patricia Gammon, who typed the many versions of the book as it evolved through testing and rewriting.

THOMAS A. DAVIS

To the Student

Programmed material such as this has the following characteristics:

(a) The subject matter is presented in carefully sequenced steps called frames.

(b) A written response is required at frequent intervals.

(c) Feedback about the correctness of the response is immediate.

To use the program effectively follow these instructions:

1. Cover the page with a piece of paper so that the frame you are working on is visible, but not its answer.

2. Read the frame carefully. Do not write your response until you have read the entire frame.

3. Make your response in the appropriate space(s) or on the appropriate diagram. If you have to solve a problem, derive a formula, or prove a theorem, put your work on a separate sheet of paper.

4. Now slide the covering paper down until the answer is visible.

5. Check your answer.

If your answer is correct, go on to the next frame and repeat steps 2 to 5. Your answer need not be exactly the same as the one provided. Use your judgment about whether your answer is close enough to the one provided. If your answer is incorrect, try to discover why, and then go on to the next frame.

The frames in each part are numbered consecutively.

Since this is not a test, it is permissible to review previous steps if necessary.

Throughout the program are so-called express frames, terminal frames, and summary pages. If you answer the question in an express frame correctly, you are told in the answer to skip the next few frames. If you do not answer correctly, you are directed to the next frame, where you will begin a sequence that will teach you the correct response. An example of an express frame is frame 119 on page 18.

Terminal frames are usually labeled "exercise" and often occur at the end of a chapter. They are used to test your knowledge of a unit of material. If you answer the terminal frame correctly, you are directed to the next frame. If you do not answer it correctly, you are told which frames to review to enable you to do so. An example of a terminal frame is frame 31 on page 6.

Summary pages occur immediately after a sequence of frames in which a formula has been derived or a theorem has been proved. The summary pages pull together the complete proof or derivation as it should appear if you were asked to prove the theorem or derive the formula. The terminal frames and summary pages should prove especially useful in reviewing the material.

Finally, a quiz containing representative questions and problems is at the end of each chapter to help you in assessing how well you have learned the material in the chapter. To use the quiz for this purpose, write out the answers and solutions in detail and check them carefully against the answers in the back of the book. Otherwise, in glancing through the quiz, you may get the impression that you understand the material in the chapter when, in fact, you do not.

Contents

Exponential and Logarithmic Functions

PART 1

In the volume on functions, we considered functions and their inverses in some detail; the illustrations used were algebraic functions. In the volume on trigonometry, we studied trigonometric functions and their inverses. In this chapter we shall investigate two more non-algebraic functions, the *exponential* function $y = a^x$ and its inverse function, the *logarithmic* function $y = \log_a x$.

1 Exponents

Upon completing this chapter, you should be able to

I. Write the five laws of exponents for positive, zero, and negative integer exponents.

II. Simplify expressions involving positive, zero, and negative exponents.

---

	1. You are familiar with the use of **exponent** notation to denote the product of several real numbers that are all the same. For example, $$5^2 = 5 \cdot 5, \quad 4^3 = \underline{\hspace{4cm}}, \text{ and}$$ $$2^7 = 2 \cdot 2 \cdot 2 \cdot 2 \cdot 2 \cdot 2 \cdot 2.$$
1. $4 \cdot 4 \cdot 4$	**2.** In general, we have the following definition. **DEFINITION:** If a is any real number and n is a positive integer, then $$a \cdot a \cdot a \cdots a \ (n \text{ factors})$$ is represented by $\underline{\hspace{1cm}}$.
2. a^n	**3.** The symbol a^n is read as "a raised to the nth power" or "the nth power of a" or simply "a to the nth." For example, 4^7 is most simply read "$\underline{\hspace{5cm}}$."
3. 4 to the 7th	**4.** $\left(\frac{1}{2}\right)^9$ is read "$\underline{\hspace{4cm}}$."
4. $\frac{1}{2}$ to the 9th	**5.** The number a is called the **base**, and the positive integer n is called the **exponent**. In 4^7, $\underline{\hspace{0.5cm}}$ is the base and $\underline{\hspace{0.5cm}}$ is the exponent.
5. 4; 7	

6. In $(-9)^{11}$, -9, is the _____ and 11 is the _____ .

---

6. base; exponent

7. A number of laws of exponents follow from the preceding definition and the associative and commutative laws of real numbers. In each of the following statements a and b are any real numbers (no denominator may equal 0), and m and n are positive integers.

---

7. Go on to the next frame.

8. $2^3 \cdot 2^5 = (2 \cdot 2 \cdot 2) \cdot \text{(a) (} \rule{5cm}{0.4pt} \text{)}$

$= \text{(b)} \rule{6cm}{0.4pt} = \text{(c) } 2^{\rule{1cm}{0.4pt}} \cdot$

---

8. (a) $2 \cdot 2 \cdot 2 \cdot 2 \cdot 2$
(b) $2 \cdot 2 \cdot 2 \cdot 2 \cdot 2 \cdot 2 \cdot 2 \cdot 2$, (c) ^{8}

9. Thus $2^3 \cdot 2^5 = 2^8 = 2^{3+5}$ and $3^4 \cdot 3^7 = $ _____ .

---

9. 3^{11}

10. In general

$$a^m \cdot a^n = \overbrace{(a \cdot a \cdots a)}^{m \text{ factors}} \overbrace{(a \cdot a \cdots a)}^{n \text{ factors}}$$

$$= \overbrace{a \cdot a \cdots a}^{m+n \text{ factors}}$$

$$= a^{\rule{1cm}{0.4pt}}$$

---

10. a^{m+n}

11. We have the first law of exponents:

E1. $a^m \cdot a^n = $ _____ .

---

11. a^{m+n}

12. Now consider $(5^4)^3 \cdot (5^4)^3 = 5^4 \cdot 5^4 \cdot 5^4 = $ _____

---

12. 5^{12}

13. Thus $(5^4)^3 = 5^{12} = 5^{4 \cdot 3} \cdot (7^2)^5 = $ _____

---

13. 7^{10}

14. In general

$$(a^m)^n = \overbrace{\rule{5cm}{0pt}}^{n \text{ factors}}$$

$$= \rule{2cm}{0.4pt} \text{ by E1.}$$

---

14. $a^m \cdot a^m \cdots a^m$;
$a^{m \cdot n}$

15. We have the second law of exponents.

E2. $(a^m)^n = $ _____ .

---

15. $a^{m \cdot n}$

16. Now we consider the third law of exponents.

E3. $(ab)^n = \overbrace{ab \cdot ab \cdots ab}^{n \text{ factors}}$

$= \overbrace{a \cdot a \cdots a}^{n \text{ factors}} \cdot \overbrace{b \cdot b \cdots b}^{n \text{ factors}}$ by the commutative and associative laws of multiplication of real numbers

$=$ _____

---

16. $a^n b^n$

17. Thus the third law of exponents is

$(ab)^n =$ _____ .

---

17. $a^n b^n$

18.

$\left(\dfrac{a}{b}\right)^n = \overbrace{\rule{3cm}{0pt}}^{n \text{ factors}}$ _____

---

18. $\overbrace{\dfrac{a}{b} \cdot \dfrac{a}{b} \cdots \dfrac{a}{b}}$

19. But by definition

$\dfrac{a}{b} \cdot \dfrac{a}{b} = \dfrac{a \cdot a}{b \cdot b}$.

Thus by the associative law of multiplication of real numbers

$\left(\dfrac{a}{b}\right)^n = \overbrace{\dfrac{a}{b} \cdot \dfrac{a}{b} \cdots \dfrac{a}{b}}^{n \text{ factors}} =$ ____ .

---

19. $\dfrac{a^n}{b^n}$

20. Thus the fourth law of exponents is

E4. $\left(\dfrac{a}{b}\right)^n =$ ____ .

---

20. $\dfrac{a^n}{b^n}$

21. Finally, we turn to the fifth law of exponents:

E5. $\dfrac{4^5}{4^3} =$ _____ $=$ _____

by cancellation.

---

21. $\dfrac{4 \cdot 4 \cdot 4 \cdot 4 \cdot 4}{4 \cdot 4 \cdot 4}$; $4 \cdot 4 = 4^2$

22. Thus

$$\frac{4^5}{4^3} = 4^2 = 4^{5-3}.$$

$$\frac{6^8}{6^5} = \underline{\qquad}$$

---

22. 6^3

23. In general, if $n > m$,

$$\frac{a^n}{a^m} = \frac{\overbrace{a \cdot a \cdots a}^{n \text{ factors}}}{\underbrace{a \cdot a \cdots a}_{m \text{ factors}}} = \underline{\qquad\qquad}$$

by cancellation since $n > m$.

---

23. a^{n-m}

24. Thus we have the first part of the fifth law of exponents. If $n > m$, then

$$\frac{a^n}{a^m} = \underline{\qquad\qquad}.$$

---

24. a^{n-m}

25. If $n = m$, then

$$\frac{a^n}{a^m} = \frac{a^n}{a^n} \qquad \text{since } n = m = \underline{\quad}.$$

---

25. 1

26. Thus the second part of the fifth rule of exponents is: If $n = m$,

$$\frac{a^n}{a^m} = \underline{\quad}.$$

---

26. 1

27. Finally,

$$\frac{4^3}{4^5} = \frac{4 \cdot 4 \cdot 4}{4 \cdot 4 \cdot 4 \cdot 4 \cdot 4} = \underline{\qquad\qquad\qquad}.$$

---

27. $\dfrac{1}{4 \cdot 4} = \dfrac{1}{4^2}$

28. In general, if $n < m$,

$$\dfrac{a^n}{a^m} = \dfrac{\overbrace{a \cdot a \cdots a}^{n \text{ factors}}}{\underbrace{a \cdot a \cdots a}_{m \text{ factors}}} = \underline{\hspace{3cm}}$$

by cancellation, since $n < m$.

---

28. $\dfrac{1}{a^{m-n}}$

29. Thus we have the third and final part of the fifth law of exponents.

If $n < m$, then

$$\dfrac{a^n}{a^m} = \underline{\hspace{3cm}}.$$

---

29. $\dfrac{1}{a^{m-n}}$

30. Putting the three parts together, we get

$$\dfrac{a^n}{a^m} = \begin{cases} \text{(a)} \underline{\hspace{2cm}} & \text{if } n > m, \\ \text{(b)} \underline{\hspace{2cm}} & \text{if } n = m, \\ \text{(c)} \underline{\hspace{2cm}} & \text{if } n < m. \end{cases}$$

---

30. (a) a^{n-m},

(b) 1,

(c) $\dfrac{1}{a^{m-n}}$

EXERCISE 1

31. Complete the statements of the following laws of exponents.

E1. $a^n \cdot a^m = \underline{\hspace{2cm}}$

---

31. a^{n+m}.

If you had difficulty, see frames 8 to 11.

32. E2. $(a^m)^n = \underline{\hspace{2cm}}$

---

32. $a^{m \cdot n}$.

If you had difficulty, see frames 12 to 15.

33. E3. $(ab)^n = \underline{\hspace{2cm}}$

---

33. $a^n b^n$.

If you had difficulty, see frames 16 and 17.

34. E4. $\left(\dfrac{a}{b}\right)^n =$ _____ .

34. $\dfrac{a^n}{b^n}$.

If you had difficulty, see
frames 18 to 20.

35. E5.

$\dfrac{a^n}{a^m} = \begin{cases} \text{(a)} \rule{3cm}{0.4pt} \quad \rule{3cm}{0.4pt} \\ \text{(b)} \rule{3cm}{0.4pt} \quad \rule{3cm}{0.4pt} \\ \text{(c)} \rule{3cm}{0.4pt} \quad \rule{3cm}{0.4pt} \end{cases}$

35.
(a) a^{n-m} if $n > m$,
(b) 1 if $n = m$,
(c) $\dfrac{1}{a^{m-n}}$ if $n < m$.

If you had difficulty, see
frames 21 to 30.

SUMMARY

Laws of Exponents

E1. $a^m a^n = a^{m+n}$

E2. $(a^m)^n = a^{mn}$

E3. $(ab)^n = a^n b^n$

E4. $\left(\dfrac{a}{b}\right)^n = \dfrac{a^n}{b^n}$

E5. $\dfrac{a^n}{a^m} = \begin{cases} a^{n-m} & \text{if } n > m \\ 1 & \text{if } n = m \\ \dfrac{1}{a^{m-n}} & \text{if } n < m \end{cases}$

	36. So far we have defined a^n for _____ integers. (all, positive, negative)
36. positive	**37.** We now want to define a^n where n is zero or negative. Moreover, we want to choose our definitions so that the laws of exponents E1 to E5 remain true if m and n are zero or negative.
37. Go on to the next frame.	**38.** First let us consider a^0. If E1 is to hold when one of the exponents is zero, then $a^m \cdot a^0 = $ _____ .
38. a^{m+0}	**39.** Thus $a^m \cdot a^0 = a^{m+0} = a^m = a^m \cdot 1$. That is, $a^m \cdot a^0 = a^m \cdot 1$. Hence $a^0 = $ ___ .
39. 1	**40.** Therefore we make the following definition. **DEFINITION:** If a is any non-zero real number, then $a^0 = $ ___ .
40. 1	**41.** Therefore, *by definition* $5^0 = $ **(a)** _____ , $(-7)^0 = $ **(b)** ___ , $(\sqrt{2})^0 = $ **(c)** ___ , etc.
41. (a) 1, **(b)** 1, **(c)** 1	**42.** But 0^0 has *not* been defined and has no meaning, since a^0 was defined to be 1 for all _____ real numbers. (what kind?)
42. Non-zero. If you had difficulty, see frame 40.	**43.** With a^0 defined to be ___ , it is easy to see that the remaining laws of exponents are also true when either m or n is zero.
43. 1	**44.** If $n = 0$ and $m > 0$, $a^m = r$ for some real number r. And $(a^m)^0 = r^0 = $ ___ .
44. 1	

	45. On the other hand, by E2, $(a^m)^0 = $ _____ .
45. $a^{m \cdot 0}$	**46.** But $a^{m \cdot 0} = $ ____ $= $ ___ . Thus the second law of exponents is true for $n = 0$.
46. a^0; 1	**47.** Similarly, if $m = 0, n > 0$, then $(a^0)^n = ($ __ $)^n = $ __ .
47. 1; 1	**48.** And, by E2, $(a^0)^n = $ _____ $= $ _____ . Thus the second law of exponents is true if $m = 0$.
48. $a^{0 \cdot n}$; $a^0 = 1$	**49.** In a similar way we can show that E3, E4, and E5 remain true if either m or n is zero.
49. Go on to the next frame.	**50.** We now turn our attention to defining a negative exponent, a^{-n}, where n is a positive integer. Again our definition will be motivated by the desire to preserve the first law of exponents, E1. Let $m = -n$; if E1 is to be preserved, then $$a^n \cdot a^{-n} = \underline{\hspace{3cm}}.$$
50. $a^{n+(-n)}$	**51.** Thus $a^n \cdot a^{-n} = a^{n+(-n)} = a^{n-n} = a^0 = $ __ .
51. 1	**52.** That is, $$a^n \cdot a^{-n} = 1 = a^n \cdot \frac{1}{a^n}.$$ Hence $a^{-n} = $ ____ .
52. $\dfrac{1}{a^n}$	**53.** Therefore we define a^{-n} as follows. **DEFINITION:** If a is any non-zero real number and n is a positive integer, then $a^{-n} = $ ____ .
53. $\dfrac{1}{a^n}$	

9

54. Thus by definition 4^{-2} = (a) _____ ,

$(-3)^{-4}$ = (b) _____ , π^{-6} = (c) _____ , etc.

---

54. (a) $\dfrac{1}{4^2} = \dfrac{1}{16}$,

(b) $\dfrac{1}{(-3)^4}$, (c) $\dfrac{1}{\pi^6}$

55. As in the zero case, the four remaining laws of exponents remain true if either m or n is negative. For example,

$\left(\dfrac{a}{b}\right)^{-n}$ = _____ by definition.

---

55. $\dfrac{1}{\left(\frac{a}{b}\right)^n}$

56. = $\dfrac{1}{\text{\underline{\hspace{1cm}}}}$ by E4.

---

56. $\dfrac{a^n}{b^n}$

57. But $\dfrac{1}{\frac{a^n}{b^n}} = \dfrac{1}{a^n \cdot \frac{1}{b^n}}$

$= \dfrac{1}{a^n \cdot \underline{\hspace{0.8cm}}}$ by definition of negative exponents.

---

57. b^{-n}

58. $\dfrac{1}{a^n b^{-n}} = \dfrac{1}{a^n} \cdot \dfrac{1}{b^{-n}}$

$= \underline{\hspace{1cm}} \cdot \dfrac{1}{b^{-n}}$ by definition of negative exponents

---

58. a^{-n}

59. Thus, by combining frames 55 through 58, we get

$\left(\dfrac{a}{b}\right)^{-n}$ = _____ .

We have shown that E4 remains true for negative exponents.

---

59. $\dfrac{a^{-n}}{b^{-n}}$

60. Similarly, we can show that E2, E3, and E5 remain true for negative exponents. We have now defined a^n for any integer n and have seen the five laws of exponents remain true for all integers.

---

60. Go on to the next frame.

61. Thus if a and b are non-zero real numbers and m and n are any integers, positive, zero, or negative, then

E1 **(a)** _____ = _____ ,

E2 **(b)** _____ ,

E3 **(c)** _____ ,

E4 **(d)** _____ ,

and

E5 $\dfrac{a^n}{a^m} = a^{n-m}$.

---

61. (a) $a^m a^n$; a^{m+n} ,
(b) $(a^m)^n = a^{mn}$,
(c) $(ab)^n = a^n b^n$,

(d) $\left(\dfrac{a}{b}\right)^n = \dfrac{a^n}{b^n}$.

It is not important that you remember which law is E1, E2, etc.

62. Note that one case now covers E5, for if $n = m$,

$\dfrac{a^n}{a^m} = a^{n-m} = $ _____ as before.

---

62. $a^0 = 1$

63. And if $n < m$, then

$\dfrac{a^n}{a^m} = a^{n-m} = $ _____ as before.

---

63. $\dfrac{1}{a^{m-n}}$

64. Thus if a is any non-zero real number and n is any integer, positive, zero, or negative, then

E5 _____ .

---

64. $\dfrac{a^n}{a^m} = a^{n-m}$

EXAMPLE 1

65. We can now use the laws of exponents to simplify expressions like $(x^2 y^{-3})^4$. By E3

$(x^2 y^{-3})^4 = ($ _____ $)($ _____ $)$.

---

65. $(x^2)^4 (y^{-3})^4$

66. And by applying E2 to both factors, we get

$(x^2 y^{-3})^4 = (x^2)^4 (y^{-3})^4 = $ _____ .

---

66. $x^8 y^{-12}$

67. Finally, by definition of negative exponents, we get

$$(x^2 y^{-3})^4 = x^8 y^{-12} = \underline{\hspace{2cm}}.$$

---

67. $\dfrac{x^8}{y^{12}}$

EXAMPLE 2

68. Simplify the expression $\dfrac{(x^{+3} y^{-4} z^{+2})^{-2}}{z^{-5}}$ so that no negative

exponents remain. $\dfrac{(x^{+3} y^{-4} z^{+2})^{-2}}{z^{-5}} = \underline{\hspace{2cm}}$

---

68. $\dfrac{y^8 z}{x^6}$.

If you had difficulty, go on to the next frame. If not, skip to frame 72.

69. By E3 and then E2,

$$\dfrac{(x^{+3} y^{-4} z^{+2})^{-2}}{z^{-5}} = \underline{\hspace{5cm}}.$$

69.

$$\dfrac{(x^{+3})^{-2}(y^{-4})^{-2}(z^{+2})^{-2}}{z^{-5}}$$

$$= \dfrac{x^{-6} y^8 z^{-4}}{z^{-5}}$$

70. Now, by E5,

$$\dfrac{x^{-6} y^8 z^{-4}}{z^{-5}} = x^{-6} y^8 \underline{\hspace{1cm}}.$$

---

70. z

71. And, finally, by the definition of negative exponents, we get

$$\dfrac{(x^{+3} y^{-4} z^{+2})^2}{z^{-5}} = x^{-6} y^8 z = \underline{\hspace{2cm}}.$$

---

71. $\dfrac{y^8 z}{x^6}$

EXAMPLE 3

72. Express $\dfrac{(x^{-2} y^{-5} z^{-1})^{-2}}{x^5 y^4}$ without zero or negative exponents.

---

72. $\dfrac{y^6 z^2}{x}$.

If you had difficulty, see frames 65 to 71.

PROBLEMS

1. Simplify the following expressions.

(a) 4^{-2}

(b) $(-4)^{-2}$

(c) $(\frac{7}{8})^{-1}$

(d) $(\frac{2}{5})^{-2}$

(e) $(x^2 y^3)^2 (xy^0)^3$

(f) $(x^{-2} y^{-1})(x^3 y^4)$

(g) $(xy^{-1})^{-2} (x^{-2} y)^3$

2. Express the following without zero or negative exponents.

(a) $2^{-1} x^2 z^0 y^{-3}$

(b) $4x^{-1} y^{-3} z$

(c) $4^{-1} x^{-2} y^0 z^4$

(d) $\dfrac{3^{-1} x^3 y^{-1}}{x^2 y^3}$

(e) $\dfrac{3x^4 y^{-2}}{x^{-2} y^{-3}}$

(f) $\dfrac{5^{-1} x^{-3} y^{-2}}{x^2 y^{-3} z^{-4}}$

(g) $\left(\dfrac{2x^4 y^0}{x^2 y^{-3}}\right)^{-1}$

(h) $\left(\dfrac{2^{-3} x^{-2} y^3 z}{xy^{-4} z}\right)^{-2}$

(i) $\left(\dfrac{-3^2 x^2 y^{-4} z^0}{x^{-1} y^3 z^{-2}}\right)^{-3}$

Answers are at end of book.

QUIZ

If you cannot answer the following questions correctly, review the appropriate frames.

1. Complete the statements of the following laws of exponents.

(a) $a^n \cdot a^m = $ _____

(b) $(a^m)^n = $ _____

(c) $(ab)^n = $ _____

(d) $(\frac{a}{b})^n = $ _____

(e) $\dfrac{a^n}{a^m} = $ _____

2. Express $\dfrac{(x^{-1} y^3 z^{-3})^{-3}}{x^2 z^4}$ without zero or negative exponents.

Answers are at end of book.

2 Radicals and Rational Exponents

Upon completing this chapter, you should be able to

I. Extend the definition of an exponent to $a^{m/n}$.

II. Simplify expressions involving rational exponents and radicals, rationalizing the denominator where necessary.

---

	73. In this chapter we want to extend the idea of exponents to include rational exponents. As in the previous section we wish to define $a^{m/n}$ in a way that will preserve _____ _____ .
73. the five laws of exponents	**74.** Let m and n be positive integers. We first define $a^{1/n}$ and then extend it to the more general case $a^{m/n}$. If $m = \dfrac{1}{n}$ and E2 is to be preserved, then $(a^{1/n})^n = $ _____ .
74. $a^{(1/n)\cdot n}$	**75.** Thus $(a^{1/n})^n = a^{(1/n)\cdot n} = a^1 = a$ and we must let $a^{1/n}$ represent a number b that satisfies $b^n = $ ___ .
75. a	**76.** Therefore, before we can assign a meaning to $a^{1/n}$ we must first discuss the meaning of $b^n = a$. **DEFINITION:** If n is a positive integer and $b^n = a$, then b is an nth **root** of a. For example, since $3^2 = 9$, 3 is a second root of 9. Since $4^2 = 16$, 4 is a _____ .
76. second root of 16	

	77. $(-3)^2 = 9$; therefore -3 is also _____ _____ .
77. a second root of 9	78. $3^4 = 81$; hence 3 is a _____ .
78. fourth root of 81	79. And, since $(-3)^4 = 81$, _____ _____ .
79. -3 is also a fourth root of 81	80. Since $3^3 = 27$, 3 is a _____ .
80. third root of 27	81. -3 _____ a third root of 27. (is, is not)
81. is not	82. $(-3)^3 = -27$, thus -3 is _____ .
82. a third root of -27	83. Since $3^5 = 243$, 3 is a _____ _____ , etc.
83. fifth root of 243	84. Depending on whether a is positive or negative and on whether n is even or odd, a may have **(i)** two real nth roots, **(ii)** one real nth root, or **(iii)** no real nth root. We saw in frames 78 and 79 that 81 has two fourth roots: ___ and ___ .
84. 3; -3	85. 4 has _____ real second root(s). They are _____ . (how many?)
85. two; 2 and -2	86. 16 has _____ real *fourth* root(s). They are _____ .
86. two; 2 and -2	

87. In general, a will have two real nth roots if **(i)** a is

_____ real number, and **(ii)** n is
(a positive, a negative, any)

_____ positive integer.
(an even, an odd, any)

---

87. a positive;
an even

88. One of the two real roots is positive; the other is negative. The positive nth root is called the **principal nth root of** a and is denoted by $\sqrt[n]{a}$. The negative nth root is denoted by $-\sqrt[n]{a}$. For example,

$\sqrt[4]{81} =$ _____ and $-\sqrt[4]{81} =$ _____ .

---

88. 3; -3

89. $\sqrt[2]{4} =$ _____ and $-\sqrt[2]{4} =$ _____

---

89. 2; -2

90. $\sqrt[4]{16}$ is called the _____ fourth root of 16.

---

90. principal

91. And the negative fourth root of 16 is denoted by _____ .

---

91. $-\sqrt[4]{16}$

92. We must emphasize again that $\sqrt[4]{16} =$ _____ 2.
$(+, -, \pm)$

---

92. $+$

93. $\sqrt[4]{16}$ does not equal ± 2. _____ $= -2$

---

93. $-\sqrt[4]{16}$

94. If a is *positive* and n is an *even* positive integer, then a has

_____ real nth root(s).
(how many?)

---

94. two

95. $\sqrt[n]{a}$ is called the _____ nth root.

---

95. principal

96. and $-\sqrt[n]{a}$ is called the _____ .

---

96. negative nth root

97. We saw in frame 80 that 3 is a third root of 27, and that -3

_____ a third root of 27.
(is, is not)

---

97. is not

16

	98. Thus 27 has _____ real third root(s). (how many?)
98. one	**99.** 8 has _____ real third root(s). (how many?)
99. one	**100.** The real third root of 8 is ___ .
100. 2	**101.** In general, a will have one and only one real nth root if **(i)** a is a positive real number, and **(ii)** n is _____ positive integer. (an even, an odd, any)
101. an odd	**102.** This one root is the principal root and is denoted by _____ .
102. $\sqrt[n]{a}$	**103.** Thus $\sqrt[3]{8} = $ ___ .
103. 2	**104.** $\sqrt[5]{32} = $ ___
104. 2	**105.** $\sqrt[5]{243} = $ ___
105. 3	**106.** If a is *positive* and n is an *odd* positive integer, then a has _____ real nth root(s). (how many?)
106. one	**107.** Thus the one real nth root is denoted by _____ .
107. $\sqrt[n]{a}$	**108.** It is called the _____ nth root.
108. principal	**109.** In frame 82 we saw that -3 is a real third root of _____ .
109. -27	**110.** How many real third root(s) does -27 have? _____
110. one	

	111. −8 has _____ real third root(s).
111. one	**112.** In general, a will have one and only one real root if **(i)** a is a negative real number, and **(ii)** n is _____ positive integer. _(an even, an odd, any)
112. an odd	**113.** This one real nth root is denoted by _____ .
113. $\sqrt[n]{a}$	**114.** And it is called the _____ nth root.
114. principal	**115.** $\sqrt[5]{-243} =$ ____
115. −3	**116.** We can combine the last two cases into one. a will have one and only one real nth root if **(i)** a is any real number and **(ii)** n is _____ positive integer.
116. an odd	**117.** If a is positive and n is even, then a has _____ real nth root(s).
117. two	**118.** If a is any real number and n is odd, then a has _____ real nth root(s).
118. one	**119.** If a is negative and n is even, then a has _____ real nth root(s). Look at some examples and decide.
119. No. If you had difficulty, go on to the next frame. If not, skip to frame 124.	**120.** Are there any real numbers b such that $b^2 = -9$? _____
120. no (since $3^2 = 9$ and $(-3)^2 = 9$)	**121.** Does −4 have any real second roots? _____
121. no	**122.** Does −16 have any real fourth roots? _____
122. no (since $2^4 = 16$ and $(-2)^4 = 16$)	

	123. Thus, if a is negative and n is even, then a has _____ real nth root(s).
123. no	**124.** Finally, if $a = 0$ and n is any positive integer, $\sqrt[n]{0} = $ ___ .
124. 0	**125.** That is, the nth root of zero is _____ for any n.
125. zero	**126.** In summary we have the following cases: **(i)** If a is a *positive* real number and n is an *even* positive integer, then a has _____ real nth root(s).
126. two	**127.** **(ii)** If a is any real number and n is an *odd* positive integer, then a has _____ real nth root(s).
127. one	**128.** **(iii)** If a is a *negative* real number and n is an *even* positive integer, then a has _____ real nth root(s).
128. no	**129.** Finally, **(iv)** $\sqrt[n]{0} = $ ___ for all n.
129. 0	**130.** The symbol $\sqrt[n]{a}$ is called a **radical**, the number a is called the **radicand**, and n is called the **index** of the radical. Thus in $\sqrt[5]{421}$, **(a)** _____ is the radical, **(b)** _____ is the radicand, and **(c)** ___ is the index.
130. (a) $\sqrt[5]{421}$, **(b)** 421, **(c)** 5	**131.** $\sqrt[6]{1024}$ is called a _____ .
131. radical	**132.** 1024 is called the _____ .
132. radicand	**133.** And 6 is the _____ .
133. index	**134.** The principal nth root of a is always represented by _____ whether a is positive or negative.
134. $\sqrt[n]{a}$	

	135. If a has two real nth roots, the negative real nth root of a is denoted by _____ .
135. $-\sqrt[n]{a}$	**136.** If the index is 2, we do not write it. Thus the second root of 9 is written $\sqrt{9}$. And, in general, the principal second (or square) root of a is written _____ .
136. $\sqrt{a}$	**137.** The negative square root of 373 is denoted by _____ .
137. $-\sqrt{373}$. Again we did not write the index 2.	**138.** Finally, we are ready to define $a^{1/n} = b$. As we saw in frames 74 and 75, if E2 is to remain true, $a^{1/n}$ must satisfy _____ .
138. $b^n = a$	**139.** Thus we make the following definition. **DEFINITION:** If a is any real number and n is a positive integer, then $a^{1/n} =$ _____ whenever _____ exists.
139. $\sqrt[n]{a}$; $\sqrt[n]{a}$	**140.** As we have seen in the preceding frames, $\sqrt[n]{a}$ will fail to exist when a is _____ and n is _____ . (positive, negative) (even, odd)
140. negative; even	**141.** By definition $9^{1/2} =$ _____ .
141. $\sqrt{9} = 3$	**142.** $27^{1/3} =$ _____
142. $\sqrt[3]{27} = 3$	**143.** $(-27)^{1/3} =$ _____ , etc.
143. $\sqrt[3]{-27} = -3$	**144.** In general, $a^{1/n} =$ _____ whenever _____ exists.
144. $\sqrt[n]{a}$; $\sqrt[n]{a}$	**145.** $(-9)^{1/2}$ and $(-81)^{1/4}$ are _____ since a is negative and n is even.
145. not defined	

146. We are now ready to define $a^{m/n}$ for m and n positive integers so that rule E2 will be preserved.

If rule E2 is to be preserved,

(1) $a^{m/n} = (a^{1/n})^m = ($_____$)^m$ by definition of $a^{1/n}$.

---

146. $\sqrt[n]{a}$

147. (2) $a^{m/n} = (a^m)^{1/n} = \sqrt{\phantom{\rule{2cm}{0pt}}}$ _____ by definition of $a^{1/n}$.

---

147. $\sqrt[n]{a^m}$

148. That is, combining (1) and (2) we see that

$a^{m/n} = $ _____ $= $ _____ whenever $\sqrt[n]{a}$ exists.

---

148. $(\sqrt[n]{a})^m$; $\sqrt[n]{a^m}$

149. We make the following definition.

DEFINITION: If a is any real number and m and n are integers with $n > 0$, then

$a^{m/n} = $ _____ $= $ _____ whenever $\sqrt[n]{a}$ exists.

---

149. $(\sqrt[n]{a})^m$; $\sqrt[n]{a^m}$

150. $\sqrt[n]{a}$ exists unless a is _____ and n is _____ .

---

150. negative; even

151. Thus $5^{2/3} = $ _____ or _____ .

---

151. $(\sqrt[3]{5})^2$; $\sqrt[3]{5^2}$

152. $7^{4/9} = $ _____ or _____

---

152. $(\sqrt[9]{7})^4$; $\sqrt[9]{7^4}$

153. While $(-29)^{3/4}$ is _____ .

---

153. not defined (or not a real number)

154. We have defined $a^{m/n}$ to preserve property E2.

It can be shown that the results E1, E3, E4, and E5 are also true for this definition whenever all the terms involved exist.

---

154. Go on to the next frame.

155. We have defined $a^{m/n}$ to be _____ whenever $\sqrt[n]{a}$ has meaning in the real number system.

---

155. $\sqrt[n]{a^m} = (\sqrt[n]{a})^m$

156. Thus we have extended our definition of exponent to a^{r^+} where $r^+ = m/n$ is a positive rational number. We have indicated that we could show that the laws of exponents remain true for rational numbers. Moreover we can extend our definition to include negative rational numbers by defining $a^{-r} = \dfrac{1}{a^r}$.

Thus if a and b are non-zero real numbers, r and s are rational numbers, and both sides have meaning

E1. $a^r \cdot a^s = $ _____ .

---

156. a^{r+s}

157. E2. $(a^r)^s = $ _____

---

157. $a^{r \cdot s}$

158. E3. $(ab)^r = $ _____

---

158. $a^r b^r$

159. E4. $\left(\dfrac{a}{b}\right)^r = $ _____

---

159. $\dfrac{a^r}{b^r}$

160. E5. $\dfrac{a^r}{a^s} = $ _____

---

160. a^{r-s}

161. We must emphasize again that the rules of exponents are true for rational exponents if and only if *each term involved has meaning in the real number system.*

For example, if we apply E3 to $(-3)^{1/2} (-3)^{1/2}$, we get

$(-3)^{1/2} (-3)^{1/2} = $ _____ .

---

161. $((-3)(-3))^{1/2}$

162. This is equal to _____ = _____ .

---

162. $9^{1/2}$; 3

163. That is, by E3, $(-3)^{1/2} (-3)^{1/2} = $ _____.

---

163. 3

164. On the other hand, by E1, $(-3)^{1/2} (-3)^{1/2} = $ _____ .

---

164. $(-3)^{1/2+1/2}$

165. But $(-3)^{1/2 + 1/2} = $ _____ = _____ .

---

165. $(-3)^1$; -3

166. That is, by E1, $(-3)^{1/2} (-3)^{1/2} = $ _____.

---

166. -3

167. $(-3)^{1/2}$ $(-3)^{1/2}$ cannot be both 3 and -3. Our error occurred when we applied the laws E2 and E3 in a situation where not all the terms had meaning. _____ is not defined in the real number system.

---

167. $(-3)^{1/2}$

EXAMPLE 1

168. The value of $\left(\frac{32}{243}\right)^{3/5}$ is given by

$$\left(\frac{32}{243}\right)^{3/5} = \frac{32^{3/5}}{243^{3/5}} = \frac{(\sqrt[5]{32})^3}{(\sqrt[5]{243})^3} = \frac{2^3}{3^3} = \frac{8}{27}.$$

$$\left(\frac{8}{27}\right)^{2/3} = \underline{\quad}.$$

---

168. $\frac{4}{9}$

EXAMPLE 2

169. The value of $\left(\frac{81}{256}\right)^{3/4}$ is _____.

---

169. $\frac{27}{64}$.

If you had difficulty, see frame 168.

EXAMPLE 3

170. Problems frequently arise in terms of radicals instead of rational exponents. We can simplify such problems by changing the radicals to exponents and applying the laws of exponents.

Simplify the expression $\dfrac{\sqrt{y}}{\sqrt[3]{y}}$. _____

---

170. $y^{1/6}$.

If you had difficulty, go on to the next frame. If not, skip to frame 173.

171. By definition $\dfrac{\sqrt{y}}{\sqrt[3]{y}} = $ _____ .

---

171. $\dfrac{y^{1/2}}{y^{1/3}}$

172. And, by E5, $\dfrac{y^{1/2}}{y^{1/3}} = $ _____ .

---

172. $y^{(1/2)-(1/3)} = y^{1/6}$

173. If a quotient contains a radical in its denominator, it is sometimes desirable to write the expression in a way that has no radical in the denominator. For example, we would write

$$\frac{4}{\sqrt{3}} = \frac{4}{\sqrt{3}} \cdot \frac{\sqrt{3}}{\sqrt{3}} = \underline{\quad}.$$

---

173. $\dfrac{4\sqrt{3}}{3}$

174. This process is called **rationalizing the denominator.**

$$\frac{7}{\sqrt{5}} = \underline{\hspace{2cm}}$$

---

174. $\dfrac{7\sqrt{5}}{5}$

EXAMPLE 4

175. To rationalize the denominator of $\dfrac{5}{\sqrt[3]{3x^5}}$, we first write the radical with rational exponents. We get

$$\frac{5}{\sqrt[3]{3x^5}} = \underline{\hspace{4cm}}.$$

---

175. $\dfrac{5}{3^{1/3}(x^5)^{1/3}}$

176. But $(x^5)^{1/3} = \underline{\hspace{2cm}}$ by E2.

---

176. $x^{5/3}$

177. Thus we have $\dfrac{5}{\sqrt[3]{3x^5}} = \dfrac{5}{3^{1/3}(x^5)^{1/3}} = \underline{\hspace{3cm}}.$

---

177. $\dfrac{5}{3^{1/3}x^{5/3}}$

178. To get a positive integral power of 3 in the denominator, we must multiply numerator and denominator by $\underline{\hspace{2cm}}$.

---

178. $3^{2/3}$

179. And to get a positive integral power of x in the denominator we multiply numerator and denominator by $\underline{\hspace{2cm}}$.

---

179. $x^{1/3}$

180. We get $\dfrac{5}{3^{1/3}x^{5/3}} \cdot \underline{\hspace{2cm}} = \underline{\hspace{2cm}}.$

---

180. $\dfrac{3^{2/3}x^{1/3}}{3^{2/3}x^{1/3}}$;

$\dfrac{5 \cdot 3^{2/3} \cdot x^{1/3}}{3x^2}$

181. Finally, if we so desire, we can put this answer in radical form and get $\dfrac{5}{\sqrt[3]{3x^5}} = \dfrac{5 \cdot 3^{2/3}x^{1/3}}{3x^2} = \underline{\hspace{3cm}}.$

---

181. $\dfrac{5\sqrt[3]{3^2 \cdot x}}{3x^2}$

EXAMPLE 5

182. Rationalize the denominator of $\dfrac{7}{\sqrt[5]{2x4}}$. _____

---

182. $\dfrac{7\sqrt[5]{2^4 \cdot x}}{2x}$.

If you had difficulty, see frames 175 to 181.

EXAMPLE 6

183. We now wish to rationalize the denominator of $\dfrac{4x}{7-\sqrt{5}}$.

Since $(a-b)(a+b) = a^2 - b^2$,

$(7-\sqrt{5})(7+\sqrt{5}) =$ _____ .

---

183. $(7)^2 - (\sqrt{5})^2 = 49 - 5 = 44$

184. Thus multiplying the numerator and denominator of

$\dfrac{4x}{7-\sqrt{5}}$ by _____

---

184. $7 + \sqrt{5}$

185. gives $\dfrac{4x}{7-\sqrt{5}}$. _____ = _____ .

---

185. $\dfrac{7+\sqrt{5}}{7+\sqrt{5}}, \dfrac{4x(7+\sqrt{5})}{44}$

EXAMPLE 7

186. Rationalize the denominator of $\dfrac{7y}{\sqrt{3}-9}$. _____

---

186. $\dfrac{7y(\sqrt{3}+9)}{-78}$.

If you had difficulty, go on to the next frame. If not, skip to frame 189.

187. Since the denominator is $\sqrt{3}-9$, we multiply the numerator and denominator of

$$\dfrac{7y}{\sqrt{3}-9} \text{ by } \underline{\hspace{2cm}} .$$

---

187. $\sqrt{3}+9$

188. We get $\dfrac{7y}{\sqrt{3}-9}$. _____ = _____ .

---

188. $\dfrac{\sqrt{3}+9}{\sqrt{3}+9} ; \dfrac{7y(\sqrt{3}+9)}{-78}$

EXAMPLE 8

189. Rationalize the denominator of $\dfrac{8z}{6+\sqrt{2}}$. _____

---

189. $\dfrac{8z(6-\sqrt{2})}{34}$.

If you had difficulty, see frames 183 to 188.

PROBLEMS

1. Find the numerical value for each of the following.

   (a) $25^{1/2}$

   (b) $27^{1/3}$

   (c) $16^{1/4}$

   (d) $8^{2/3}$

   (e) $(-64)^{2/3}$

   (f) $64^{-2/3}$

   (g) $128^{3/7}$

   (h) $(-128)^{3/7}$

   (i) $128^{-3/7}$

   (j) $\left(\frac{243}{1024}\right)^{1/5}$

2. Write each of the following in exponent form with no denominator.

   (a) $\sqrt{y^4}$

   (b) $\sqrt[4]{\frac{y}{z}}$

   (c) $\sqrt{64x^4y^6}$

   (d) $\sqrt[3]{4} \cdot \sqrt[3]{54}$

   (e) $\sqrt[6]{2} \cdot \sqrt[6]{32}$

   (f) $\sqrt[6]{x^3} \ \sqrt[4]{xy^{-2}}$

   (g) $\sqrt[3]{x^2} \ \sqrt[4]{x}$

   (h) $\sqrt{\frac{4y}{3z^2}}$

   (i) $\sqrt[3]{-x}$

   (j) $\sqrt[3]{\frac{5x^2y^3}{3z^5}}$

3. Simplify the following, rationalizing the denominator where necessary.

   (a) $(2 - \sqrt{3})(2 + \sqrt{3})$

   (b) $(\sqrt{7} + \sqrt{4})(\sqrt{7} - \sqrt{4})$

   (c) $(2\sqrt{5} - 9)(2\sqrt{5} + 9)$

   (d) $\frac{\sqrt{7} + 4}{\sqrt{7} - 4}$

   (e) $\frac{\sqrt{5} - 3}{\sqrt{5} + 3}$

   (f) $\frac{\sqrt{6} + \sqrt{5}}{\sqrt{6} - \sqrt{5}}$

   (g) $\frac{\sqrt{x} - \sqrt{y}}{\sqrt{x} + \sqrt{y}}$

   (h) $\frac{5}{\sqrt{3} - 2}$

   (i) $\frac{x}{\sqrt{y} - x}$

   (j) $\frac{x}{x - \sqrt{y^2 - 9}}$

4. Simplify the following problems, eliminating zero and negative exponents and rationalizing the denominator where necessary.

   (a) $(x - 1)x^{-1/3} + x^{2/3}$

   (b) $(x^2 + 1)x^{-2/5} + (2x)x^{3/5}$

   (c) $y^{2/3}x^{1/3} + y^{-1/3}x^{4/3}$

   (d) $y^{2/3}x^{-2/3} + 2y^{-1/3}x^{1/3} + y^{-4/3}x^{4/3}$

Answers are at end of book.

If you cannot answer the following questions correctly, review the appropriate frames.

1. Complete the following:

    (a) If a is a *positive* real number and n is an *even* positive integer, then a has

    _____ nth root(s).
    (how many?)

    (b) If a is *any* real number and n is an *odd* positive integer, then a has _____ real nth root(s).

    (c) If a is a *negative* real number and n is an even positive integer, then a has

    _____ real nth root(s).

2. Find the numerical value for each of the following:

    (a) $(81)^{3/4}$ (b) $\left(-\dfrac{1}{1024}\right)^{1/5}$

3. Simplify $\dfrac{\sqrt{10}+3}{\sqrt{10}-3}$ by rationalizing the denominator.

Answers are at end of book.

3   Exponential Function $y=a^x$

Upon completing this chapter, you should be able to

I. Extend the definition of a^x, $a > 0$, to all real numbers x.

II. Graph the function $y = a^x$ for any real number $a > 0$.

III. Give the properties of the function $y = a^x$.

IV. Use the graph of the function $y = a^x$ to find an approximate value
for a^b, where b is any real number.

---

190. In the volume on functions we saw that a function is completely defined by specifying

    (a) ——————————————— ,

    (b) ——————————————— ,

and

    (c) ——————————————————— .

---

190. (a) its domain,
(b) its second set,
(c) its rule of association.

If you had difficulty, see the
volume on functions, frames 10 to 19.

191. We also noted that whenever the domain is not specified, it is
taken to be the subset of the real numbers for which ——————————
———————————————— .

---

191. the rule gives another real
number (or makes sense)

192. And, finally, in the previous chapter we saw that if a is a
positive number, then a^r is a real number for all rational
exponents r.
    Thus if $a > 0$, and we define a function f by $f(x) = a^x$, the

domain of f would consist of the set of ——————————— .

---

192. all rational numbers

193. We now want to extend the definition of a^x to all real numbers x for $a > 0$ and then examine some of the properties of the function $f(x) = a^x$.

In the first volume we saw that any irrational number can be represented by a non-repeating, non-terminating decimal. We also saw that we can approximate any unending decimal to any desired degree of accuracy by terminating decimals and that these terminating decimals represent rational numbers. That is, we can approximate any irrational number as accurately as we wish by

——————————— numbers.

---

193. rational

194. Thus if $a > 0$ and x is irrational, it is possible to approximate a^x by replacing x by one of its ——————————— approximations.

---

194. rational

195. The proof that a^x is defined for all irrational numbers x is beyond the scope of this book, but we shall illustrate the process with the following example.

Let us consider the meaning of $3^{\sqrt{2}}$. Since $\sqrt{2}$ can be approximated by the rational numbers 1.4, 1.41, 1.414, etc., $3^{\sqrt{2}}$ can be approximated by **(a)** ———— , **(b)** ———— , **(c)** ———— , etc.

---

195. (a) $3^{1.4}$, **(b)** $3^{1.41}$, **(c)** $3^{1.414}$

196. If we write the exponents in fractional form, these approximations would be $3^{14/10}$, $3^{141/100}$, $3^{1414/1000}$, etc.

These numbers all have meaning, since a^r was defined for all

——————————— numbers r in the previous section, even though it would be difficult to represent them by decimals.

---

196. rational

197. Therefore it is possible, in theory, to get an unending decimal expression for ———— .

---

197. $3^{\sqrt{2}}$

198. In a similar manner, if a is any positive real number and x is any irrational number that can be approximated by r_1, r_2, r_3, etc., then a^x can be approximated by **(a)** ———— , **(b)** ———— , **(c)** ———— , etc.

---

198. (a) a^{r_1}, **(b)** a^{r_2}, **(c)** a^{r_3}

199. Thus it is possible to get a unique unending decimal expression for ——— .

---

199. a^x

200. Hence we accept (1) the fact that for $a > 0$ and x real a^x represents a unique ——————— number and (2) that the laws of exponents E1–E5 are preserved.

---

200. real

201. We can now make the following definition.

DEFINITION: If $a > 0$, then $f(x) = a^x$ is defined for all real numbers x and is called an **exponential function** with base a.

Thus $f(x) = 5^x$ is an exponential function with base ——— . (We shall show later that $f(x) = a^x$ is in fact a function.)

---

201. 5

202. $f(x) = 3^x$ is an ———————————— function with ——————— 3.

---

202. exponential; base

EXAMPLE 1

203. We can graph an exponential function as we have graphed other functions by plotting several points and connecting them by a smooth curve.

To sketch the graph of $f(x) = 2^x$, we first calculate a table of ordered pairs. Complete the table.

x	-2	-1	0	1	2
2^x					

203.

x	-2	-1	0	1	2
2^x	$\frac{1}{4}$	$\frac{1}{2}$	1	2	4

204. Now plot the points and connect them by a smooth curve.

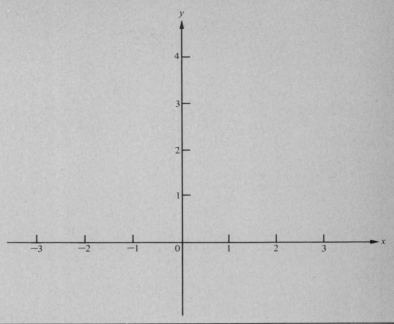

204.

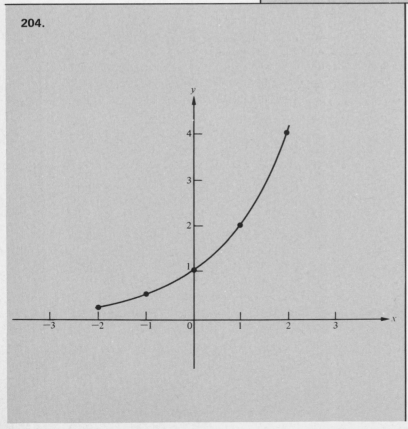

EXAMPLE 2

205. Graph $f(x) = (\frac{1}{2})^x$.

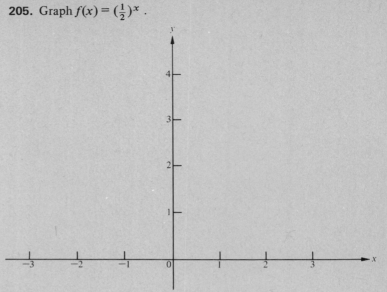

205.

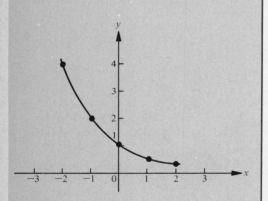

If you had difficulty, go on to the next frame. If not, skip to frame 208.

206. To graph $f(x) = (\frac{1}{2})^x$, we again calculate a number of ordered pairs.

x	-2	-1	0	1	2
$(\frac{1}{2})^x$					

206.

x	-2	-1	0	1	2
$(\frac{1}{2})^x$	4	2	1	$\frac{1}{2}$	$\frac{1}{4}$

207. Now plot the points and connect them by a smooth curve.

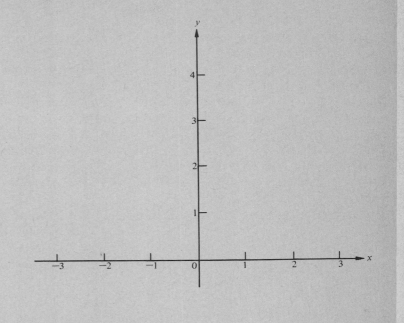

207.

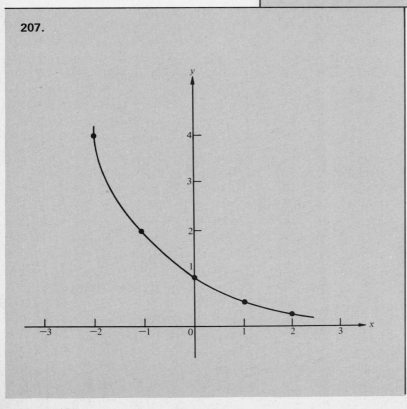

EXAMPLE 3

208. Graph $f(x) = 3^x$.

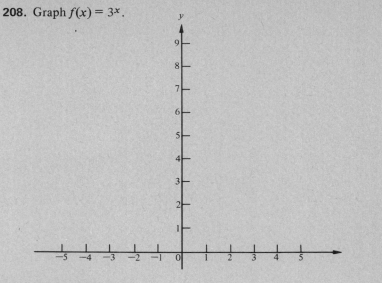

208.

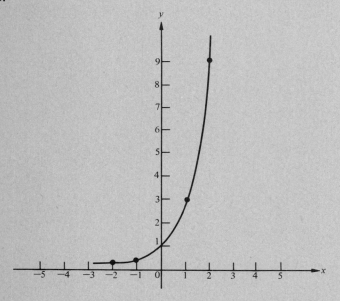

If you had difficulty, see frames
203 to 207.

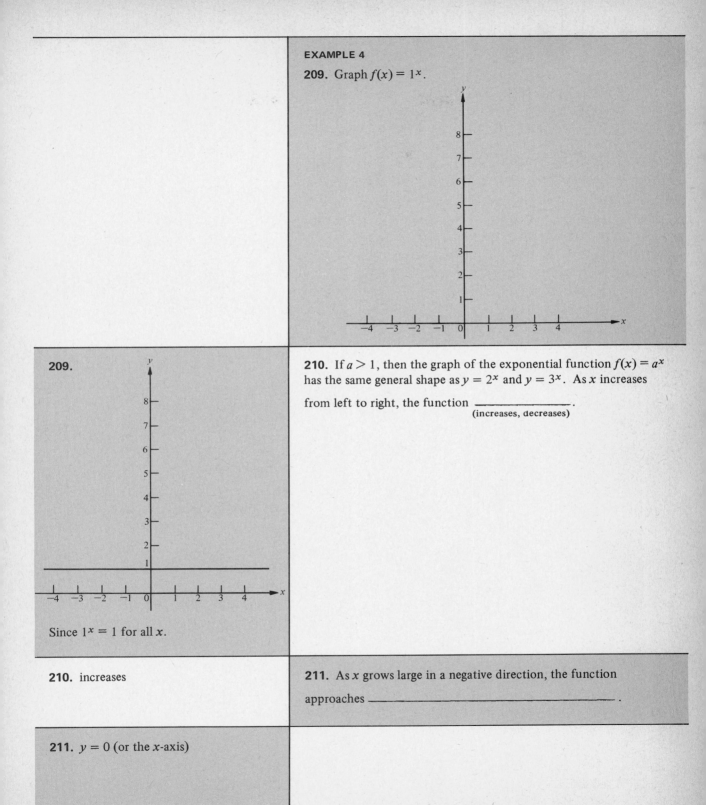

EXAMPLE 4

209. Graph $f(x) = 1^x$.

209.

Since $1^x = 1$ for all x.

210. If $a > 1$, then the graph of the exponential function $f(x) = a^x$ has the same general shape as $y = 2^x$ and $y = 3^x$. As x increases from left to right, the function _____.
(increases, decreases)

210. increases

211. As x grows large in a negative direction, the function approaches _____.

211. $y = 0$ (or the x-axis)

212. Thus _____ is a horizontal asymptote.

---

212. the x-axis (or $y = 0$)

213. We see from the graphs that the exponential function $f(x) = a^x$ has the following properties that we accept without proof.

---

213. Go on to the next frame.

214. If $a > 1$,

(1) $y = a^x$ does indeed define a function. That is, for each real

number x in the domain, there is associated _____

_____ .

---

214. one and only one number y in the range

215. **(2)** The function is

(a) positive for all values of x, or
(b) negative for all values of x, or
(c) positive for some values, negative for others.

(Choose one.)

---

215. (a)

216. **(3)** The value of the function _____ as x increases.

---

216. increases

217. That is, if $x_2 > x_1$, then $a^{x_2} \underset{(>,\,=,\,<)}{\rule{2cm}{0.4pt}} a^{x_1}$.

---

217. $>$

218.
(4) $a^x > 1$ if x **(a)** _____

$a^x = 1$ if x **(b)** _____

$a^x < 1$ if x **(c)** _____

---

218. **(a)** > 0,
(b) $= 0$,
(c) < 0.

If you had difficulty, see frames 204 and 208.

219. Summarizing frames 214 to 218, we see that, if $a > 1$, then $f(x) = a^x$

(a) _____

(b) _____

(c) _____

_____

(d) _____ ,

_____ ,

_____

---

219. (a) is a function.
(b) The function is positive for all x.
(c) The value of the function increases as x increases.
(d) $a^x > 1$ if $x > 0$,
   $a^x = 1$ if $x = 0$,
   $a^x < 1$ if $x < 0$

220. On the other hand, if $a < 1$, then the graph of the exponential function $f(x) = a^x$ has the same general shape as $y = (\frac{1}{2})^x$. That is, the function _____ as x increases from left to right.

---

220. Decreases.

If you had difficulty, see frames 205 to 207.

221. $y = a^x, a < 1$, has properties similar to those of $y = a$, $a > 1$. Again we list them without proof.

(1) If $a < 1$, _____ .

---

221. $y = a^x$ defines a function

222. (2) The function $y = a^x$, $a < 1$, is

(a) positive for all values of x, or
(b) negative for all values of x, or
(c) positive for some values, negative for others.

(Choose one.)

---

222. (a)

223. (3) The value of the function _____ as x increases. That is, if $x_2 > x_1, a^{x_2} \_\_ a^{x_1}$.

---

223. decreases;
$<$

224. (a) a^x _____ if $x > 0$

(b) a^x _____ if $x = 0$

(c) a^x _____ if $x < 0$

---

224. (a) < 1,
(b) $= 1$
(c) > 1

EXAMPLE 5

225. If the graph of $y = a^x, a > 0$, passes through the point $(4, 81)$, then $a =$ ___ .

---

225. 3.

If you had difficulty, go on to the next frame. If not, skip to frame 229.

226. Since $y = a^x, a > 0$, passes through the point $(4, 81)$, we have ___ $= a^4$.

---

226. 81

227. But $81 =$ ___^{4}.

---

227. 3

228. Hence $a =$ ___ .

---

228. 3

229.

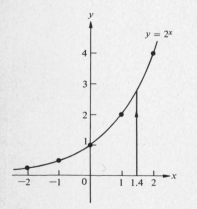

EXAMPLE 6

229. We can use the graph of $y = 2^x$ to find an approximate value for $2^{\sqrt{2}}$.

Since 1.4 is an approximation of $\sqrt{2}$, draw a vertical line through 1.4 on the x-axis that meets the graph of $y = 2^x$.

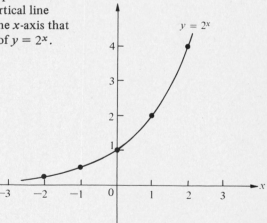

230. A horizontal line through the point of intersection of this line and the graph will meet the y-axis at the point that approximates _____ .

230. $2^{\sqrt{2}}$

231. Draw the horizontal line on the figure below. Hence, we see from the graph that _____ is an approximation for $2^{\sqrt{2}}$.

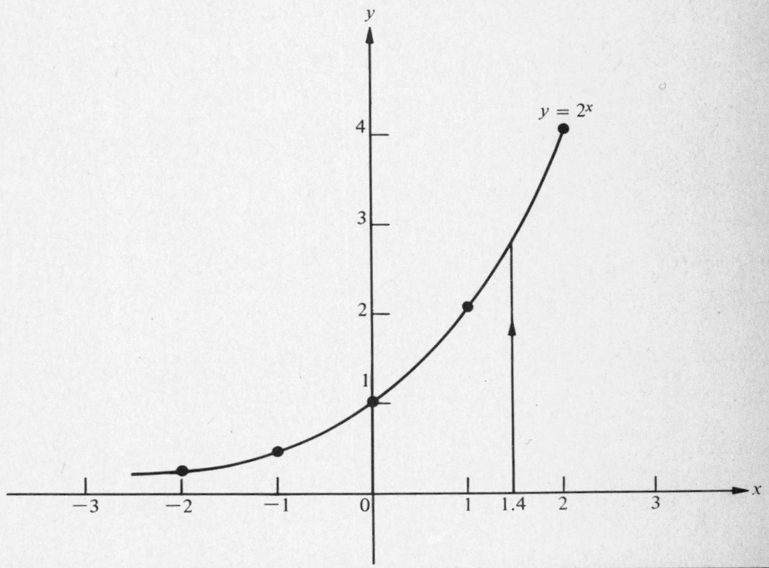

231. 2.7

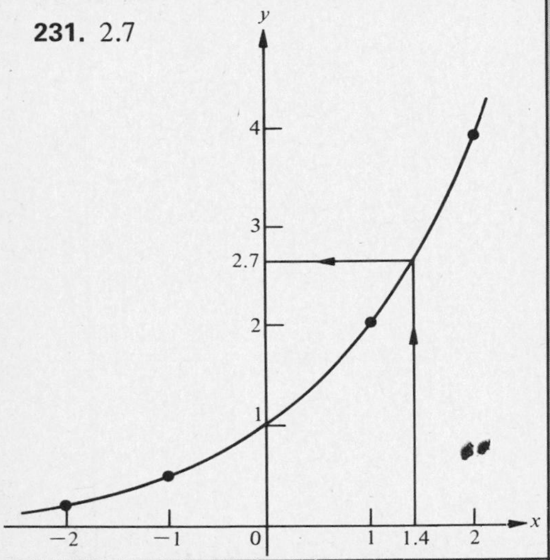

EXAMPLE 7

232. Use the graph of $y = 2^x$ to find an approximate value for $\sqrt[4]{2}$. $\sqrt[4]{2} \approx$ _____

232. 1.2 (since $\sqrt[4]{2} = 2^{1/4}$)

39

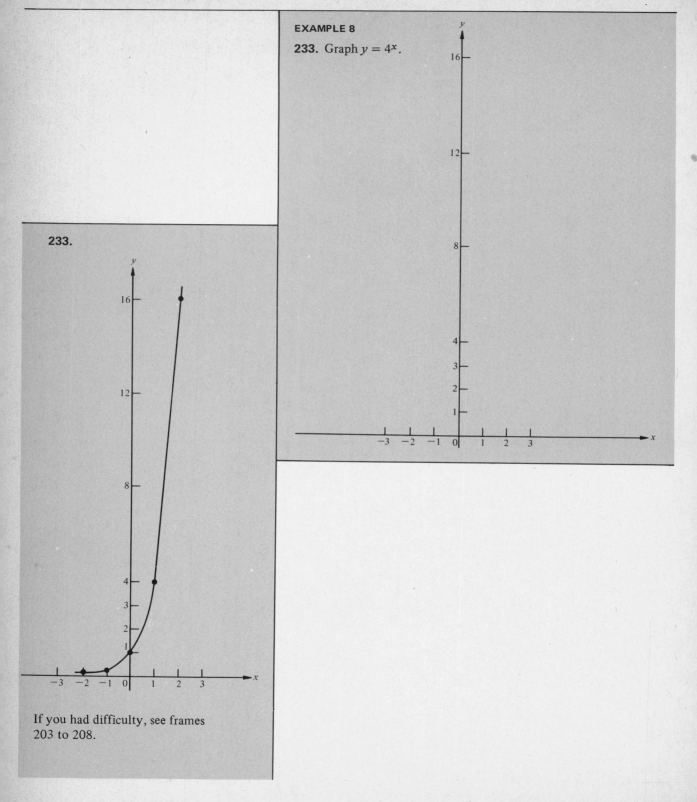

EXAMPLE 8

233. Graph $y = 4^x$.

233.

If you had difficulty, see frames 203 to 208.

EXAMPLE 9

234. Use the graph of $y = 4^x$ to find an approximate value for $4^{7/5}$. $4^{7/5} \approx$ ___

234. 7.

If you had difficulty, see frames 229 to 232.

235. If $a > 1$, then $y = a^x$ is **(a)** _____ .

The function is **(b)** _____ for all x.

The function **(c)** _____ as x increases.

(d) a^x ___ if $x > 0$

(e) a^x ___ if $x = 0$

(f) a^x ___ if $x < 0$

235. (a) a function,
(b) positive,
(c) increases,
(d) > 1,
(e) $= 1$,
(f) < 1.

If you had difficulty, see frames 213 to 224.

PROBLEMS

1. Use the graph of $y = 2^x$ to find approximate values for the following.

   (a) $\sqrt{2}$ (b) $\sqrt[3]{2}$ (c) $2^{\pi/2}$

2. Graph $y = 4^x$ and find approximate values for the following.

   (a) $\sqrt[3]{4}$ (b) $4^{\sqrt{2}}$ (c) $4^{\pi/2}$

3. If $y = a^x, a > 0$, find the number a whose graph passes through the following points.

   (a) $(6, 729)$ (b) $(7, 128)$ (c) $(3, 343)$

Answers are at end of book.

QUIZ

If you cannot answer the following questions correctly, review the appropriate frames.

1. Sketch the graph of $y = 2^x$.

2. Give four properties of $y = a^x, a > 1$.

3. Use the graph of $y = 2^x$ to find an approximate value for $2^{3/2}$.

Answers are at end of book.

4 Logarithmic Functions

Upon completing this chapter, you should be able to

I. Define the logarithm function $f(x) = \log_a x$.

II. Give the domain and range of the logarithm function.

III. Use the properties

(A) $\log_a a^x = x$,

(B) $a^{\log_a y} = y$,

(C) $a^x = y$ if and only if $x = \log_a y$
to solve simple logarithmic equations.

---

	236. In Volume II in the chapter on inverse functions we saw that a function f has an inverse if and only if f is _____ .
236. One-to-one. If you had difficulty, see frames 248 to 251 of chapter 8, Volume II.	**237.** Furthermore, a function is one-to-one if and only if _____ _____ _____ .
237. Each element in the range is associated with one and only one element in the domain. If you had difficulty, see frames 248 to 251 of chapter 8, Volume II.	**238.** And we can tell from the graph that a function is one-to-one if a _____ line through any point in the _____ (horizontal, vertical) (domain, range) meets the graph once and only once.
238. horizontal; range	

239. Look at the graph of the function $f(x) = 2^x$. Does it have an inverse? _____

Why? _____

_____

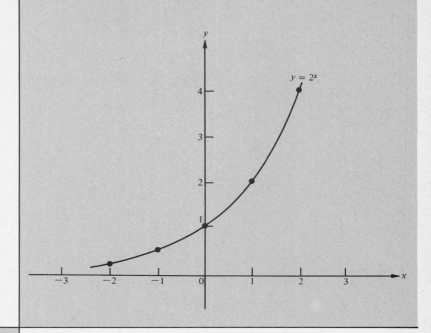

239. Yes.

A horizontal line through any point in the range meets the graph once and only once. Thus $f(x) = 2^x$ is one-to-one and hence has an inverse.

240. If $a > 0$ is any positive real number, $a \neq 1$, then the graph of $f(x) = a^x$ has the same general shape as $y = 2^x$ or $y = (\frac{1}{2})^x$.

Does $f(x) = a^x$, $a > 0$, $a \neq 1$, have an inverse? _____

Why? _____

_____

_____

240. Yes.

A horizontal line through any point in the range meets the graph once and only once. Thus $f(x) = a^x$ is one-to-one and hence has an inverse.

241. The domain of $f(x) = a^x$ is _____

_____ and the range of $f(x) = a^x$ is _____

_____.

241. R, the set of real numbers; $\{y \in R \mid y > 0\}$, the set of positive real numbers.

242. In general, the domain of an inverse function f^{-1} is equal to the _____ of the function f, and the range of f^{-1} is equal to the _____ of f.

---

242. range; domain.

If you had difficulty, see frames 242 to 248 of the chapter on inverse functions in Volume II.

243. Thus f^{-1}, the inverse of $f(x) = a^x$, has as its domain

_____

and as its range _____

_____ .

---

243. $\{x \in R \mid x > 0\}$, the set of positive real numbers; R, the set of real numbers

244. The inverse of $f(x) = a^x, a > 0, a \neq 1$, is called the **logarithm function to the base a** and is denoted by $\log_a x$.

DEFINITION: $y = a^x$ if and only if $x = \log_a y$. The domain of the logarithm function is _____

and the range is _____ .

---

244. the set of positive real numbers; R, the set of all real numbers

245. $x = \log_a y$ is read "x is the logarithm of y to base a."

$x = \log_a y$ is defined by

_____ if and only if $x = \log_a y$.

---

245. $y = a^x$

246. The base of the logarithm function $x = \log_a y$ is ____ .

---

246. a

247. $x = \log_a y$ is read " _____

_____ ."

---

247. x is the logarithm of y to base a

248. And, by definition, $y = a^x$ if and only if $x =$ _____ .

---

248. $\log_a y$

249. As we have seen in frame 239, a horizontal line through any point in the range of $y = a^x$ will intersect the graph of the function

_____ .

(how many times?)

---

249. once and only once

250. Thus, the equation $N = a^x$, for any given positive number N, has one and only one solution z as illustrated below.

We also see from the illustration that $x =$ _____ is the only solution of the equation $M = a^x$.

---

250. c

251. In Volume II, in the chapter on inverse functions we proved that if a function f from D_f, the domain, onto $\mathcal{R}_f$, the range, is one-to-one, then f^{-1} is a function from _____ onto _____ .

---

251. $\mathcal{R}_f$; D_f

252. Furthermore the composite function $f \circ f^{-1}$ is a function from **(a)** _____ to **(b)** _____ defined by $(f \circ f^{-1})(x) =$ **(c)** ___ for all $x \in$ **(d)** _____ .

---

252. (a) $\mathcal{R}_f$, **(b)** $\mathcal{R}_f$,
(c) x, **(d)** $\mathcal{R}_f$.
If you had difficulty, see frames
286 to 294 in chapter 8, Volume II.

253. Similarly, $f^{-1} \circ f$ is a function from **(a)** _____ to **(b)** _____ defined by $(f^{-1} \circ f)(x) =$ **(c)** ___ for all $x \in$ **(d)** _____ .

---

253. (a) D_f, **(b)** D_f,
(c) x, **(d)** D_f.
If you had difficulty, see frames
286 to 294 in chapter 8, Volume II.

254. Thus, if we start with any real number x, first apply the exponential function to x and then apply its inverse, the logarithm function, to the result, we get ___ .

---

254. x

255. That is, if $y = a^x$, then $\log_a y =$ ___ .

---

255. x

256. That is, **(1)** $\log_a a^x =$ ___ for all real numbers x.

---

256. x

257. Similarly, if we start with any positive real number y, first apply the logarithm function to y and then apply its inverse, the exponential function, to the result, we get ___ .

---

257. y

258. That is, if $x = \log_a y$, then $a^x =$ ___ .

---

258. y

259. That is, **(2)** $a^{\log_a y} =$ ___ .

---

259. y

260. And, by definition, **(3)** $y = a^x$ if and only if _____ .

---

260. $\log_a y = x$

261. The three relationships

(1) $\log_a a^x = $ **(a)** _____ , (2) $a^{\log_a y} = $ **(b)** _____ , and

(3) **(c)** _____ if and only if **(d)** _____ are the key relationships involving logarithmic and exponential functions.

---

261. (a) x, **(b)** y,
(c) $y = a^x$, **(d)** $\log_a y = x$

262. Many problems involve little more than shifting from the equation $y = a^x$ to the equivalent equation _____ or vice versa.

---

262. $\log_a y = x$

EXAMPLE 1
263. To find the value of $\log_2 32$, we change from $x = \log_2 32$ to the equivalent equation **(a)** _____ since the base $a = $ **(b)** _____ and $y = $ **(c)** _____ .

---

263. (a) $2^x = 32$,
(b) 2, **(c)** 32

264. Thus $x = $ _____ and $\log_2 32 = $ _____ .

NOTE: The solution is unique since $x = \log_2 y$ is a function and hence associates a unique value with each y in the domain.

---

264. 5; 5

EXAMPLE 2
265. $\log_3 81 = $ _____

---

265. 4.

If you had difficulty, go on to the next frame. If not, skip to frame 268.

266. To find the value of $\log_3 81$, we replace the equation $x = \log_3 81$ by the equivalent equation **(a)** _____ since the base $a = $ **(b)** _____ and $y = $ **(c)** _____ .

---

266. (a) $3^x = 81$, **(b)** 3, **(c)** 81

267. Thus $x = $ _____ and $\log_3 81 = $ _____ .

---

267. 4; 4

EXAMPLE 3
268. $\log_4 \frac{1}{64} = $ _____

---

268. -3.

If you had difficulty, go on to the next frame. If not, skip to frame 272.

	269. If $x = \log_4 \frac{1}{64}$, the base $a =$ ___ and $y =$ ___ .
269. 4; $\frac{1}{64}$	**270.** We can replace $x = \log_4 \frac{1}{64}$ by the equivalent equation _____ .
270. $\frac{1}{64} = 4^x$	**271.** Hence $x =$ ___ and $\log_4 \frac{1}{64} =$ ___ .
271. $^-3$; $^-3$	**EXAMPLE 4** **272.** If $\log_5 N = 3, N =$ ___ .
272. 125. If you had difficulty, go on to the next frame. If not, skip to frame 276.	**273.** If $\log_5 N = 3$, then the base $a =$ **(a)** ___ , $y =$ **(b)** ___ , and $x =$ **(c)** ___ .
273. (a) 5, **(b)** N, **(c)** 3	**274.** We can replace $\log_5 N = 3$ by the equivalent equation _____ .
274. $N = 5^3$	**275.** Thus $N =$ ___ .
275. 125	**EXAMPLE 5** **276.** If $\log_a 216 = 3, a =$ ___ .
276. 6. If you had difficulty, go on to the next frame. If not, skip to frame 280.	**277.** If $\log_a 216 = 3$, then $y =$ ___ and $x =$ ___ .
277. 216; 3	

278. We can replace $\log_a 216 = 3$ by the equivalent equation

_____ .

---

278. $a^3 = 216$

279. Thus $a =$ ___ .

---

279. 6

EXAMPLE 6

280. $7^3 = 343$ expressed in equivalent logarithmic form is

_____ .

---

280. $3 = \log_7 343$.

If you had difficulty, go on to the next frame. If not, skip to frame 283.

281. If $7^3 = 343$, the base $a =$ **(a)** ___ , $x =$ **(b)** _____ , and $y =$ **(c)** _____ .

---

281. (a) 7, **(b)** 3, **(c)** 343

282. Thus, in logarithmic form, we get _____ .

---

282. $3 = \log_7 343$

EXAMPLE 7

283. $10^{-3} = \frac{1}{1000}$ expressed in equivalent logarithmic form is

_____ .

---

283. $-3 = \log_{10} \frac{1}{1000}$.

If you had difficulty, see frames 280 to 282.

EXAMPLE 8

284. To solve $2^{\log_2 y} = 13$, we see by property **(2)** of frame 259

that $a^{\log_a y} = $ ___ for all y.

---

284. y

285. Thus if $2^{\log_2 y} = 13$, $y = $ ___ .

---

285. 13

EXAMPLE 9

286. Solve $x^{\log_7 14} = 14$ for x. $x = $ ___

---

286. 7.

If you had difficulty, go on to the next frame. If not, skip to frame 289.

287. By property **(2)** $a^{\log_a y} = \underline{\quad}$ for all y.

---

287. y

288. Thus $x = \underline{\quad}$.

---

288. 7

289. $9^{\log_9 12} = \underline{\quad}$

---

289. 12.
If you had difficulty, see frames 284 to 288.

290. $6^{\log_x 11} = 11$ if and only if $x = \underline{\quad}$.

---

290. 6
If you had difficulty, see frames 284 to 289.

EXAMPLE 10

291. To express 7^5 as a power of 10, we have by property **(2)**
$a^{\log_a y} = \underline{\quad}$.

---

291. y

292. Thus if $y = 7$ and $a = 10$, we get $7 = \underline{\hspace{3cm}}$.

---

292. $10^{\log_{10} 7}$

293. And $7^5 = \underline{\hspace{4cm}}$.

---

293. $\left(10^{\log_{10} 7}\right)^5 = 10^{(\log_{10} 7)5}$

EXAMPLE 11

294. 9^{11} expressed as a power of 10 is $\underline{\hspace{3cm}}$.

---

294. $10^{11 \log_{10} 9}$.
If you had difficulty, go on to the next frame. If not, skip to frame 298.

295. By property **(2)** $\underline{\hspace{3cm}}$ for all y.

---

295. $a^{\log_a y} = y$

296. Thus if $y = 9$ and $a = 10$, we get $9 = \underline{\hspace{2.5cm}}$.

---

296. $10^{\log_{10} 9}$

297. And $9^{11} = \underline{\hspace{4cm}}$.

---

297. $\left(10^{\log_{10} 9}\right)^{11} = 10^{11(\log_{10} 9)}$

298. If $y = a^x$, we define the logarithm function by
$x = \underline{\hspace{2cm}}$.

---

298. $\log_a y$

299. The domain of $x = \log_a y$ is ———————— ———————— and the range is ————————
————————.

---

299. the set of positive real numbers; R, the set of all real numbers.

If you had difficulty, see frames 241 to 244.

300. The three key relationships between the exponential function and its inverse, the logarithm function, are

(1) $\log_a a^x = $ **(a)** —— ,

(2) $a^{\log_a y} = $ **(b)** —— ,

(3) **(c)** ———————— if and only if **(d)** ————————.

---

300. (a) x,
(b) y,
(c) $y = a^x$, **(d)** $\log_a y = x$

EXERCISE 1

301. $\log_5 625 = $ ——

---

301. 4.

If you had difficulty, see frames 262 to 271.

EXERCISE 2

302. If $\log_6 N = 3$, $N = $ ————.

---

302. 216.

If you had difficulty, see frames 272 to 275.

EXERCISE 3

303. Solve $6^{\log_6 x} = 21$ for x. $x = $ ——

---

303. 21.

If you had difficulty, see frames 284 to 290.

EXERCISE 4

304. 4^7 expressed as a power of 10 is ——————— .

304. $10^{7\log_{10}4}$.

If you had difficulty, see frames 291 to 297.

PROBLEMS

1. Write each of the following equations in equivalent logarithmic form.

(a) $2^6 = 64$ (c) $8^3 = 512$ (e) $5^{-3} = \frac{1}{125}$ (g) $k^4 = N$

(b) $10^2 = 100$ (d) $64^{1/3} = 4$ (f) $9^0 = 1$ (h) $4^K = N$

2. Solve each of the following equations for x.

(a) $\log_{10}\frac{1}{1000} = x$ (c) $\log_{16} 2 = x$ (e) $\log_4 x = -2$

(b) $\log_6 x = 3$ (d) $\log_x \frac{1}{49} = -2$ (f) $\log_x 625 = 4$

3. Solve each of the following equations for x.

(a) $4^{\log_4 x} = 9$ (c) $5^{\log_5 7} = x$ (e) $8^{\log_8 x} = 14$ (g) $K^{\log_K 4} = x$

(b) $x^{\log_4 6} = 6$ (d) $3^{\log_x 5} = 5$ (f) $x^{\log_3 2} = 2$ (h) $7^{\log_x K} = K$

Answers are at end of book.

If you cannot answer the following questions correctly, review the appropriate frames.

1. The three key relationships between the exponential function and its inverse, the logarithm function, are

   (a) _____

   (b) _____

   (c) _____ if and only if _____ .

2. Find the value of $\log_7 343$.

3. If $\log_5 N = 3$, find N.

4. Solve $8^{\log_8 x} = 37$ for x.

5. Express 5^6 as a power of 10.

Answers are at end of book. $P\ 282$

5   Properties of Logarithms

Upon completing this chapter, you should be able to

I. Graph $y = \log_a x$.

II. Write the properties of $f(x) = \log_a x$.

III. Given the values for $\log_a 2$, $\log_a 3$, $\log_a 5$, and $\log_a 7$ for a fixed positive real number a, calculate $\log_a k$ for values of k that are multiples or reciprocals of multiples of 2, 3, 5, and 7.

IV. Use the properties of logarithms to simplify expressions involving logarithms.

V. Change a logarithm from one base to another base.

---

305. We saw in Volume II in the chapter on inverse functions that the graphs of a function f and its inverse f^{-1} are symmetric with respect to _____ .

305. The line $y = x$.

If you had difficulty, see frames 252 to 271 in chapter 8, Volume II.

306. That is, if the point (a, b) is on the graph of f, then the point $(\_\_\_ , \_\_\_)$ is on the graph of f^{-1} .

306. b, a.

If you had difficulty, see frames 252 to 271 in chapter 8, Volume II.

307. Therefore we can use the graph of $f(x) = 2^x$ to obtain the graph of its inverse $f^{-1}(x) = $ _____ .

307. $\log_2 x$

308. Below is the graph of $f(x) = 2^x$ along with a table of values. Complete the table of values for $f^{-1}(x) = \log_2 x$ and sketch the graph on the same axes.

x	2^x
−2	$\frac{1}{4}$
−1	$\frac{1}{2}$
0	1
1	2
2	4

x	$\log_2 x$

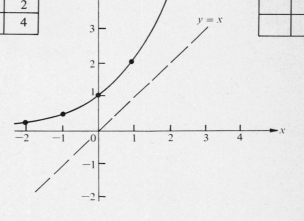

308.

x	$\log_2 x$
$\frac{1}{4}$	−2
$\frac{1}{2}$	−1
1	0
2	1
4	2

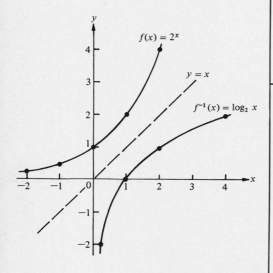

309. The domain of $f^{-1}(x) = \log_2 x$ is _____

_____ and the range is _____

_____ .

---

309. the set of positive real numbers;
R, the set of all real numbers

310. If $a > 1$, then the graph of the logarithmic function $f(x) = \log_a x$ has the same general shape as $\log_2 x$. We see from the graph in frame 308 that the logarithm function has the following properties that we accept without proof.

---

310. Go on to the next frame.

311. (1) $y = \log_a x, a > 1$, does indeed define a function. That is, for each real number x in the domain $\log_a x$ associates _____

_____ .

---

311. one and only one number y in the range

312. (2) $\log_a x$ **(a)** _____ if $x \leqslant 0$.

$\log_a x <$ **(b)** ___ if $0 < x < 1$.

$\log_a x$ **(c)** ___ if $x = 1$.

$\log_a x$ **(d)** ___ if $1 < x$.

---

312. (a) is not defined,
(b) 0,
(c) $= 0$,
(d) > 0

313. (3) The value of the function _____ as x increases.

---

313. increases

314. That is, if $x_2 > x_1$, then $\log_a x_2 \underset{(>,\,=,\,<)}{\underline{\hspace{1.5cm}}} \log_a x_1$.

---

314. $>$

315. A number of properties of logarithms follow immediately from the definition.

(4) $\log_a a =$ ___ . That is, the logarithm of any number a to the base a is ___ .

---

315. 1;
1.

If you had difficulty, go on to the next frame. If not, skip to frame 318.

316. If $\log_a a = x$, then $y = $ ___ , and we can replace $\log_a a = x$ by the equivalent equation _____ .

---

316. a; $a = a^x$

317. Thus $x = $ ___ , and $\log_a a = $ ___ .

---

317. 1; 1

318. Summarizing frames 311 to 317, we see that if $a > 1$, then

(1) $f(x) = \log_a x$ **(a)** _____ ;

(2) $\log_a x$ **(b)** _____ if $x \leqslant 0$,

$\log_a x$ **(c)** ___ if $0 < x < 1$,

$\log_a x$ **(d)** ___ if $x = 1$,

$\log_a x$ **(e)** ___ if $1 < x$;

(3) the values of $\log_a x$ **(f)** _____ as x increases;

(4) $\log_a a = $ **(g)** ___ .

---

318. **(a)** is a function,
(b) is not defined,
(c) < 0,
(d) $= 0$,
(e) > 0,
(f) increase,
(g) 1

319. We now prove three more properties of $y = \log_a x$.

Let M, N, and $a \neq 1$ be positive real numbers and let **(1)** $m = \log_a M$ and **(2)** $n = \log_a N$. We can replace equations **(1)** and **(2)** by the equivalent equations _____ and _____ .

---

319. $M = a^m$; $N = a^n$

320. Hence $M \cdot N = a^m \cdot a^n = $ _____ , by a law of exponents.

---

320. a^{m+n}

321. And $\log_a (M \cdot N) = \log_a a^{m+n} = $ _____ , since $\log_a x$ and a^x are inverse functions.

---

321. $m + n$

322. Finally, from **(1)** and **(2)** in frame 319 $m = $ _____ and $n = $ _____ .

---

322. $\log_a M$; $\log_a N$

323. Thus we have shown that $\log_a (M \cdot N) = $ _____ .

---

323. $\log_a M + \log_a N$

324. We have proved the following theorem that will be our fifth property.

THEOREM 5:   If M, N, and $a \neq 1$ are positive real numbers, then

_____ .

324. $\log_a (M \cdot N) = \log_a M + \log_a N$

■■■■■   ■■■■■

SUMMARY

■■■■■   ■■■■■

Theorem 5

If M, N, and $a \neq 1$ are positive real numbers, then
$$\log_a (M \cdot N) = \log_a M + \log_a N.$$
Proof: Let (1) $m = \log_a M$ and (2) $n = \log_a N$.

We can replace equations (1) and (2) by the equivalent equations
$$M = a^m \quad \text{and} \quad N = a^n.$$
Hence $M \cdot N = a^m \cdot a^n = a^{m+n}$ and
$$\log_a (M \cdot N) = \log_a a^{m+n} = m + n,$$
since $\log_a x$ and a^x are inverse functions.

Finally, from (1) and (2)
$$m = \log_a M \quad \text{and} \quad n = \log_a N.$$
Thus
$$\log_a (M \cdot N) = \log_a M + \log_a N.$$

---

325. We now turn to property **(6)**. Let M, N, and $a \neq 1$ be positive real numbers and let **(1)** $m = \log_a M$ and **(2)** $n = \log_a N$. As before we can replace (1) and (2) by the equivalent equations _____

and _____ .

325. $M = a^m$; $N = a^n$

326. Hence $\dfrac{M}{N} = $ _____ = _____ by a law of exponents.

---

326. $\dfrac{a^m}{a^n}$; a^{m-n}

327. And $\log_a \dfrac{M}{N} = $ _____ = _____ , since $\log_a x$ and a^x are inverse functions.

---

327. $\log_a a^{m-n}$; $m-n$

328. Finally, from (1) and (2) in frame 325, $m = $ _____ and $n = $ _____ .

---

328. $\log_a M$; $\log_a N$

329. Thus we have shown that $\log_a \dfrac{M}{N} = $ _____ .

---

329. $\log_a M - \log_a N$

330. We have proved the following theorem that we shall accept as property (6).

THEOREM 6: If M, N, and $a \neq 1$ are positive real numbers, then

_____ .

---

330. $\log_a \dfrac{M}{N} = \log_a M - \log_a N$

Theorem 6

If M, N, and $a \neq 1$ are positive real numbers, then

$$\log_a \frac{M}{N} = \log_a M - \log_a N$$

Proof: Let (1) $m = \log_a M$ and (2) $n = \log_a N$.

We can replace equations (1) and (2) by the equivalent equations

$$M = a^m \quad \text{and} \quad N = a^n.$$

Hence

$$\frac{M}{N} = \frac{a^m}{a^n} = a^{m-n} \quad \text{by a law of exponents, and}$$

$$\log_a \frac{M}{N} = \log_a a^{m-n} = m - n,$$

since $\log_a x$ and a^x are inverse functions.

Finally, from (1) and (2)

$$m = \log_a M \quad \text{and} \quad n = \log_a N.$$

Thus

$$\log_a \frac{M}{N} = \log_a M - \log_a N.$$

---

	331. We have an immediate corollary to theorem (6). Since $\log_a 1 = \underline{\quad}$,
331. 0	**332.** it follows from theorem (6) that $\log_a \frac{1}{N} = \underline{\hspace{3cm}}$.
332. $-\log_a N$	

	333. We now prove our final property for $y = \log_a x$. Let M and $a \neq 1$ be positive real numbers, p be any real number, and let $m = \log_a M$. We can replace $m = \log_a M$ by the equivalent equation _____ .
333. $M = a^m$	**334.** Hence, $M^p = (a^m)^p =$ _____ by the laws of exponents.
334. $a^{mp} = a^{pm}$	**335.** Therefore $\log_a M^p =$ _____ $=$ ____ , since $\log_a x$ and a^x are inverse functions.
335. $\log_a a^{pm}$; pm	**336.** But $m =$ _____ .
336. $\log_a M$	**337.** Thus we have shown that $\log_a M^p =$ _____ .
337. $p \log_a M$	**338.** We have proved the following theorem. **THEOREM (7):** If M and $a \neq 1$ are positive real numbers and p is any real number, then _____ .
338. $\log_a M^p = p \log_a M$	

SUMMARY

Theorem 7

If M and $a \neq 1$ are positive real numbers and p is any real number, then
$$\log_a M^p = p \log_a M.$$

Proof: Let $m = \log_a M$, then we can replace $m = \log_a M$ by the equivalent equation $M = a^m$.

Hence $M^p = (a^m)^p = a^{mp} = a^{pm}$ by a law of exponents.

Therefore $\log_a M^p = \log_a a^{pm} = pm,$

since $\log_a x$ and a^x are inverse functions.

Finally,
$$m = \log_a M$$

Thus we have shown that
$$\log_a M^p = p \log_a M.$$

339. Summarizing theorems (5), (6), and (7) we have

(5) $\log_a (M \cdot N) = $ **(a)** _____ ,

(6) $\log_a \dfrac{M}{N} = $ **(b)** _____ ,

(7) $\log_a M^p = $ **(c)** _____ .

---

339. (a) $\log_a M + \log_a N$,
(b) $\log_a M - \log_a N$,
(c) $p \log_a M$

340. Theorem (5) indicates that a logarithm of the product of two numbers is equal to the _____ of the logarithms of the numbers.

---

340. sum

341. Theorem (6) indicates that a logarithm of the quotient of two numbers is equal to the _____

_____ .

---

341. difference of the logarithms of the numbers

342. And theorem (7) says that the logarithm of a number to the power p is equal to _____ the logarithm of the number.

---

342. p times

343. The seven properties of $f(x) = \log_a x$ are

(1) $f(x) = \log_a x$ **(a)** _____ ;

(2) $\log_a x$ **(b)** _____ if $x \leqslant 0$,

   $\log_a x$ **(c)** ____ if $0 < x < 1$,

   $\log_a x$ **(d)** ____ if $x = 1$,

   $\log_a x$ **(e)** ____ if $1 < x$;

(3) the values of $\log_a x$ **(f)** _____ as x increases;

(4) $\log_a a = $ **(g)** ___ ;

Theorem (5) $\log_a (M \cdot N) = $ **(h)** _____ ;

Theorem (6) $\log_a \dfrac{M}{N} = $ **(i)** _____ ;

Theorem (7) $\log_a M^p = $ **(j)** _____ .

---

343. (a) is a function,
(b) is not defined, **(c)** < 0,
(d) $= 0$, **(e)** > 0, **(f)** increase, **(g)** 1,
(h) $\log_a M + \log_a N$,
(i) $\log_a M - \log_a N$,
(j) $p \log_a M$

EXAMPLE 1

344. We are now ready to use the seven properties.

If $\log_{10} 3 = .4771$ and $\log_{10} 4 = .6021$, then we can calculate $\log_{10} 12$.

Since $12 = 3 \cdot 4$, we apply theorem (5) and get

$\log_{10} 12 = \log_{10} (3 \cdot 4) = \underline{\hspace{4cm}}$

$\underline{\hspace{5cm}}$.

---

344. $\log_{10} 3 + \log_{10} 4$
$= .4771 + .6021 = 1.0792$

EXAMPLE 2

345. Use theorem (7) and the information in frame 344 to find $\log_{10} 64$.

$\log_{10} 64 = \underline{\hspace{2cm}}$

---

345. 1.8063.

If you had difficulty, go on to the next frame. If not, skip to frame 348.

346. Since $64 = 4^3$, $\log_{10} 64 = \log_{10} 4^3 = \underline{\hspace{2cm}}$ by theorem (7).

---

346. $3 \log_{10} 4$

347. And $\log_{10} 4 = .6021$. Thus $\log_{10} 64 = \underline{\hspace{3cm}}$

$\underline{\hspace{3cm}}$.

---

347. $3(.6021) = 1.8063$

EXAMPLE 3

348. Use the data in frame 344 to find $\log_{10} \sqrt[3]{4}$.

$\log_{10} \sqrt[3]{4} = \underline{\hspace{2cm}}$

---

348. .2007.

If you had difficulty, go on to the next frame. If not, skip to frame 351.

349. Since $\sqrt[3]{4} = 4^{1/3}$, we can apply theorem (7). We get

$\log_{10} 4^{1/3} = \underline{\hspace{3cm}}$.

---

349. $\frac{1}{3} \log_{10} 4$

350. And, since $\log_{10} 4 = .6021$,

$\log_{10} 4^{1/3} = \underline{\hspace{4cm}}$.

---

350. $\frac{1}{3}(.6021) = .2007$

EXAMPLE 4

351. Use the data of frame 344 to find $\log_{10} \frac{4}{3}$.

$\log_{10} \frac{4}{3} = \underline{\hspace{4cm}}$

---

351. .1250 by theorem (6).

If you had difficulty, see frames 344 to 350.

EXAMPLE 5

352. We can also use the properties of logarithms to simplify expressions involving logarithms.

To simplify $3 \log_a x - \log_a xy$
we first apply theorem (7) to $3 \log_a x$ and get

$3 \log_a x = \underline{\hspace{3cm}}$.

---

352. $\log_a x^3$

353. Now we can apply theorem (6) and get

$\log_a x^3 - \log_a xy = \underline{\hspace{4cm}}$.

---

353. $\log_a \dfrac{x^3}{xy} = \log_a \dfrac{x^2}{y}$

EXAMPLE 6

354. Write the following expression as a single logarithm.

$2 \log_a y + 4 \log_a x - \log_a x^2 yz = \log_a \underline{\hspace{3cm}}$

---

354. $\dfrac{x^2 y}{z}$.

If you had difficulty, go on to the next frame. If not, skip to frame 357.

355. By theorem (7), $2 \log_a y = \underline{\hspace{2cm}}$ and

$4 \log_a x = \underline{\hspace{2cm}}$.

---

355. $\log_a y^2$; $\log_a x^4$

356. Now by theorems (5) and (6)

$$2 \log_a y + 4 \log_a x - \log_a x^2 yz = \log_a y^2 + \log_a x^4 - \log_a x^2 yz$$
$$= \underline{\hspace{4cm}} .$$

---

356. $\log_a \dfrac{y^2 x^4}{x^2 yz} = \log_a \dfrac{x^2 y}{z}$

EXAMPLE 7

357. $2 \log_a ax - \log_a x^2 = \underline{\hspace{1cm}}$

---

357. 2.

If you had difficulty, go on to the next frame. If not, skip to frame 363.

358. By theorem (7), $\log_a x^2 = \underline{\hspace{3cm}} .$

---

358. $2 \log_a x$

359. Hence $2 \log_a ax - \log_a x^2 = 2(\underline{\hspace{3cm}}).$

---

359. $\log_a ax - \log_a x$

360. And by theorem (6),

$$2(\log_a ax - \log_a x) = \underline{\hspace{5cm}} .$$

---

360. $2 \log_a \dfrac{ax}{x} = 2 \log_a a$

361. But $\log_a a = \underline{\hspace{1cm}} .$

---

361. 1

362. Hence $2 \log_a ax - \log_a x^2 = \underline{\hspace{1cm}} .$

---

362. 2

363. Many books provide a table of logarithms to the base 10. And in order to find the logarithm to another base it is necessary to express that logarithm in terms of base 10 logarithms. We now prove a result that allows us to change from one base to another.

---

363. Go on to the next frame.

364. If a and b are two logarithmic bases and N is any positive number, we have $a^{\log_a N} = \underline{\hspace{0.5cm}} .$

---

364. N

365. Hence $\log_b N = \log_b a^{\log_a N} = \underline{\hspace{3cm}}$ by theorem (7).

---

365. $\log_a N \log_b a$

	366. Or $\log_a N =$ _____ .
366. $\dfrac{\log_b N}{\log_b a}$	**367.** Thus we have proved the following theorem. **THEOREM 8:** If a and b are two logarithmic bases and N is any positive number, then $\log_a N =$ _____ .
367. $\dfrac{\log_b N}{\log_b a}$	

SUMMARY

Theorem 8

If a and b are two logarithmic bases and N is any positive number, then

$$\log_a N = \frac{\log_b N}{\log_b a} \, .$$

Proof: For any positive number N,

$$N = a^{\log_a N}.$$

Hence

$$\log_b N = \log_b a^{\log_a N}$$
$$= \log_a N \cdot \log_b a \quad \text{by theorem (7).}$$

That is,

$$\log_a N = \frac{\log_b N}{\log_b a} \, .$$

	368. We have an immediate corollary. If $N = b$, then, by theorem (8), $\log_a b =$ _____ .
368. $\dfrac{1}{\log_b a}$, (since $\log_b b = 1$)	

EXAMPLE 8

369. If we let $a = 3$, $N = 4$, and $b = 10$, then, by theorem (8),

$\log_3 4 = $ _____ .

---

369. $\dfrac{\log_{10} 4}{\log_{10} 3}$

370. But $\log_{10} 3 = .4771$ and $\log_{10} 4 = .6021$. Hence

$\log_3 4 = $ _____ .

---

370. $\dfrac{.6021}{.4771} = 1.2620$

EXAMPLE 9

371. $\log_4 3 = $ _____

---

371. .7924.

If you had difficulty, see frames 369 and 370.

EXAMPLE 10

372. If $\log_{10} 2 = .3010$ and $\log_{10} 3 = .4771$, $\log_8 3 = $ _____ .

_____

---

372. .5283.

If you had difficulty, go on to the next frame. If not, skip to frame 377.

373. We can apply theorem (8) if we let $N = $ **(a)** ___, $a = $ **(b)** ___, and $b = $ **(c)** ___ . We get $\log_8 3 = $ **(d)** _____ .

---

373. **(a)** 3, **(b)** 8, **(c)** 10,

(d) $\dfrac{\log_{10} 3}{\log_{10} 8}$

374. But $8 = 2^3$; hence, by theorem (5),

$\log_{10} 8 = $ _____ .

---

374. $\log_{10} 2^3 = 3 \log_{10} 2$

375. $\log_{10} 2 = .3010$. Hence $\log_{10} 8 = $ _____ .

---

375. $3(.3010) = .9030$

376. And $\log_{10} 3 = .4771$. Hence

$$\log_8 3 = \frac{\log_{10} 3}{\log_{10} 8} = \underline{\hspace{4cm}}.$$

---

376. $\dfrac{.4771}{.9030} = .5283$

EXAMPLE 11

377. If $\log_{10} 2 = .3010$ and $\log_{10} 3 = .4771$, then

$$\log_6 4 = \underline{\hspace{2cm}}.$$

---

377. .7737.

If you had difficulty, go on to the next frame. If not, skip to frame 382.

378. We can apply theorem (8) if $N = $ **(a)** ___ , $a = $ **(b)** ___ ,

and $b = $ **(c)** ___ . We get $\log_6 4 = $ **(d)** $\underline{\hspace{3cm}}$.

---

378. **(a)** 4, **(b)** 6, **(c)** 10,

(d) $\dfrac{\log_{10} 4}{\log_{10} 6}$

379. But $4 = 2^2$, and $\log_{10} 2 = .3010$. Hence

$$\log_{10} 4 = \underline{\hspace{6cm}}.$$

---

379. $2 \log_{10} 2 = 2(.3010) = .6020$

380. $6 = 2 \cdot 3$ and $\log_{10} 3 = .4771$. Hence $\log_{10} 6 = \log_{10} (2 \cdot 3)$

$$= \underline{\hspace{6cm}}.$$

---

380. $\log_{10} 2 + \log_{10} 3$

$= .3010 + .4771 = .7781$

381. Thus $\log_6 4 = \dfrac{\log_{10} 4}{\log_{10} 6} = \underline{\hspace{4cm}}$.

---

381. $\dfrac{.6020}{.7781} = .7737$

382. Graph $f(x) = \log_3 x$.

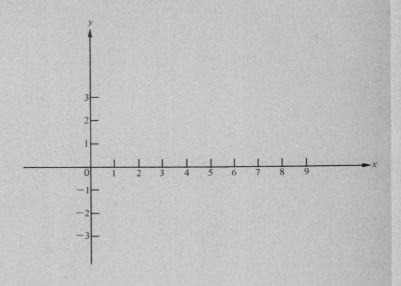

382.

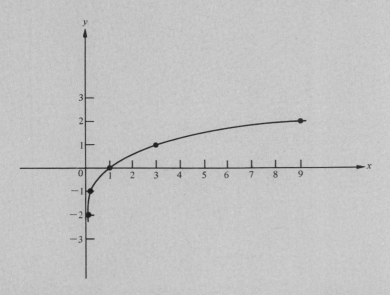

If you had difficulty, see frames 305 to 309.

	EXERCISE 2
	383. The domain of $f(x) = \log_a x, a \neq 1$, is _____
	_____ and the range is _____
	_____ .
383. the set of positive real numbers; R, the set of all real numbers	**EXERCISE 3**
	384. We observed three properties of the logarithm function from its graph.
	(1) $f(x) = \log_a x$ **(a)** _____ ;
	(2) $\log_a x$ **(b)** _____ if $x \leqslant 0$,
	$\log_a x$ **(c)** _____ if $0 < x < 1$,
	$\log_a x$ **(d)** _____ if $x = 1$,
	$\log_a x$ **(e)** _____ if $1 < x$;
	(3) the values of the function **(f)** _____ as x increases.
384. (a) is a function, **(b)** is not defined, **(c)** < 0, **(d)** $= 0$, **(e)** > 0, **(f)** increase. If you had difficulty, see frames 310 to 318.	**EXERCISE 4**
	385. Property (4) followed immediately from the definition of the logarithm function. We have (4) $\log_a a = $ ___ .
385. 1. If you had difficulty, see frames 315 to 317.	**EXERCISE 5**
	386. We proved properties (5), (6), and (7).
	(5) $\log_a (M \cdot N) = $ **(a)** _____
	(6) $\log_a \dfrac{M}{N} = $ **(b)** _____
	(7) $\log_a M^p = $ **(c)** _____
386. (a) $\log_a M + \log_a N$, **(b)** $\log_a M - \log_a N$, **(c)** $p \log_a M$. If you had difficulty, see frames 319 to 339.	

EXERCISE 6

387. If $\log_{10} 2 = .3010$ and $\log_{10} 3 = .4771$, then

$\log_{10} 6 = $ _____ .

387. .7781.

If you had difficulty, see frame 344.

EXERCISE 7

388. $\log_{10} \frac{2}{3} = $ _____

388. $-.1761$.

NOTE: $\log_{10} \frac{2}{3}$ is negative since $\frac{2}{3} < 1$;

If you had difficulty, see frames 344 to 351.

EXERCISE 8

389. $\log_{10} 8 = $ _____

389. .9030.

If you had difficulty, see frames 344 to 351.

EXERCISE 9

390. Express $3 \log_{10} x - 4 \log_{10} y + 2 \log_{10} xy$ as a single logarithm.

$3 \log_{10} x - 4 \log_{10} y + 2 \log_{10} xy = $ _____

390. $\log_{10} \dfrac{x^5}{y^2}$.

If you had difficulty, see frames 352 to 362.

EXERCISE 10

391. If a and b are two logarithmic bases and N is any positive number, then $\log_a N = $ _____ .

391. $\dfrac{\log_b N}{\log_b a}$

EXERCISE 11

392. If $\log_{10} 6 = .7781$ and $\log_{10} 8 = .9030$, then

$\log_8 6 = $ _____ .

392. .8617.

If you had difficulty, see frames 369 to 381.

PROBLEMS

1. Given that $\log_a 2 = .3010$, $\log_a 3 = .4771$, $\log_a 5 = .6990$, and $\log_a 7 = .8451$, find

   (a) $\log_a 4$ (d) $\log_a 9$ (g) $\log_a \frac{3}{7}$ (j) $\log_a \frac{1}{7}$

   (b) $\log_a 6$ (e) $\log_a 10$ (h) $\log_a \frac{16}{9}$ (k) $\log_a 192$

   (c) $\log_a 8$ (f) $\log_a 1$ (i) $\log_a 32$ (l) $\log_a a$

2. Simplify the following expressions.

   (a) $\log_a x - \log_a y + 2 \log_a z$ (c) $\log_a (x - 3) - \log_a (x + 4)$

   (b) $\frac{1}{2} \log_a x + 3 \log_a y - \log_a xyz$ (d) $\log_a (x/a) - \log_a (a/x)$

3. Use the data in problem 1 to determine the following.

   (a) $\log_a 7$ (d) $\log_7 32$ (g) $\log_8 1$

   (b) $\log_3 10$ (e) $\log_5 \frac{1}{7}$ (h) $\log_3 a$

   (c) $\log_4 9$ (f) $\log_6 \frac{16}{9}$

Answers are at end of book.

QUIZ

If you cannot answer the following questions correctly, review the appropriate frames.

1. Sketch the graph of $y = \log_2 x$.

2. Give the domain and range of the logarithm function $y = \log_a x$, $a \neq 1$.

3. Fill in the blanks on the left with the appropriate statement on the right.

    (a) $\log_a x$ _____ if $x < 0$ > 0

    (b) $\log_a x$ _____ if $0 < x < 1$ $= 0$

    (c) $\log_a x$ _____ if $x = 1$ < 0

    (d) $\log_a x$ _____ if $1 < x$ not defined

4. Complete the following.

    (a) $\log_a a =$ _____ for all a.

    (b) $\log_a M \cdot N =$ _____

    (c) $\log_a \dfrac{M}{N} =$ _____

    (d) $\log_a M^p =$ _____

5. If $\log_{10} 2 = .3010$ and $\log_{10} 3 = .4771$, then

    (a) $\log_{10} \frac{3}{2} =$ _____   (b) $\log_2 3 =$ _____

Answers are at end of book.

6 Logarithms to the Base 10 (Common Logarithms)

Upon completing this chapter, you should be able to

I. Express any positive number in scientific notation.

II. Find log N for any positive number N with three significant digits.

III. Express logarithms in standard form.

IV. Find N if log N is given.

V. Use logarithms to solve simple exponential problems.

---

393. We have seen earlier that any positive number, except 1, can be used as an exponential or logarithmic base. In practice, however, two numbers are almost always used as bases in logarithmic work. The integer 10 is most frequently used as the base for computational work, and the irrational number e occurs as a base in many theoretical considerations.

---

393. Go on to the next frame.

394. Logarithms to the base 10 are called **common logarithms** and it is customary to omit the subscript denoting the base.

Thus instead of $\log_{10} x$ we write _____ .

---

394. $\log x$

395. That is, $\log x$ means _____ , and we shall use the word "log" to mean "common logarithm."

---

395. $\log_{10} x$

396. Logarithms to the base 10 are called _____ _____ .

---

396. common logarithms

397. And they are denoted by _____ .

---

397. $\log x$

398. To find the logarithm to the base 10 of a positive number N, $x = \log_{10} N$, we use the equivalent equation _____ .

---

398. $10^x = N$

399. We can find $\log N$ for those values of N where $10^x = N$ is easily solved. For example, if $N = 1 = 10^0$, then $\log 1 = $ ___ .

---

399. 0

400. If $N = 10 = $ _____ , then $\log 10 = $ ___ .

---

400. 10^1; 1

401. If $N = 100 = $ _____ , then $\log 100 = $ ___ .

---

401. 10^2; 2

402. If $N = \frac{1}{10} = $ _____ , then $\log \frac{1}{10} = $ _____ .
And if $N = \frac{1}{100} = $ _____ , then $\log \frac{1}{100} = $ _____ , etc.

---

402. 10^{-1}; -1;
10^{-2}; -2

403. But for most values of N we must look up the value for $\log N$ in a table of common logarithms. Table I at the end of this book is a table of common logarithms.

Table I gives the *approximate* (correct to four decimal places) value of the common logarithm of each number from 1.00 to 9.99 in steps of .01. We must emphasize that in most cases the value of a logarithm is irrational and that the table gives only a rational approximation.

---

403. Go on to the next frame.

EXAMPLE 1

404. To find log 3.45, look at table I, part of which is shown below. Look down the column headed by N until you find the row headed by 3.4. Then move along that row until you come to the column headed by the third digit 5. This is the desired number. Thus

log 3.45 = _____ .

TABLE I LOGARITHMS OF NUMBERS FROM 1.00 TO 9.99

N	0	1	2	3	4	5	6	7	8	9
1.0	0.0000	0.004321	0.008600	0.01284	0.01703	0.02119	0.02531	0.02938	0.03342	0.03743
1.1	0.04139	0.04532	0.04922	0.05308	0.05690	0.06070	0.06446	0.06819	0.07188	0.07555
1.2	0.07918	0.08279	0.08636	0.08991	0.09342	0.09691	0.1004	0.1038	0.1072	0.1106
1.3	0.1139	0.1173	0.1206	0.1239	0.1271	0.1303	0.1335	0.1367	0.1399	0.1430
1.4	0.1461	0.1492	0.1523	0.1553	0.1584	0.1614	0.1644	0.1673	0.1703	0.1732
1.5	0.1761	0.1790	0.1818	0.1847	·	·	0.1931	0.1959	0.1987	·
1.6	0.2041	0.2068	0.2095	0.2122	·	·	·	·	·	·
1.7	0.2304		0.2355	·	·	·	·	·	·	·
⋮	⋮			0.4518	0.4533	0.4548	0.4564	·	·	0.4609
2.9	0.4624		0.4654	0.4669	0.4683	0.4698	0.4713	0.4728	0.4742	0.4757
3.0	0.4771	0.4786	0.4800	0.4814	0.4829	0.4843	0.4857	0.4871	0.4886	0.4900
3.1	0.4914	0.4928	0.4942	0.4955	0.4969	0.4983	0.4997	0.5011	0.5024	0.5038
3.2	0.5051	0.5065	0.5079	0.5092	0.5105	0.5119	0.5132	0.5145	0.5159	0.5172
3.3	0.5185	0.5198	0.5211	0.5224	0.5237	0.5250	0.5263	0.5276	0.5289	0.5302
3.4	0.5315	0.5328	0.5340	0.5353	0.5366	0.5378	0.5391	0.5403	0.5416	0.5428
3.5	0.5441	0.5453	0.5465	0.5478	0.5490	0.5502	0.5514	0.5527	0.5539	0.5551
3.6	0.5563	0.5575	0.5587	0.5599	0.5611	0.5623	0.5635	0.5647	0.5658	0.5670
3.7	0.5682	0.5694	0.5705	0.5717	0.5729	0.5740	0.5752	0.5763	0.5775	0.5786
3.8	0.5798	0.5809	0.5821	0.5832	0.5843	0.5855	0.5866	0.5877	0.5888	0.5899
		0.5922		0.5944	0.5955	0.5966	0.5977	0.5988	0.5000	0.6010

---

404. .5378

EXAMPLE 2

405. Find the value for log 7.31 in table I. log 7.31 = _____

---

405. .8639.

If you had difficulty, go on to the next frame. If not skip to frame 409.

406. To find log 7.31, look down the left-hand column headed by N of table I until you find the row headed by _____ .

---

406. 7.3

407. Then move across the row to the column headed by ____ .

---

407. 1

408. The number there is _____ . Thus log 7.31 = _____ .

---

408. .8639;
.8639

EXAMPLE 3
409. log 1.42 = _____

---

409. .1523.

If you had difficulty, see frames
404 to 408.

EXAMPLE 4
410. We may also use the table to find N if we know log N. For example, if log N = .9222, we look at the values in table I until we find .9222. The number at the head of the row gives us the first two digits, which are _____ .

---

410. 8.3

411. And the number at the head of the column above .9222 gives us the third digit, which is _____ .

---

411. 6

412. Thus if log N = .9222, then N = _____ .

---

412. 8.36

EXAMPLE 5
413. If log N = .6839, then N = _____ .

---

413. 4.83.

If you had difficulty, go on to the next frame. If not, skip to frame 417.

414. To find N, we scan table I until we find the number .6839. The number at the head of the row gives us the first two digits, which are _____ .

---

414. 4.8

415. The number at the head of the column above .6839 gives us the third digit which is _____ .

---

415. 3

416. Thus if log N = .6839, then N = _____ .

---

416. 4.83

EXAMPLE 6
417. If log N = .5775, then N = _____ .

---

417. 3.78.

If you had difficulty, see frames
410 to 416.

418. So far we have found the value of log N only for the numbers N between 1 and 10, since table I contains only those values. However, we can write any positive number in the form

$$N = n \times 10^c$$

where $1 \leqslant n < 10$ and c is an integer.

For example,

$3750 = 3.75 \times 10^3$ where $n =$ _____ and $c =$ ___ .

---

418. 3.75; 3

419. $375 = 3.75 \times$ **(a)** _____ where $n =$ **(b)** _____ and $c =$ **(c)** ___ .

---

419. **(a)** 10^2,
(b) 3.75, **(c)** 2

420. $37.5 =$ **(a)** _____ $\times$ **(b)** _____ where $n =$ **(c)** _____ and $c =$ **(d)** ___ .

---

420. **(a)** 3.75, **(b)** 10^1,
(c) 3.75, **(d)** 1

421. $3.75 =$ **(a)** _____ $\times$ **(b)** _____ where $n =$ **(c)** _____ and $c =$ **(d)** ___ .

---

421. **(a)** 3.75, **(b)** 10^0,
(c) 3.75, **(d)** 0

422. $.375 = 3.75 \times$ **(a)** _____ where $n =$ **(b)** _____ and $c =$ **(c)** ___

---

422. **(a)** 10^{-1},
(b) 3.75, **(c)** -1

423. And $.0375 =$ **(a)** _____ where $n =$ **(b)** _____ and $c =$ **(c)** ___ .

---

423. **(a)** 3.75×10^{-2},
(b) 3.75, **(c)** -2

EXAMPLE 7

424. This notation is called **scientific notation**. Express the number 746 in scientific notation.

$746 =$ **(a)** _____ , where $n =$ **(b)** _____ and $c =$ **(c)** ___ .

---

424. **(a)** 7.46×10^2, **(b)** 7.46,
(c) 2.

If you had difficulty, see frames 418 to 423.

	EXAMPLE 8 **425.** Express 8970 in scientific notation. 8970 = _____
425. 8.97×10^3. If you had difficulty, see frames 418 to 424.	**426.** In scientific notation, we write $N = n \times 10^c$ where _____ $\leqslant n <$ _____ and c is an integer.
426. 1; 10. If you had difficulty, see frame 418.	**EXAMPLE 9** **427.** Express .0527 in scientific notation. .0527 = _____
427. 5.27×10^{-2}	**428.** The number 486 written as 4.86×10^2 is said to be in _____ .
428. scientific notation	**429.** Scientific notation enables us to determine the common logarithm of any positive number from table I. If $N = n \times 10^c$ where $1 \leqslant n < 10$ and c is an integer, then $\log N = \log (n \cdot 10^c)$ $\qquad = $ _____ by property (5) of logarithms.
429. $\log n + \log 10^c$	**430.** But $\log 10^c = $ _____ by property (7).
430. $c \log 10$	**431.** And, since $\log 10 = \log_{10} 10 = $ ___ ,
431. 1	**432.** $\log 10^c = c \log 10 = $ ___ .
432. c	**433.** Thus, $\log N = $ _____ where $1 \leqslant n < 10$ and c is an integer.
433. $\log n + c$	

434. $\log n$ is called the **mantissa** of $\log N$ and c is called the **characteristic** of $\log N$ where $N =$ _____ .

---

434. $n \times 10^c$

435. Since $1 \leqslant n < 10$, we can find $\log n$ in table I and hence find the common logarithm for any positive number N by the following procedure.

We first write N in the scientific notation $N = n \times 10^c$. Then

$\log N =$ _____ .

---

435. $\log n + c$.

If you had difficulty, see frames 429 to 433.

436. Since $1 \leqslant n < 10$, we can look up $\log n$ in table I and add c to that value.

$\log n$ is called the _____ .

---

436. mantissa

437. c is called the _____ .

---

437. characteristic

EXAMPLE 10

438. To find $\log 729$, we first write 729 in scientific notation.

$729 =$ **(a)** _____ where

$n =$ **(b)** _____ and $c =$ **(c)** ___ .

---

438. **(a)** 7.29×10^2, **(b)** 7.29, **(c)** 2

439. Thus $\log 729 =$ _____ + __ .

---

439. $\log 7.29; 2$

440. From table I we see that $\log 7.29 =$ _____ .

---

440. .8627

441. Thus $\log 729 = \log 7.29 + 2 =$ _____ .

---

441. 2.8627

EXAMPLE 11

442. $\log 1620 =$ _____

---

442. 3.2095.

If you had difficulty, go on to the next frame. If not, skip to frame 447.

443. First write 1620 in scientific notation.

$1620 =$ **(a)** _____ where $n =$ **(b)** _____

and $c =$ **(c)** ___ .

---

443. (a) 1.62×10^3, **(b)** 1.62, **(c)** 3

444. Thus log $1620 =$ _____ .

---

444. log $1.62 + 3$

445. From table I, we see that log $1.62 =$ _____ .

---

445. $.2095$

446. Thus log $1620 =$ log $1.62 + 3 =$ _____ .

---

446. 3.2095

EXAMPLE 12

447. log $32.7 =$ _____

---

447. 1.5145

If you had difficulty, see frames 438 to 446.

EXAMPLE 13

448. To find log $.0315$, first write $.0315$ in scientific notation.

$.0315 =$ _____

---

448. 3.15×10^{-2}

449. Thus log $.0315 =$ _____ .

---

449. log $3.15 - 2$

450. From table I, we see that log $3.15 =$ _____ . Thus log

$.0315 =$ _____ $- 2$.

---

450. $.4983$;
$.4983$

451. In the equation log $.0315 = .4983 - 2$, the mantissa is

_____ , and the characteristic is ___ .

---

451. $.4983$; -2

452. We shall leave the answer in two parts, $.4983 - 2$, to preserve the mantissa. If we subtract 2 from $.4983$, we get -1.5017 and

the decimal part, $.5017$, is clearly no longer the _____ .

---

452. mantissa

	453. In fact, it is common practice for computational purposes to write any negative characteristic as a positive integer minus a multiple of 10. Thus we could write -2 as $8 - 10$ and $\log .0315 = \underline{\quad} .4983 - \underline{\quad}$.
453. 8; 10	**454.** Or we could write -2 as $18 - 20$ and $\log .0315 = \underline{\hspace{5cm}}$, etc.
454. $18.4983 - 20$	**EXAMPLE 14** **455.** To find $\frac{1}{4}$ ($\log .00528$), we first express $.00528$ as $\underline{\hspace{4cm}}$.
455. 5.28×10^{-3}	**456.** Hence $\log .00528 = \underline{\hspace{5cm}}$.
456. $\log 5.28 - 3$	**457.** From table I we see that $\log 5.28 = \underline{\hspace{2cm}}$. Thus $\log .00528 = \underline{\hspace{2.5cm}}$.
457. $.7226$; $.7226 - 3$	**458.** To obtain $\frac{1}{4}$ of this answer, we shall write -3 as $17 - 20$ so that the negative part can be divided conveniently by 4. We get $\log .00528 = \underline{\hspace{4cm}}$.
458. $17.7226 - 20$	**459.** Hence $\frac{1}{4}$ ($\log .00528$) $= \frac{1}{4}$ ($\underline{\hspace{4cm}}$) $\qquad\qquad\qquad = 4.4307 - \underline{\quad}$.
459. $17.7226 - 20$; 5	**460.** $\frac{1}{4}(17.7226) = 4.43065$. But we rounded it off to four decimal places since table I is correct only to $\underline{\hspace{1.5cm}}$ places.
460. four	**461.** We wish to keep the negative part a multiple of 10. Therefore if we add 5 to the first number and subtract 5 from the second, we get $\frac{1}{4}$ ($\log .00528$) $= 4.4307 - 5 = \underline{\hspace{3cm}}$.
461. $9.4307 - 10$	

	462. To avoid adding and subtracting 5, we could write -3 as $37 - 40$. Then $\log .00528 = $ _____ .
462. $37.7226 - 40$	**463.** And $\frac{1}{4}(\log .00528) = \frac{1}{4}($ _____ $)$ $\qquad = 9.4307 - $ ____ .
463. $37.7226 - 40$; 10	**EXAMPLE 15** **464.** $\frac{1}{3}(\log .0302) = $ _____
464. $9.4933 - 10$. If you had difficulty, go on to the next frame. If not, skip to frame 472.	**465.** To find $\log .0302$ we first write $.0302$ as _____ .
465. 3.02×10^{-2}	**466.** Thus $\log .0302 = $ _____ .
466. $\log 3.02 - 2$	**467.** From table I, we see that $\log 3.02 = $ _____ .
467. $.4800$	**468.** Thus $\log .0302 = $ _____ .
468. $.4800 - 2$	**469.** We want to obtain $\frac{1}{3}$ of this answer and leave the negative part a multiple of 10. Thus we write -2 as _____ .
469. $28 - 30$	**470.** Then $\log .0302 = $ _____ .
470. $28.4800 - 30$	**471.** And $\frac{1}{3} \log .0302 = \frac{1}{3}($ _____ $)$ $\qquad = 9.4933 - $ ____ .
471. $28.4800 - 30$; 10	**EXAMPLE 16** **472.** $\frac{1}{5}(\log .139) = $ _____ .
472. $9.8286 - 10$. If you had difficulty, see frames 455 to 471.	

EXAMPLE 17

473. We have been finding $\log N$ for any positive number N. We can also find N if we know its logarithm, $\log N$, simply by using table I in reverse. For example, if $\log N = 2.5340$, we write $\log N = \log n + c =$ _____ $+$ ___ .

---

473. .5340; 2

474. If $\log n = .5340$, we see from table I that $n =$ _____ .

---

474. 3.42.

If you had difficulty, see frames 410 to 417.

475. Hence $N =$ _____ $\times$ _____ .

---

475. 3.42 10^2

(since $N = n \times 10^c$)

476. That is, $N =$ _____ .

---

476. 342

477. In general, if we are given $\log N$, we write it as $\log N = m + c$.

This is called **standard form**, where $m = \log n$ is the

_____ , $0 \leqslant m < 1$, and c is the _____

of $\log N$.

---

477. mantissa; characteristic

478. If $\log N = m + c$ and $m = \log n$, then $N =$ _____ .

---

478. $n \times 10^c$

EXAMPLE 18

479. If $\log N = 3.8162$, then $N =$ _____ .

---

479. 6550.

If you had difficulty, go on to the next frame. If not, skip to frame 484.

480. If $\log N = 3.8162$, then in standard form $\log N =$

_____ .

---

480. .8162 $+$ 3

481. If $\log n = .8162$, we see from table I that $n =$ _____ .

---

481. 6.55

---

	482. Hence $N =$ _____ $\times$ _____ .
482. 6.55; 10^3	**483.** That is, $N =$ _____ .
483. 6550	**EXAMPLE 19** **484.** If $\log N = .6693 - 2$, then $N =$ _____ .
484. $.0467$. If you had difficulty, see frames 473 to 483.	**EXAMPLE 20** **485.** To find N if $\log N = 7.8825 - 10$, we first write $\log N$ in standard form. $\log N =$ _____
485. $.8825 - 3$	**486.** Thus from table I, $n =$ _____ and hence $N =$ _____ .
486. 7.63; $7.63 \times 10^{-3} = .00763$	**487.** It is essential to write $\log N$ in standard form. $\log N = m + c$, where ___ $\leqslant m <$ ___ .
487. 0; 1	**EXAMPLE 21** **488.** That is, the mantissa must be positive and between 0 and 1. For example, if $\log N = -1.6271$, we must write $\log N$ as $\log N = -1.6271 = 2 - 1.6271 - 2 =$ _____ $- 2$.
488. $.3729$	**489.** $\log N = .3729 - 2$ is now in standard form with the mantissa _____ and the characteristic _____ .
489. $.3729$; -2	**490.** Thus from table I, $n =$ **(a)** _____ and $N =$ **(b)** _____ $\times$ **(c)** _____ . That is, $N =$ **(d)** _____ .
490. (a) 2.36, **(b)** 2.36, **(c)** 10^{-2}, **(d)** $.0236$	**EXAMPLE 22** **491.** If $\log N = -3.1463$, then $N =$ _____ .
491. $.000714$. If you had difficulty, go on to the next frame. If not, skip to frame 495.	

492. 4; 4

492. To put $\log N = -3.1463$ in standard form, we add ____

and subtract ____ .

---

493. $.8537 - 4$

493. We get $\log N = -3.1463 = (4 - 3.1463) - 4$

$= $ _____ .

---

494. **(a)** 7.14,
(b) 7.14, **(c)** 10^{-4},
(d) .000714

494. Thus, from table I, $n =$ **(a)** _____ and $N =$ **(b)** _____ $\times$

(c) _____ . That is, $N =$ **(d)** _____ .

---

495. .00383.

If you had difficulty, see
frames 487 to 494.

EXAMPLE 23
495. If $\log N = -2.4168$, then $N =$ _____ .

---

496. $x - 3 = \log 15.3$.

If you had difficulty, go on to the
next frame. If not, skip to frame 502.

EXAMPLE 24
496. It is often convenient to solve an exponential problem by
expressing it in terms of logarithms. For example, if
(1) $10^{x-3} = 15.3$
and we wish to find x, we can replace equation (1) by the

equivalent equation _____ .

---

497. $\log 10^{x-3}$; $\log 15.3$

497. To replace $10^{x-3} = 15.3$ by a logarithmic equation, we
take the log of both sides and get

_____ $=$ _____ .

---

498. $(x - 3) \log 10$

498. And by property (7) of logarithms,

$\log 10^{x-3} = $ _____ .

---

499. 1

499. But $\log 10 =$ ___ .

---

500. $x - 3$

500. Hence $\log 10^{x-3} =$ _____ .

---

501. $x - 3 = \log 15.3$

501. And the equation $10^{x-3} = 15.3$ becomes

_____ .

502. From table I, we see that log $1.53 =$ _____ . Hence
log $15.3 =$ _____ .

---

502. .1847;
1.1847

503. Hence $x - 3 =$ _____
and
$$x = \text{_____} .$$

---

503. 1.1847;
4.1847

EXAMPLE 25
504. If $10^{3x+1} = 64$, then $x =$ _____ .

---

504. .2687.

If you had difficulty, go on to the
next frame. If not, skip to frame 508.

505. To solve for x, we replace $10^{3x+1} = 64$ by the equivalent
equation _____ .

---

505. $3x + 1 = \log 64$

506. From table I, we see that log $6.4 =$ _____ .
Hence log $64 =$ _____ .

---

506. .8062;
1.8062

507. Thus $3x + 1 =$ _____ and
$$x = \text{_____} .$$

---

507. 1.8062;

$\dfrac{.8062}{3} = .2687$

EXAMPLE 26
508. If $10^{2x} = 845$, then $x =$ _____ .

---

508. 1.4635.

If you had difficulty, see frames
496 to 507.

EXERCISE 1
509. log $5.73 =$ _____

---

509. .7582.

If you had difficulty, see frames
403 to 409.

EXERCISE 2
510. Express .00437 in scientific notation.

$.00437 =$ _____

---

510. 4.37×10^{-3} .

If you had difficulty, see frames
418 to 428.

	EXERCISE 3 **511.** log .00437 = _____
511. .6405 − 3. If you had difficulty, see frames 418 to 446.	**EXERCISE 4** **512.** If log N = .4669, then N = _____ .
512. 2.93. If you had difficulty, see frames 410 to 417.	**EXERCISE 5** **513.** Write log N = 3.7466 in standard form. log N = _____
513. .7466 + 3. If you had difficulty, see frames 473 to 478.	**EXERCISE 6** **514.** If log N = 3.7466, then N = _____ .
514. 5580. If you had difficulty, see frames 473 to 484.	**EXERCISE 7** **515.** If log N = −3.0511, then N = _____ .
515. .000889. If you had difficulty, see frames 487 to 495.	**EXERCISE 8** **516.** $\frac{1}{2}$ (log .00602) = _____
516. 8.8898 − 10. If you had difficulty, see frames 451 to 472.	**EXERCISE 9** **517.** If 10^{1-x} = 247, then x = _____ .
517. −1.3927. If you had difficulty, see frames 496 to 508.	

PROBLEMS

1. Write the following numbers in scientific notation.

    (a) 37.5   **(c)** .592   **(e)** 8130   **(g)** 138

    (b) 485   **(d)** 7.19   **(f)** .00269   **(h)** 83.7

2. If log 3.54 = .5490, find each of the following.

    (a) log 3540   **(c)** log 35.4   **(e)** log .354   **(g)** log .00354

    (b) log 354   **(d)** log 3.54   **(f)** log .0354   **(h)** log .000354

3. Use table I to find the following logarithms.

    (a) log 237   **(c)** log 7.29   **(e)** log .0615   **(g)** $1 - \log 6.73$

    (b) log 58.3   **(d)** log .841   **(f)** log .00486   **(h)** $\log (19.8)^2$

4. Solve for N.

    (a) $\log N = .4742$ **(c)** $\log N = 4.8899$ **(e)** $\log N = -1.5560$

    (b) $\log N = 2.6937$ **(d)** $\log N = 6.7218 - 10$ **(f)** $\log N = -2.0670$

5. Use logarithms and table I to solve the following equations for x.

    (a) $10^x = 16$ **(c)** $10^{4x} = 4.95$ **(e)** $10^{2x+4} = 8.60$

    (b) $10^x = 39.6$ **(d)** $10^{x-5} = 718$ **(f)** $10^{-x} = 62$

Answers are at end of book.

QUIZ

If you cannot answer the following questions correctly, review the appropriate frames.

1. Express the number 47,100 in scientific notation.

2. Use table I to find log 4.37.

3. Use table I to find log .0756.

4. Write $\log N = 2.7292$ in standard form.

5. If $\log N = 2.7292$, then $N =$ _____ .

6. If $10^{x-4} = 843$, then $x =$ _____ .

7

Interpolation

Upon completing this chapter, you should be able to

I. Use interpolation to find log *N* for any positive number *N* with more than three significant digits.

II. Given log *N* not in table I, find *N* by interpolation.

From table I we can determine the logarithm of 5.29 and the number *N* whose logarithm is .8274. But the logarithm of 5.274 is not in table I, nor is the number whose logarithm is .8725.

When a number has four significant digits, for example 5.274 or 52,740, we can find its logarithm by **interpolation**. Similarly, when the logarithm of a number is not in the table, we can find the number by interpolation. We shall illustrate the use of interpolation with examples.

EXAMPLE 1

518. To find log 5.274, we observe that 5.274 is $\frac{4}{10}$ of the way from 5.27 to 5.28. Thus log 5.274 will be approximately **(a)** _____ of the way from **(b)** _____ to

(c) _____ .

NOTE: The logarithm function is not a linear function, hence the $\frac{4}{10}$ is an approximation. Moreover, in most cases the values in the four-place table I are correct to only four places. Hence throughout the next three sections our calculations will be accurate to three and in most cases four decimal places. We shall use "=" throughout these sections even though it will represent an approximation in many cases.

518. **(a)** $\frac{4}{10}$,

(b) log 5.27, **(c)** log 5.28

	519. That is, $\log 5.274 = \log 5.27 + \underline{\quad}$ $(\log 5.28 - \log 5.27)$.
519. $\frac{4}{10}$	**520.** From table I we see that $\log 5.27 = \underline{\quad\quad}$ and $\log 5.28 = \underline{\quad\quad}$.
520. .7218; .7226	**521.** Thus $\log 5.274 = \underline{\quad\quad} + \frac{4}{10}$ ($\underline{\quad\quad\quad\quad}$),
521. .7218; .7226 − .7218	**522.** Thus $\log 5.274 = .7218 + \frac{4}{10}$ **(a)** ($\underline{\quad\quad\quad}$) $= .7218 +$ **(b)** $\underline{\quad\quad\quad}$ $=$ **(c)** $\underline{\quad\quad\quad\quad}$.
522. (a) .0008, **(b)** .00032, **(c)** .7221	**523.** Since the table is accurate to only $\underline{\quad\quad}$ decimal places, our problem is not accurate to five decimal places.
523. four	**524.** Hence we round off .00032 to four decimal places and get $\underline{\quad\quad}$.
524. .0003	**525.** Thus $.7218 + .0003 = .7221$ is a close approximation to four decimal places of $\underline{\quad\quad\quad}$.
525. $\log 5.274$	**EXAMPLE 2** **526.** $\log 3426 = \underline{\quad\quad}$
526. 3.5348. If you had difficulty, go on to the next frame. If not, skip to frame 534.	**527.** In scientific notation $3426 = \underline{\quad\quad\quad\quad}$.
527. 3.426×10^3	**528.** Thus $\log 3426 = \underline{\quad\quad\quad\quad}$.
528. $\log 3.426 + 3$	

	529. To find log 3.426 from table I, we see that 3.426 is (a) _____ of the way from (b) _____ to (c) _____ .
529. (a) $\frac{6}{10}$, (b) 3.42, (c) 3.43	**530.** Hence, log 3.426 is (a) _____ of the way from (b) _____ to (c) _____ .
530. (a) $\frac{6}{10}$, (b) log 3.42, (c) log 3.43	**531.** That is, log 3.426 = _____ + $\frac{6}{10}$ _____ .
531. log 3.42; (log 3.43 − log 3.42)	**532.** From table I, we get log 3.42 = _____ and log 3.43 = _____ .
532. .5340; 5353	**533.** Hence log 3.426 = (a) _____ + $\frac{6}{10}$ (b) (_____) = (c) _____ + $\frac{6}{10}$ (d) (_____) = (e) _____ + (f) _____ = (g) _____ . and log 3426 = (h) _____ .
533. (a) .5340, (b) .5353 − .5340, (c) .5340, (d) .0013, (e) .5340, (f) .00078, (g) .5348, (h) 3.5348	**EXAMPLE 3** **534.** To find the logarithm of a number with more than four significant digits, we must first round off the number to four significant digits and then interpolate. For example, to find log 65,737, we first round off 65,737 to _____ .
534. 65,740	**535.** And log 65,740 = _____ .
535. 4.8178. If you had difficulty, go on to the next frame. If not, skip to frame 543.	**536.** In scientific notation 65,740 = _____ .
536. 6.574×10^4	

	537. Thus log 65,740 = _____ .
537. log 6.574 + 4	**538.** To find log 6.574 from table I, we see that 6.574 is (a) ____ of the way from (b) _____ to (c) _____ .
538. (a) $\frac{4}{10}$, (b) 6.57, (c) 6.58	**539.** That is, log 6.574 = _____ + $\frac{4}{10}$ (_____).
539. log 6.57; log 6.58 − log 6.57	**540.** From table I, we get log 6.57 = _____ and log 6.58 = _____ .
540. .8176; .8182	**541.** Hence, log 6.574 = _____ .
541. .8178 (since .8176 + $\frac{4}{10}$ (.8182 − .8176) = .8176 + $\frac{4}{10}$ (.0006) = .8176 + .00024 = .8178)	**542.** Thus log 65,740 = _____ .
542. 4.8178	**543.** Hence log 65,737 is approximately _____ .
543. 4.8178	**EXAMPLE 4** **544.** We now turn to the problem of finding N if we are given a value for log N that does not appear in table I. To find N if log N = .4720, we see from table I that .4720 is between the entries _____ and _____ .
544. .4713; .4728	**545.** In fact, .4720 is (a) ____ of the way from (b) _____ to (c) _____ .
545. (a) $\frac{7}{15}$, (b) .4713, (c) .4728	

546. $.4713 = $ _____ and $.4728 = $ _____

---

546. log 2.96; log 2.97

547. Thus N will be approximately **(a)** ____ of the way from **(b)** _____ to **(c)** _____ .

---

547. **(a)** $\frac{7}{15}$,

(b) 2.96, **(c)** 2.97

548. That is, $N = $ **(a)** _____ $+ \frac{7}{15}$ **(b)** (_____)

$= $ **(c)** _____ $+ \frac{7}{15}$ **(d)** (_____).

---

548. **(a)** 2.96; **(b)** $2.97 - 2.96$, **(c)** 2.96, **(d)** .01

549. We note here that the difference in parentheses will always be ____ .

---

549. .01

550. Hence

$N = $ _____ $+$ _____ $= $ _____ .

---

550. 2.96; .0047; 2.965 (since $\frac{7}{15} = .4667$ and

$\frac{7}{15}(.01) = .0047$ to four decimal places)

EXAMPLE 5

551. If $\log N = 3.5692$, then $N = $ _____ .

---

551. 3708.

If you had difficulty, go on to the next frame. If not, skip to frame 559.

552. In standard form $\log N = 3.5692 = $ _____ .

---

552. $.5692 + 3$

553. We see from table I that $.5692$ is **(a)** ____ of the way from **(b)** _____ to **(c)** _____ .

---

553. **(a)** $\frac{10}{12}$,

(b) .5682, **(c)** .5694

554. $.5682 = $ _____ and $.5694 = $ _____

---

554. log 3.70; log 3.71

---

555. Thus n will be **(a)** _____ of the way from **(b)** _____ to **(c)** _____ .

555. (a) $\frac{10}{12}$,
(b) 3.70, **(c)** 3.71

556. That is,

$n =$ **(a)** _____ $+ \frac{10}{12}$ **(b)** (_____)

$=$ **(c)** _____ $+$ **(d)** _____ $=$ **(e)** _____ .

556. (a) 3.70, **(b)** .01,
(c) 3.70, **(d)** .008, **(e)** 3.708

557. Finally, since $\log N = .5692 + 3$ and $n = 3.708$,

$N =$ _____ $\times$ _____ .

557. 3.708; 10^3

558. That is, $N =$ _____ .

558. 3708

EXERCISE 1

559. $\log 1433 =$ _____ approximately.

559. 3.1562.

If you had difficulty, see frames 518 to 543.

EXERCISE 2

560. If $\log N = 2.1683$, then $N =$ _____ .

560. 147.3.

If you had difficulty, see frames 544 to 558.

PROBLEMS

1. Use interpolation to find the following.

(a) log 3962   **(c)** log 74.35   **(e)** log .4013   **(g)** log .006454

(b) log 548.1   **(d)** log 9.118   **(f)** log .05692   **(h)** log 27,643

2. Find N to four significant digits.

(a) $\log N = .2840$ **(c)** $\log N = 3.6604$ **(e)** $\log N = 7.5420 - 10$

(b) $\log N = 1.5400$ **(d)** $\log N = 6.8100 - 10$ **(f)** $\log N = 9.9802 - 10$

Answers are at end of book.

If you cannot answer the following questions correctly, review the appropriate frames.

1. Use interpolation to find log 4752.
2. Find N to four significant digits if log $N = 3.6005$.

Answers are at end of book.

8   Computations with Logarithms

Upon completing this chapter, you should be able to

I. Use logarithms to solve problems involving multiplication and division by addition and subtraction.

II. Use logarithms to solve problems involving powers by multiplication.

---

561. Logarithms were once studied because of their usefulness in calculating products and powers.

If $N = a \cdot b$, then $\log N = \log (a \cdot b) = $ _____ by property (5) of logarithms.

---

561. $\log a + \log b$

562. Thus to find the product $a \cdot b = N$, we can take the log of both sides and obtain $\log N = \log a + \log b$.

We look up $\log a$ and $\log b$, add them, and then find N from table I. We have changed the product $a \cdot b$ into a sum,

_____ .

---

562. $\log a + \log b$

563. Similarly, if $N = a^b$, then $\log N = \log a^b = $ _____

by property (7) of logarithms.

---

563. $b \log a$

564. Thus to find a to the power b, $a^b = N$, we take the log of both sides and obtain $\log N = b \log a$.

We look up $\log a$, multiply it by b, and then find N from table I. We have changed the calculation a^b to a multiplication,

_____ .

---

564. $b \log a$

565. Thus the properties of logarithms enable us to reduce

multiplications to _____ and to reduce calculations involving powers to calculations that involve

_____ .

---

565. additions;
multiplications

566. However, with the increasing use of high-speed computers, logarithms are no longer needed for performing complicated calculations.

---

566. Go on to the next frame.

567. Logarithms are still important in mathematical theory, and performing a few computations with logarithms will increase your skill with them.

---

567. Go on to the next frame.

EXAMPLE 1

568. To calculate $N = \dfrac{473 \times .0157}{2.69}$, we take the log of

both sides and obtain $\log N =$ _____

$=$ _____

by theorems (5) and (6).

---

568. $\log \dfrac{473 \times .0157}{2.69}$;

$\log 473 + \log .0157 - \log 2.69$

569. Using table I and the techniques of the last chapter,

we see that $\log 473 =$ **(a)** _____ ,

$\log .0157 =$ **(b)** _____ , and $\log 2.69 =$ **(c)** _____ .

---

569. (a) 2.6749, **(b)** .1959 − 2, **(c)** .4298

570. Thus

$\log N =$ **(a)** _____ + **(b)** _____ − **(c)** _____

$=$ **(d)** _____ .

---

570. (a) 2.6749, **(b)** (.1959 − 2), **(c)** .4298, **(d)** .4410

571. If $\log N = .4410$, we see from table I that $.4410$ is

(a) _____ of the way from (b) _____ to (c) _____ .

---

571. (a) $\frac{1}{16}$,
(b) .4409, (c) .4425

572. Hence N is (a) _____ of the way from (b) _____ to

(c) _____ .

---

572. (a) $\frac{1}{16}$,
(b) 2.76, (c) 2.77

573. That is,

$N =$ (a) _____ $+ \frac{1}{16}$ (b) (_____)

　　 $=$ (c) _____ $+$ (d) _____

　　 $=$ (e) _____ .

---

573. (a) 2.76, (b) .01,
(c) 2.76, (d) .00062,
(e) 2.761

574. Hence we have shown that

$$\frac{473 \times .0157}{2.69} = \underline{\hspace{2cm}} .$$

---

574. 2.761

EXAMPLE 2

575. To calculate $N = \sqrt[3]{30}$, we take the log of both sides

and obtain $\log N = \underline{\hspace{2.5cm}}$

　　　　　　　　　 $= \underline{\hspace{2.5cm}}$

by theorem (7).

---

575. $\log 30^{1/3}$;
$\frac{1}{3}$ $(\log 30)$

576. Using table I and the techniques of the last chapter,

we see that $\log 30 = \underline{\hspace{2.5cm}}$.

---

576. 1.4771

577. Thus $\log N =$ (a) $\underline{\hspace{3cm}}$

　　　　　　 $=$ (b) $\underline{\hspace{3cm}}$

　　　　　　 $=$ (c) $\underline{\hspace{3cm}}$ (rounded to four

decimal places).

---

577. (a) $\frac{1}{3}(1.4771)$,
　(b) .49236
　(c) .4924

578. We see from table I that log $N = .4924$ is **(a)** _____ of the way from **(b)** _____ to **(c)** _____ .

---

578. **(a)** $\frac{10}{14}$,
(b) .4914, **(c)** .4928

579. Hence N is **(a)** _____ of the way from **(b)** _____ to **(c)** _____ .

---

579. **(a)** $\frac{10}{14}$,
(b) 3.10, **(c)** 3.11

580. That is,

$N =$ **(a)** _____ $+ \frac{10}{14}$ **(b)** (_____)

$=$ **(c)** _____ $+$ **(d)** _____

$=$ **(e)** _____ .

---

580. **(a)** 3.10, **(b)** .01,
(c) 3.10, **(d)** .0071
(e) 3.107

581. Hence we have shown that $\sqrt[3]{30} =$ _____ .

---

581. 3.107

EXAMPLE 3

582. $\dfrac{512 \times .617}{1742} =$ _____

---

582. 0.1814.

If you had difficulty, see frames 568 to 574 and the previous chapter.

EXAMPLE 4

583. $\sqrt[5]{823} =$ _____

---

583. 3.829.

If you had difficulty, see frames 575 to 581 and the previous chapter.

Use logarithms to solve the following:

1. $\dfrac{24.9 \times 7.35}{372 \times .0165}$ 2. $\dfrac{943 \times .00721}{.384 \times 60.3}$

3. 75^7 4. 31.5^3

5. $(31)^4 (93.2)^5$ 6. $(19)^7 (41)^3$

7. $\sqrt{417}$ 8. $\sqrt{93.6}$

9. $\sqrt[3]{71.5}$ 10. $\dfrac{\sqrt[4]{36.5}}{\sqrt{134}}$

Answers are at end of book.

If you cannot answer the following questions correctly, review the appropriate frames.

Use logarithms to solve the following problems.

1. $\sqrt[3]{6.73} =$ _____

2. $\dfrac{237 \times .0015}{7.58} =$ _____

Answers are at end of book.

9 Exponential and Logarithmic Equations

Upon completing this chapter, you should be able to use the techniques of the previous chapters to solve

I. Equations of the form $x^a = b$, $a^x = b$, and $a^b = x$.

II. Equations of the form $\log (ax + b) - \log (cx + d) = e$.

III. Inequalities of the form $a^x < b$.

In previous chapters we have solved equations of the form $\log_a x = b$, $x = \log_a b$, and $a^x = b$ for x. These represent the three basic types of exponential equations, $x^a = b$, $a^x = b$, and $a^b = x$ where a and b are suitable real numbers.

In this chapter, by working examples of the three types above, we shall review the methods for solving equations that involve exponential or logarithmic expressions.

EXAMPLE 1

584. To solve $x^4 = 3.94$, we take the log of both sides and get

_____ = _____ .

584. $\log x^4$; $\log 3.94$

585. And by theorem (7), $\log x^4 = $ _____ .

585. $4 \log x$

586. Hence we get _____ = _____ .

586. $4 \log x$; $\log 3.94$

587. $\dfrac{\log 3.94}{4}$

588. .5955

589. $\dfrac{.5955}{4}$; .14887

.1489 rounded to four places

590. 1.409.

If you had difficulty, see the chapter on common logarithms.

591. 225,200.

If you had difficulty, go on to the next frame. If not, skip to frame 597.

592. $\log x$; $\log 7.8^6$

593. $6 \log 7.8$

594. .8921;
6(.8921); 5.3526

595. .3526 + 5

596. $2.252 \times 10^5 = 225{,}200.$

If you had difficulty, see the chapter on interpolation.

---

587. And $\log x = $ _____ .

588. From table I, $\log 3.94 = $ _____ .

589. Hence $\log x = $ _____ = _____ rounded to four decimal places.

590. Finally, by table I, $x = $ _____ approximately.

EXAMPLE 2

591. If $x = 7.8^6$, then $x = $ _____ approximately.

592. Taking the log of both sides of $x = 7.8^6$, we get

_____ = _____ .

593. And by theorem (7), $\log 7.8^6 = $ _____ .

594. From table I, $\log 7.8 = $ _____ . Thus

$\log x = 6$ _____ = _____ .

595. Finally, in standard form $\log x = $ _____ .

596. And, by table I, $x = $ _____
approximately.

EXAMPLE 3

597. If $4.6^x = 447.9$, then $x = $ ___ approximately.

---

597. 4.

If you had difficulty, go on to the next frame. If not, skip to frame 603.

598. Taking the log of both sides of $4.6^x = 447.9$, we get

_____ = _____ .

---

598. $\log 4.6^x$; $\log 447.9$

599. And by theorem (7), $\log 4.6^x = $ **(a)** _____ .

Hence we get **(b)** _____ = **(c)** _____ .

---

599. **(a)** $x \log 4.6$,
(b) $x \log 4.6$, **(c)** $\log 447.9$

600. And $x = $ _____ .

---

600. $\dfrac{\log 447.9}{\log 4.6}$

601. From table I and the techniques of the previous chapters,

$\log 447.9 = $ _____ and $\log 4.6 = $ _____ .

---

601. 2.6512; .6628

602. Thus $x = $ _____

= _____ = _____ .

This last step can be accomplished by either long division or logarithms.

---

602. $\dfrac{2.6512}{.6628}$; 4 (or 3.999)

EXAMPLE 4

603. If $5^x = 2^{3x-1}$, then $x = $ _____ approximately.

---

603. 1.476

If you had difficulty, go on to the next frame. If not, skip to frame 611.

604. Taking the log of both sides of $5^x = 2^{3x-1}$, we obtain

_____ = _____ .

---

604. $\log 5^x$; $\log 2^{3x-1}$

605. And by theorem (7), we have

_____ = _____ .

---

605. $x \log 5$; $(3x - 1) \log 2$

606. From table I, $\log 5 = $ **(a)** _____ and $\log 2 = $ **(b)** _____ .

Hence **(c)** x (_____) $= $ **(d)** $(3x - 1)$ (_____).

---

606. (a) .6990, **(b)** .3010,
(c) .6990, **(d)** .3010

607. Thus x (_____) $= -.3010$.

---

607. $.6990 - .9030$

608. _____ $x = -.3010$

---

608. $-.2040$

609. And $x = \dfrac{\underline{\hspace{2cm}}}{\underline{\hspace{2cm}}}$

$= \underline{\hspace{2cm}}$.

---

609. $\dfrac{-.3010}{.2040}$;

1.4755

610. Thus we have shown that if $5^x = 2^{3x-1}$, then

$x = \underline{\hspace{2cm}}$.

---

610. 1.476

EXAMPLE 5

611. To solve $\log (3x - 2) - \log (x + 4) = 1$ for x, we apply theorem (6) and get

$1 = \log (3x - 2) - \log (x + 4) = \underline{\hspace{3cm}}$.

---

611. $\log \dfrac{3x - 2}{x + 4}$

612. That is, $1 = \log \dfrac{3x - 2}{x + 4}$, and if we replace $1 = \log \dfrac{3x - 2}{x + 4}$

by the equivalent exponential equation, we get _____ .

---

612. $10^1 = \dfrac{3x - 2}{x + 4}$

(since $x = \log y$ iff $10^x = y$)

613. Thus **(a)** 10 (_____) $= 3x - 2$,

$7x = $ **(b)** _____ ,

and $\qquad\qquad x = $ **(c)** _____ .

---

613. (a) $x + 4$,
(b) -42,
(c) -6

EXAMPLE 6

614. If $\log (x - 99) - \log (2x + 1) = 2$, then $x = \underline{\hspace{1.5cm}}$.

---

614. -1.

If you had difficulty, go on to the next frame. If not, skip to frame 618.

615. We first apply theorem (6) and get

$$2 = \log(x - 99) - \log(2x + 1) = \underline{\hspace{5cm}}.$$

---

615. $\log \dfrac{x - 99}{2x + 1}$

616. If we replace $2 = \log \dfrac{x - 99}{2x + 1}$ by the equivalent exponential

equation, we get $\underline{\hspace{1cm}} = \underline{\hspace{2cm}}$.

---

616. $10^2 \, ; \, \dfrac{x - 99}{2x + 1}$

(since $x = \log y$ iff $10^x = y$)

617. Thus **(a)** $100 \, (\underline{\hspace{3cm}}) = $ **(b)** $\underline{\hspace{2cm}}$

         (c) $\underline{\hspace{2cm}} \, x = $ **(d)** $\underline{\hspace{2cm}}$

and $x = $ **(e)** $\underline{\hspace{2cm}}$.

---

617. **(a)** $2x + 1$, **(b)** $x - 99$,
(c) 199, **(d)** -199, **(e)** -1

EXAMPLE 7

618. If $\log(13 - x) - \log(2x - 5) = 1$, then $x = \underline{\hspace{1cm}}$.

---

618. 3.

If you had difficulty, see
frames 611 to 617.

619. In the chapter on properties of logarithms we saw that

$a < b$ if and only if $\log a \underset{(<, \, =, \, >)}{\underline{\hspace{2cm}}} \log b$.

---

619. $<$

620. We can make use of this fact and the preceding methods to
solve *inequalities* involving exponential and logarithmic expressions.

---

620. Go on to the next frame.

EXAMPLE 8

621. Solve the inequality $2^x < \frac{5}{8}$.

$\underline{\hspace{5cm}}$

---

621. $x < -1010$ approximately.

If you had difficulty, go on to the
next frame. If not, skip to frame 627.

622. Taking the log of both sides of $2^x < \frac{5}{8}$, we get

$\underline{\hspace{5cm}}$.

---

622. $\log 2^x < \log \frac{5}{8}$

623. By theorem (7), $\log 2^x =$ **(a)** _____ ,

and by theorem (6), $\log \frac{5}{8} =$ **(b)** _____ .

Thus, we get **(c)** _____ $<$ **(d)** _____ .

---

623. (a) $x \log 2$,
(b) $\log 5 - \log 8$,
(c) $x \log 2$,   **(d)** $\log 5 - \log 8$

624. Hence $x <$ _____ .

---

624. $\dfrac{\log 5 - \log 8}{\log 2}$

625. From table I, $\log 5 =$ **(a)** _____ , $\log 8 =$ **(b)** _____ ,

and $\log 2 =$ **(c)** _____ .

---

625. (a) .6990,
(b) .9031,   **(c)** .3010

626. Thus

$x <$ **(a)** _____ $=$ **(b)** _____ .

That is, $x <$ **(c)** _____ .

---

626. **(a)** $\dfrac{.6990 - .9031}{.3010}$, **(b)** $\dfrac{-.2041}{.3010}$,

(c) $-.6781$

EXAMPLE 9

627. Solve the inequality $8^x > \frac{2}{5}$.

_____

---

627. $x > -.4407$.

If you had difficulty, see
frames 621 to 626.

Solve the following equations for x.

1. $4^x = 7$

2. $5^{x+1} = 9$

3. $7.1^x = 9.3$

4. $6^{2x+3} = 354$

5. $x^5 = 873$

6. $x^4 = 687$

7. $x^{7/2} = 51.4$

8. $x^{10} = 37$

9. $x = 6.2^3$

10. $x = 5^{8.4}$

11. $3^x = 6^{x+3}$

12. $7^x = 4^{2x-1}$

13. $2^{x-1} = 5^{2x+1}$

14. $8^{x+2} = 3^{3x-1}$

15. $\log (3x - 1) - \log (x + 2) = 2$

16. $\log (x - \sqrt{6}) + \log (x + \sqrt{6}) = 1$

17. $\log (x^2 - 1) - \log (x + 1) = 1$

18. $\log (x^2 - 4) - 2 \log (x - 2) = 2$

Solve the following inequalities for x.

19. $4^x > \frac{2}{5}$

20. $3^x < \frac{4}{7}$

21. $2^{3x} < 6$

22. $5^{2x} > 8$

Answers are at end of book.

QUIZ

If you cannot answer the following questions correctly, review the appropriate frames.

Solve the following equations for x.

1. $3^x = 8$

2. $x^5 = 94.4$

3. $\log (x - 3) - \log (2x + 1) = 1$

Answers are at end of book.

Theory of Equations

PART **II**

In Volume II, we studied the concept of a function and its graph and in Volume III we studied trigonometric functions and their graphs. In this volume, we have considered exponential and logarithmic functions and their graphs. In the remainder of this volume we shall study **polynomial** and **rational** functions. We shall find the zeros of polynomial functions, $f(x)$. That is, we shall find the solutions of the equation $f(x) = 0$. And we shall sketch the graphs of polynomial functions.

10 Polynomials

Upon completing this chapter, you should be able to

I. Identify polynomials in a list of expressions.

II. Given a polynomial, give its degree.

III. Given two polynomials $P(x)$ and $Q(x)$, add, subtract, and multiply them.

IV. Find the quotient and remainder obtained by dividing one polynomial by another.

	1. $5x^6$, $\frac{1}{2}x^4$, $\sqrt{2}\,x$, r, and $a_n x^n$ are all **terms** in x. The **degree** of the term $5x^6$ is 6, the degree of the term $\sqrt{2}\,x$ is 1, the degree of the term $\frac{1}{2}x^4$ is ___ , and the degree of the term $a_n x^n$ is ___ .
1. $4; n$	**2.** What is the degree of each of the following terms? (a) $4x$ ___ (b) Bx^2 ___ (c) $7x^5$ ___ (d) $\sqrt{5}\,x^3$ ___
2. (a) 1, (b) 2, (c) 5, (d) 3	**3.** The numbers $4, B, 7$, and $\sqrt{5}$ are called the **coefficients** of the terms $4x$, Bx^2, $7x^5$, and $\sqrt{5}\,x^3$. The coefficient of $8x^7$ is ___ .
3. 8	

4. Since $x^0 = 1$ by definition, we can write 5 as $5x^0$ or a as ax^0. Thus the degree of the terms 5 and a is _____ .

---

4. zero

5. That is, the coefficients themselves may be thought of as terms of degree _____ .

---

5. zero

6. A **polynomial** is an expression consisting of a sum of terms. $3x^3 - \sqrt{2}\,x + \frac{1}{2}$ is a polynomial. Which of the following expressions are polynomials?

(a) $5x^3 + 2x^2 - 5$

(b) $\sqrt{3x^2 + 5x}$

(c) $2x^4 - \frac{1}{2}x^3 + \sqrt{3}\,x + \frac{1}{5}$

---

6. (a), (c)

7. The coefficients of the terms are the *coefficients of the polynomial*. List the coefficients of the polynomial

$2x^3 - \frac{1}{2}x^2 + \sqrt{3}\,x + \frac{1}{5}$. _____

---

7. $2, -\frac{1}{2}, \sqrt{3}, \frac{1}{5}$

8. The coefficients will be chosen from either the field of real numbers or the field of complex numbers. The coefficients of the polynomial $7x^4 - ix^2 + \pi x + 12$ are all in the field of (a) _____ numbers but are not all in the field of (b) _____ numbers since i is not a (c) _____ number.

---

8. (a) complex,
(b) real,
(c) real

9. Polynomials are usually written in descending powers of x, as follows:

$$a_n x^n + a_{n-1} x^{n-1} + \ldots + a_1 x + a_0.$$

And we shall denote them by $P(x), Q(x), R(x)$, etc.

For example, let

$\quad$ **(1)** $P(x) = 7x^4 + \sqrt{2}\, x^2 - ix + 5,$

$\quad$ **(2)** $Q(x) = 8x^6 - \sqrt{7}\,,$

$\quad$ **(3)** $R(x) = 3x^2 - 5x + \frac{1}{2}.$

Notice that in each example above the coefficient of the highest power of x is not 0 but that some of the other coefficients may be 0. In example **(1)**, the coefficient of x^3 is 0, and in example **(2)** the coefficients of _____ , _____ , _____ , _____ , and _____ are all 0.

---

9. $x^5; x^4; x^3; x^2;$ and x

10. We could write **(1)** and **(2)** of frame 9 as

(1) $P(x) = 7x^4 + 0x^3 + \sqrt{2}\, x^2 - ix + 5$

and

(2) $Q(x) = 8x^6 + 0x^5 + 0x^4 + 0x^3 + 0x^2 + 0x - \sqrt{7}\,.$

However, we shall write only terms with non-zero coefficients as we did in frame 9. Write the polynomial

$R(x) = 4x^5 + 0x^4 + 0x^3 - 3x^2 + 0x - 5$ in its proper form.

$R(x) = $ _____

---

10. $4x^5 - 3x^2 - 5$

EXAMPLE 1

11. List the coefficients of the polynomial

$3x^4 - \sqrt{2}\, x^3 + 4x - \frac{2}{3}.$ _____

---

11. $3, -\sqrt{2}, 0, 4, -\frac{2}{3}.$

NOTE: x^2 has coefficient 0.

12. The coefficient a_n of the highest power n is assumed not to be zero and n is called the **degree** of the polynomial. What is the degree of the polynomial $4x^5 + 3x^4 - x - 17?$ ___

---

12. 5

EXAMPLE 2

13. What is the degree of each of the following polynomials?

(a) $P(x) = 7x^4 + \sqrt{2}\,x^2 - ix + 5$ ____

(b) $Q(x) = 8x^6 - \sqrt{7}$ ____

(c) $R(x) = 3x^2 - 5x + \frac{1}{2}$ ____

---

13. (a) 4,
(b) 6,
(c) 2

14. Since we may write 5 as $5x^0$ or a as ax^0, the coefficients them-selves may be considered as polynomials of degree _____ . We may write $P(x) = ax^0 = a$ for any real or complex number a.

---

14. zero

15. Thus $P(x) = 7$, $Q(x) = \sqrt{3}$, and $R(x) = i$ are polynomials of degree _____ .

---

15. zero

16. The number 0 is also considered to be a polynomial, but *no degree* is assigned to it. What is the degree of each of the following polynomials?

(a) $P(x) = 4x^7 - 3x^2 - x + 5$ ____

(b) $Q(x) = 5$ ____

(c) $R(x) = 0$ ____

(d) $D(x) = ix^2 + \pi x - \sqrt{2}$ ____

(e) $M(x) = \sqrt{3}$ ____

---

16. (a) 7,
(b) 0,
(c) no degree,
(d) 2,
(e) 0

17. The terms $a_k x^k$ of a polynomial consist of the product of a number a_k, called a _____ , and x raised to a non-negative integral power k. k is the _____ of the term $a_k x^k$.

---

17. coefficient;
degree

EXAMPLE 3

18. Since x must be raised to a non-negative integral power, $3x^{-2}$, $7\sqrt{x}$, and 4^x cannot be terms of polynomials. Which of the following can be terms of a polynomial?

(a) $4x^3$ (d) ix^6

(b) $2x^{-5}$ (e) 5^x

(c) $4x^{1/3}$ (f) 7

---

18. (a), (d), (f)

19. Two polynomials are **equal** if and only if the corresponding coefficients are equal. For example, $ax^3 + bx^2 + cx + d = 4x^3 - ix^2 + 5$ if and only if $a = 4$, $b = -i$, $c = 0$, and $d = 5$, and $qx^4 + rx^3 + sx^2 + tx + w = 5x^4 - 2x^2 + 2$ if and only if

$q = $ (a) _____ , $r = $ (b) _____ , $s = $ (c) _____ , $t = $ (d) _____ ,

and $w = $ (e) _____ .

---

19. (a) 5, (b) 0, (c) -2,
(d) 0, (e) 2

EXAMPLE 4

20. If the rule of a function f is given by a polynomial equation $f(x) = a_n x^n + a_{n-1} x^{n-1} + \ldots + a_1 x + a_0$, then f is called a **polynomial function**. For example, the functions f and g defined by $f(x) = 7x^3 - 4x^2 - 6$ and $g(x) = 5x^2 + ix + \sqrt{7}$ are polynomial functions. Which of the following functions are polynomial functions?

(a) $f(x) = \sin^2 x$

(b) $g(x) = 4x^3 - \sqrt{2}\,x + 5$

(c) $h(x) = 6x^{-3} + 4x^{1/3} - 6$

(d) $k(x) = x^4 - ix^2 + 3$

---

20. (b), (d).
(a) is a trigonometric function and
(c) is not a polynomial since
polynomial terms have only
non-negative integral powers
of x.

21. Let $f : R \to R$ be a polynomial function defined by $f(x) = x^3 + 2x^2 - 5$. Then

(a) $f(0) = $ _____ ,

(b) $f(1) = $ _____ ,

(c) $f(-1) = $ _____ .

---

21. (a) -5,
(b) -2,
(c) -4.

If you had difficulty, see
Volume II on functions.

22. Let $g : C \to C$ be a polynomial function defined by $g(x) = x^2 + ix - 2$. Then

(a) $g(1) = $ _____ ,

(b) $g(i) = $ _____ ,

(c) $g(-i) = $ _____ .

---

22. (a) $i - 1$,
(b) -4
(c) -2.

If you had difficulty, see the volumes that contain functions and complex numbers.

23. Since polynomials define functions, we can add, subtract, and multiply polynomials just as we did with functions in Volume II. To add polynomials we add the corresponding terms of the polynomials. For example,

$P(x) = 3x^3 - 4x^2 + 5$ and $Q(x) = 7x^4 - 5x^3 + x - 2$.

Then $P(x) + Q(x) = (3x^3 - 4x^2 + 5) + (7x^4 - 5x^3 + x - 2)$

$$= 7x^4 - 2x^3 - 4x^2 + x + 3.$$

Add $R(x) = 5x^4 + 4x^2 - 3$ and $D(x) = 2x^3 - 3x^2 + 5$.

$R(x) + D(x) = $ _____

---

23. $5x^4 + 2x^3 + x^2 + 2$

24. To subtract one polynomial from another, we subtract the corresponding terms. Thus

$(8x^4 - 4x^3 + 6x^2 - 9) - (2x^3 - 5x^2 + 4x) = $

_____ .

---

24. $8x^4 - 6x^3 + 11x^2 - 4x - 9$

EXAMPLE 5

25. Let $P(x) = x^5 - 3x^3 + 4x^2 - 5$ and $Q(x) = x^3 + 3x^2 - x + 4$. Then

$P(x) + Q(x) = $ _____ ,

$P(x) - Q(x) = $ _____ .

---

25. $x^5 - 2x^3 + 7x^2 - x - 1$;
$x^5 - 4x^3 + x^2 + x - 9$

26. To multiply two polynomials $P(x)$ and $Q(x)$, we multiply each term of one by each term of the other. For example, if

$P(x) = 5x^3 - 4x^2 - 7x + 2$ and $Q(x) = 3x^2 + 4$, then

$P(x) \cdot Q(x) = (5x^3 - 4x^2 - 7x + 2) \cdot (3x^2 + 4)$

$\qquad = 15x^5 - 12x^4 - 21x^3 + 6x^2 + 20x^3 - 16x^2 - 28x + 8$

$\qquad = 15x^5 - 12x^4 - x^3 - 10x^2 - 28x + 8.$

Multiply $P(x) = x^3 - 5x^2 + 3$ and $Q(x) = 2x^2 - x + 1$.

$P(x) \cdot Q(x) =$ _____

_____

---

26. $(x^3 - 5x^2 + 3) \cdot (2x^2 - x + 1) =$
$2x^5 - x^4 + x^3 - 10x^4 + 5x^3 - 5x^2 + 6x^2 - 3x + 3 =$
$2x^5 - 11x^4 + 6x^3 + x^2 - 3x + 3$

EXAMPLE 6

27. Multiply $P(x) = 2x^2 - 5$ and

$Q(x) = x^4 + 3x^3 - x + 2.$

$P(x) \cdot (Q(x) =$ _____

_____

_____

_____

---

27. $(2x^2 - 5)(x^4 + 3x^3 - x + 2) =$
$2x^6 + 6x^5 - 2x^3 + 4x^2 - 5x^4 - 15x^3 + 5x - 10 =$
$2x^6 + 6x^5 - 5x^4 - 17x^3 + 4x^2 + 5x - 10$

EXERCISE 1

28. Let $P(x) = 3x^4 - x^2 + 2x + 3$ and

$Q(x) = 4x^3 - 2$. Then

$P(x) + Q(x) = $ **(a)** _____ ,

$P(x) - Q(x) = $ **(b)** _____ ,

$P(x) \cdot Q(x) = $ **(c)** _____

_____

_____ .

---

28. (a) $3x^4 + 4x^3 - x^2 + 2x + 1,$
(b) $3x^4 - 4x^3 - x^2 + 2x + 5,$
(c) $(3x^4 - x^2 + 2x + 3)(4x^3 - 2) =$
$12x^7 - 4x^5 + 8x^4 + 12x^3 - 6x^4 + 2x^2 - 4x - 6 =$
$12x^7 - 4x^5 + 2x^4 + 12x^3 + 2x^2 - 4x - 6$

---

29. Look at frames 23 to 28. We see that the sum,

difference, or product of two polynomials _____
$\overset{}{\underset{\text{(is, is not)}}{}}$

always a polynomial.

---

29. is

EXAMPLE 7

30. Division of one polynomial $P(x)$ by another $Q(x)$ does not always result in a polynomial. We shall now discuss what we mean by the quotient of two polynomials, $P(x)/Q(x)$. The situation is similar to the division of integers where it is also the case that two integers need not have a quotient that is an integer. But we did have for integers the following result:

For any two integers a and $b > 0$, there are integers q and r such that $a = bq + r$ where $0 \leqslant r < b$.

For example, if $a = 93$ and $b = 7$,

$$
\begin{array}{r}
13 = q \\
7\overline{)93} \\
7 \\
\hline
23 \\
21 \\
\hline
2 = r
\end{array}
$$

and $a = b \cdot q + r$ with $0 \leqslant r < b$
  $93 = 7 \cdot 13 + 2$ with $0 \leqslant 2 < 7$.

Let $a = 89$ and $b = 5$. Find q and r and write

$a = (b \cdot q) + r, 0 \leqslant r < b.$ _____

30.
$$
\begin{array}{r}
17 = q \\
5\overline{)89} \\
5 \\
\hline
39 \\
35 \\
\hline
4 = r
\end{array}
$$

Thus $89 = 5 \cdot 17 + 4, 0 \leqslant 4 < 5.$

31. In this division process q is called the **quotient** and r is called the **remainder**.

If $a = 137$ and $b = 12$, find the quotient and remainder obtained by dividing a by b.

quotient = _____

remainder = _____

31. 11;
5,

(since
$$
\begin{array}{r}
11 \\
12\overline{)137} \\
12 \\
\hline
17 \\
12 \\
\hline
5
\end{array}
$$
)

EXAMPLE 8

32. If $a = 131$ and $b = 27$, find the quotient q and the remainder r obtained by dividing a by b and write a in the form $a = b \cdot q + r$, $0 \leqslant r < b$.

quotient $q =$ **(a)** ____

remainder $r =$ **(b)** ____

$131 = 27 \cdot$ **(c)** ___ $+$ **(d)** _____ , $0 \leqslant$ **(e)** ____ < 27

---

32. (a) 4,
(b) 23,
(c) 4, **(d)** 23, **(e)** 23

EXAMPLE 9

33. If $a = 589$ and $b = 19$, find the quotient q and the remainder r obtained by dividing a by b and write a in the form $a = b \cdot q + r$, $0 \leqslant r < b$.

quotient $=$ **(a)** ____

remainder $=$ **(b)** ____

$589 =$ **(c)** _____ , $0 \leqslant$ **(d)** _____

---

33. (a) 31,
(b) 0,
(c) $19 \cdot 31 + 0$, **(d)** $0 < 19$

34. We can apply a similar algorithm to the system of polynomials with either real or complex coefficients. We state the algorithm as a theorem without proof.

THEOREM 1. If $P(x)$ is any polynomial and $D(x)$ is any polynomial other than the polynomial 0, then there exist polynomials $Q(x)$ and $R(x)$, where $R(x) = 0$ or has degree lower than $D(x)$, such that $P(x) = D(x) \cdot Q(x) + R(x)$. As in the case of the integers $Q(x)$ is

called the _____ and $R(x)$ is the _____ .

---

34. quotient; remainder

35. We can determine the quotient and remainder of two polynomials by a process similar to the long-division process of ordinary arithmetic. For example, to find the quotient $Q(x)$ and remainder $R(x)$ when $P(x) = 2x^3 - 3x^2 + 4$ and $D(x) = x^2 - x + 1$, we set up the problem as we would ordinary long division and get

$$x^2 - x + 1 \, \overline{\big)\, 2x^3 - 3x^2 + 0x + 4} \; .$$

As a first step we see that x^2 will go into $2x^3$ _____ times.

---

35. $2x$

36. Thus we write

$$x^2 - x + 1 \overline{\smash{\big)}\, 2x^3 - 3x^2 + 0x + 4} \quad \overset{\displaystyle 2x}{}$$

and multiplying the divisor by $2x$ and subtracting from $2x^3 - 3x^2 + 0x + 4$ we get as in ordinary long division

$$x^2 - x + 1 \overline{\smash{\big)}\, 2x^3 - 3x^2 + 0x + 4} \quad \overset{\displaystyle 2x}{}$$

$$\underline{}$$

$$\underline{} \, .$$

---

36. $2x^3 - 2x^2 + 2x;$
  $-x^2 - 2x + 4$

37. Now we see that x^2 will go into $-x^2$ -1 times, and we get

$$x^2 - x + 1 \overline{\smash{\big)}\, 2x^3 - 3x^2 + 0x + 4} \quad \overset{\displaystyle 2x - 1}{}$$
$$\underline{2x^3 - 2x^2 + 2x}$$
$$-x^2 - 2x + 4$$

and multiplying the divisor by -1 and subtracting from $-x^2 - 2x + 4$ gives

$$x^2 - x + 1 \overline{\smash{\big)}\, 2x^3 - 3x^2 + 0x + 4} \quad \overset{\displaystyle 2x - 1}{}$$
$$\underline{2x^3 - 2x^2 + 2x}$$
$$-x^2 - 2x + 4$$

$$\underline{}$$

$$\underline{} \, .$$

---

37. $-x^2 + x - 1;$
  $-3x + 5$

38. Since $-3x + 5$ has degree lower than $D(x) = x^2 - x + 1$, x^2 will not go into $-3x + 5$. Thus the process is complete.

The quotient is **(a)** _____ ,

the remainder is **(b)** _____ ,
and we can write

$2x^3 - 3x^2 + 4 = (x^2 - x + 1)\,\text{(c)}\,(_____) + \text{(d)}\,(_____)$.

---

38. (a) $2x - 1$,
(b) $-3x + 5$,
(c) $2x - 1$, **(d)** $-3x + 5$

EXAMPLE 10

39. Find the quotient $Q(x)$ and remainder $R(x)$ when $P(x) = 5x^4 - 4x^3 + 6x^2 - 9$ is divided by $D(x) = x^2 + 2x - 1$. And write $P(x)$ in the form $P(x) = D(x) \cdot Q(x) + R(x)$.

quotient $Q(x) = $ **(a)** _____

remainder $R(x) = $ **(b)** _____

$5x^4 - 4x^3 + 6x^2 - 9 = $ **(c)** _____

_____

---

39. (a) $5x^2 - 14x + 39$,
(b) $-92x + 30$,
(c) $(x^2 + 2x - 1)(5x^2 - 14x + 39) - 92x + 30$.

If you had difficulty, go on to the next frame. If not, skip to frame 49.

---

40. To divide $P(x) = 5x^4 - 4x^3 + 6x^2 - 9$ by $D(x) = x^2 + 2x - 1$, we use long division. Put the problem in the form used for long division.

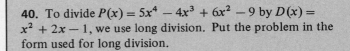

40.

$x^2 + 2x - 1 \,\overline{\big)\, 5x^4 - 4x^3 + 6x^2 + 0x - 9}$

---

41. x^2 will go into $5x^4$ _____ times, and we write

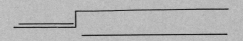

$x^2 + 2x - 1 \,\overline{\big)\, 5x^4 - 4x^3 + 6x^2 + 0x - 9}$.

---

41. $5x^2$;
$5x^2$

---

42. Multiplying the divisor $x^2 + 2x - 1$ by _____ and subtracting the result from $5x^4 - 4x^3 + 6x^2 + 0x - 9$ gives

$$x^2 + 2x - 1 \overline{\smash{\big)} \begin{array}{l} 5x^2 \\ 5x^4 - 4x^3 + 6x^2 + 0x - 9 \end{array}}$$

_____

_____ .

42. $5x^2$;
$5x^4 + 10x^3 - 5x^2$;
$ -14x^3 + 11x^2 + 0x - 9$

43. The next step is to see how many times x^2 will go into

_____ .

43. $-14x^3$

44. Since x^2 will go into $-14x^3$ _____ times, we write

$$x^2 + 2x - 1 \overline{\smash{\big)} \begin{array}{l} 5x^2 \underline{} \\ 5x^4 - 4x^3 + 6x^2 + 0x - 9 \\ 5x^4 + 10x^3 - 5x^2 \\ -14x^3 + 11x^2 + 0x - 9 \, . \end{array}}$$

44. $-14x$;
$-14x$

45. Multiplying _____ by $-14x$ and subtracting the result from $-14x^3 + 11x^2 + 0x - 9$ gives

$$x^2 + 2x - 1 \overline{\smash{\big)} \begin{array}{l} 5x^2 - 14x - 14x \\ 5x^4 - 4x^3 + 6x^2 + 0x - 9 \\ 5x^4 + 10x^3 - 5x^2 \\ -14x^3 + 11x^2 + 0x - 9 \end{array}}$$

_____

_____ .

45. $x^2 + 2x - 1$;
$-14x^3 - 28x^2 + 14x$;
$ +39x^2 - 14x - 9$

46. Finally, **(a)** _____ will go into **(b)** _____ **(c)** _____ times. Thus we write

$$
\begin{array}{r}
5x^2 - 14x\ \textbf{(d)} \underline{\hspace{1cm}} \\
x^2 + 2x - 1 \overline{\smash{\big)}\ 5x^4 -\ 4x^3 +\ 6x^2 + 0x - 9} \\
\underline{5x^4 + 10x^3 -\ 5x^2} \\
-14x^3 + 11x^2 + 0x - 9 \\
\underline{-14x^3 - 28x^2 + 14x} \\
39x^2 - 14x - 9\ .
\end{array}
$$

---

46. (a) x^2, (b) $39x^2$, (c) 39, (d) $+39$

---

47. Multiplying **(a)** _____ by **(b)** _____ and subtracting the result gives

$$
\begin{array}{r}
5x^2 - 14x + 39 \\
x^2 + 2x - 1 \overline{\smash{\big)}\ 5x^4 -\ 4x^3 +\ 6x^2 + 0x - 9} \\
\underline{5x^4 + 10x^3 -\ 5x^2} \\
-14x^3 + 11x^2 + 0x - 9 \\
\underline{-14x^3 - 28x^2 + 14x} \\
39x^2 - 14x - 9
\end{array}
$$

(c) $\underline{\hspace{3cm}}$

$\underline{\hspace{3cm}}\ .$

---

47. (a) $x^2 + 2x - 1$, (b) 39, (c) $39x^2 + 78x - 34$; $-92x + 30$

---

48. Since $-92x + 30$ has degree lower than $D(x) = x^2 + 2x - 1$, x^2 will not go into $-92x + 30$. Thus the process is complete.

The quotient is **(a)** $\underline{\hspace{4cm}}$,

the remainder is **(b)** $\underline{\hspace{4cm}}$, and we can write

$5x^4 - 4x^3 + 6x^2 + 0x - 9 = $ **(c)** $\underline{\hspace{4cm}}$

$\underline{\hspace{4cm}}\ .$

---

48. (a) $5x^2 - 14x + 39$,
(b) $-92x + 30$,
(c) $(x^2 + 2x - 1)(5x^2 - 14x + 39) -92x + 30$

EXAMPLE 11

49. Find the quotient $Q(x)$ and remainder $R(x)$ when $P(x) = x^3 - 4x^2 - 2x - 3$ is divided by $D(x) = 4x^2 + 1$ and write $P(x)$ in the form $P(x) = D(x) \cdot Q(x) + R(x)$.

$Q(x) = $ **(a)** _____

$R(x) = $ **(b)** _____

$x^3 - 4x^2 - 2x - 4 = $ **(c)** _____

---

49. **(a)** $\frac{1}{4}x - 1$,

(b) $-\frac{9}{4}x - 2$,

(c) $(4x^2 + 1)(\frac{1}{4}x - 1) - \frac{9}{4}x - 2$.

If you had difficulty, see frames 35 to 48.

EXAMPLE 12

50. Find the quotient $Q(x)$ and remainder $R(x)$ when $P(x) = 3x^4 - 4x^2 - 5x + 7$ is divided by $D(x) = x + 3$ and write $P(x)$ in the form $P(x) = D(x) \cdot Q(x) + R(x)$.

$Q(x) = $ **(a)** _____

$R(x) = $ **(b)** _____

$3x^4 - 4x^2 - 5x + 7 = $ **(c)** _____

---

50. **(a)** $3x^3 - 9x^2 + 23x - 74$,
(b) 229,
(c) $(x + 3)(3x^3 - 9x^2 + 23x - 74) + 229$

51. In a later section we shall suggest a much shorter method of finding the quotient and remainder when the divisor is of the form $x + b$. That method is known as "synthetic division."

---

51. Go on to the next frame.

52. If $P(x)$ is a polynomial, we shall denote $P(x) + P(x)$ by $2P(x)$, $P(x) + P(x) + P(x)$ by $3P(x)$, and $P(x) + P(x) + \ldots + P(x)$ with n terms by _____ .

---

52. $nP(x)$

53. By definition

$3P(x) = $ _____ .

---

53. $P(x) + P(x) + P(x)$

54. If $P(x) = x^2 + 3x - 1$, then

$3P(x) = $ _____ .

---

54. $3x^2 + 9x - 3$

55. Thus to calculate $3P(x)$ we multiply each coefficient of $P(x)$ by ___ .

---

55. 3

56. And to find $8P(x)$ we multiply each coefficient of $P(x)$ by ___ .

---

56. 8

57. Similarly, we shall denote $P(x) \cdot P(x)$ by $P(x)^2$, $P(x) \cdot P(x) \cdot P(x)$ by $P(x)^3$, and $P(x) \cdot P(x) \ldots P(x)$ times itself n times

by ___ .

---

57. $P(x)^n$

58. Let $P(x) = x^2 - 2$; then $P(x)^2 =$ ___

___ .

---

58. $(x^2 - 2)(x^2 - 2) =$
$x^4 - 4x^2 + 4$

59. Let $Q(x) = 3x^2 - x + 1$; then

$Q(x)^2 =$ ___

___ .

---

59. $(3x^2 - x + 1)(3x^2 - x + 1) =$
$9x^4 - 3x^3 + 3x^2 - 3x^3 + x^2 - x + 3x^2 - x + 1 =$
$9x^4 - 6x^3 + 7x^2 - 2x + 1$

EXAMPLE 13

60. Let $P(x) = x^3 - 2x + 1$ and $Q(x) = 2x^2 + 3$.
Find $3P(x) + Q(x)^2$ and put it in polynomial form.

$3P(x) + Q(x)^2 =$ ___

___ .

---

60. $4x^4 + 3x^3 + 12x^2 - 6x + 12$,

(since $3P(x) = 3x^3 - 6x + 3$ and
$Q(x)^2 = (2x^2 + 3)(2x^2 + 3)$
$\qquad = 4x^4 + 12x^2 + 9$)

EXERCISE 2

61. Which of the following expressions are polynomials?

(a) $\sqrt{x^2 - 3x + 4}$

(b) $3x^2 + 2x - \sqrt{3}$

(c) $4x^{-2} + 3x^{1/3} + 2$

(d) $4^x + x^3 - 17$

(e) $4x^3 - ix^2 + 14$

---

61. (b), (e).

If you had difficulty, see
frames 1 to 18.

EXERCISE 3

62. Give the degree of each of the following polynomials.

Polynomial	Degree
(a) $x^7 - 5x^3 + 16$	____
(b) $4x^3 - 6x^2 - 7x + 5$	____
(c) $ix^4 + \sqrt{3}x^2 - 6x + 4$	____

---

62. (a) 7,
(b) 3,
(c) 4.

If you had difficulty,
see frames 6 to 16.

EXERCISE 4

63. Given $P(x) = 7x^4 - 2x^3 + 5x - 7$ and
$Q(x) = 4x^3 - 5x^2 + 4$, find

(a) $P(x) + Q(x)$ _____ ,

(b) $P(x) - Q(x)$ _____ ,

(c) $P(x) \cdot Q(x)$ _____

_____ .

---

63. (a) $7x^4 + 2x^3 - 5x^2 + 5x - 3$,
(b) $7x^4 - 6x^3 + 5x^2 + 5x - 11$,
(c) $28x^7 - 8x^6 + 20x^4 - 28x^3 - 35x^6 + 10x^5 - 25x^3 + 35x^2 + 28x^4 - 8x^3 + 20x - 28 =$
$28x^7 - 43x^6 + 10x^5 + 48x^4 - 61x^3 + 35x^2 + 20x - 28$.

If you had difficulty, see
frames 23 to 28.

EXERCISE 5

64. Find the quotient $Q(x)$ and remainder $R(x)$ when
$P(x) = 5x^4 + 6x^3 - x + 3$ is divided by $D(x) = 2x^2 - x + 2$
and write $P(x)$ in the form $P(x) = D(x) \cdot Q(x) + R(x)$.

$Q(x) =$ **(a)** _____ ,

$R(x) =$ **(b)** _____ ,

$5x^4 + 6x^3 - x + 3 =$ **(c)** _____

_____ .

---

64. (a) $\frac{5}{2}x^2 + \frac{17}{4}x - \frac{3}{8}$,

(b) $-\frac{79}{8}x + \frac{15}{4}$,

(c) $(2x^2 - x + 2)(\frac{5}{2}x^2 + \frac{17}{4}x - \frac{3}{8}) - \frac{79}{8}x + \frac{15}{4}$.

If you had difficulty, see frames 30 to 49.

EXERCISE 6

65. Let $P(x) = x^4 - 4x^3 + 2x - 5$ and $Q(x) = 2x - 3$. Find $4P(x) + Q(x)^3$ and put it in polynomial form.

$4P(x) + Q(x)^3 = $ _____

65. $4x^4 - 8x^3 - 36x^2 + 62x - 47$
(since $4P(x) = 4x^4 - 16x^3 + 8x - 20$
and $Q(x)^3 = 8x^3 - 36x^2 + 54x - 27$)

If you had difficulty, see
frames 52 to 60.

EXERCISE 7

66. Let $f: C \to C$ be a polynomial function defined by
$f(x) = x^3 - 2x^2 + x - 1$. Find

(a) $f(0)$ _____ ,

(b) $f(1)$ _____ ,

(c) $f(-1)$ _____ ,

(d) $f(i)$ _____ .

66. (a) -1,
(b) -1,
(c) -5,
(d) 1.

If you had difficulty, see
frames 21 and 22.

PROBLEMS

1. Indicate whether or not the following expressions are polynomials.

(a) $7x^9 - 4x^3 - 5$ (c) $x^2 - ix + \pi$

(b) $4x^3 + 6\sqrt{x} - 5$ (d) $5x^4 - 4x + 2x^{-3} + 8$

2. Give the degree of each of the following polynomials.

(a) $4x^3 - x^2 + 1$ (c) $7x^4 + \pi x^2 - \sqrt{2}\,x + 3$

(b) $5x^6 + 3$ (d) $x^5 - ix^2 + 5x + 7$

3. For each of the following, find $P(x) + Q(x), P(x) - Q(x)$, and $P(x) \cdot Q(x)$.

(a) $P(x) = 2x^3 - 4x^2 - 5$, $Q(x) = x^2 + 6$

(b) $P(x) = 5x^4 - x + 5$, $Q(x) = 3x^2 + 4x - 1$

(c) $P(x) = 5x^2 + 2x + 3$, $Q(x) = x^3 - 5x^2 - x$

4. If $P(x)$ has degree n and $Q(x)$ has degree m and $n \geqslant m$, what is the degree of each of the following?

(a) $P(x) + Q(x)$ (b) $P(x) - Q(x)$ (c) $P(x) \cdot Q(x)$

5. For each $P(x)$ and $D(x)$, find the quotient $Q(x)$ and remainder $R(x)$ that are obtained by dividing $P(x)$ by $D(x)$.

(a) $P(x) = x^4 + 2x^3 - x + 2$, $D(x) = x^2 + 2x + 2$

(b) $P(x) = 2x^3 + x^2 + 3x + 4$, $D(x) = x - 4$

(c) $P(x) = 4x^3 - 5x^2 + x - 3$, $D(x) = x^2 + 3$

(d) $P(x) = x^4 + 2$, $D(x) = 2x^2 - 4x + 1$

6. Let $P(x) = 3x + 1$, $Q(x) = x^2 + 2$, and $R(x) = x^3 - 2x - 1$. Find each of the following in polynomial form.

(a) $P(x)^2 + 2R(x)$ (c) $3P(x) \cdot Q(x) + 2R(x)$

(b) $P(x) \cdot Q(x) + 2R(x)$ (d) $P(x)^2 \cdot Q(x)^2 + 3P(x)^2$

7. Find each of the following if $f : R \to R$ is a polynomial function defined by $f(x) = x^3 - 4x^2 + 2x + 1$.

(a) $f(2)$ (c) $f(1)$

(b) $f(0)$ (d) $f(-1)$

8. Find each of the following if $g : C \to C$ is a polynomial function from the field of complex numbers to the field of complex numbers, defined by $g(z) = z^2 - 2iz + 3$.

(a) $g(1)$ (c) $g(-i)$

(b) $g(i)$ (d) $g(1 + i)$

Answers are at end of book.

QUIZ

If you cannot answer the following questions correctly, review the appropriate frames.

1. Which of the following expressions are polynomials?

(a) $x^3 + 3x - 17$

(b) $3x^2 + 2\sqrt{x} + 5$

(c) $4^x + 5x - 2$

(d) $4x^2 - \sqrt{3}x + i$

(e) $3x^{-4} + 6x^{1/2} - 8$

2. Give the degree of each of the following polynomials.

   (a) $x^9 - 5x^4 + 6x^2$

   (b) $3x^4 - 2x^3 + 5x^2 + x - 8$

   (c) $ix^3 + \sqrt{5}x^2 + 4x - 2$

3. Given $P(x) = 4x^3 - 5x^2 + 7$ and $Q(x) = 2x^2 - x + 1$, then

   $P(x) + Q(x) =$ _____

   $P(x) - Q(x) =$ _____

   $P(x) \cdot Q(x) =$ _____

4. Find the quotient $Q(x)$ and remainder $R(x)$ when $P(x) = 4x^5 + 3x^2 - 6$ is divided by $D(x) = x^3 - 2x + 3$ and write $P(x)$ in the form $P(x) = D(x) \cdot Q(x) + R(x)$.

   $Q(x) =$ _____

   $R(x) =$ _____

   $4x^5 + 3x^2 - 6 =$ _____

Answers are at end of book.

11 Polynomials of the First and Second Degree

In this chapter our primary concern will be solving polynomial equations of the form $P(x) = 0$. We mean not that $P(x)$ is the 0 polynomial but that $P(x)$ is a function whose domain is the field of complex numbers. That is, we may replace x in $P(x)$ by any complex number. And the equation $P(x) = 0$ may be true for some values of x and not true for other values of x. At one extreme $P(x) = 0$ may be true for all x, in which case it is an identity and $P(x)$ will, in fact, be the 0 polynomial.

To solve an equation $P(x) = 0$, we must find all complex numbers that make it true or satisfy it. Such a value is called a **solution** of the equation, and the set of all solutions is called the **solution set** of the equation. The solutions of the equation $P(x) = 0$ are called the **zeros** of the polynomial $P(x)$.

It is not difficult to see that 3 is a solution for the equation

$$x^3 - 4x^2 + 6x - 9 = 0.$$

However, it is more difficult to start with the equation $x^3 - 4x^2 + 6x - 9 = 0$ and discover its solutions. This latter problem will concern us in this chapter.

Upon completing this chapter, you should be able to

I. Given a list of expressions, choose which are polynomials of the first degree and which are polynomials of the second degree.

II. Find the zero of first-degree polynomials.

III. Given a linear function,
   (A) find the slope,
   (B) find the x-intercept and y-intercept,
   (C) sketch the graph of the function.

IV. Find the zeros of second-degree polynomials by
   (A) factoring,
   (B) completing the square,
   (C) quadratic formulas.

V. By looking at the discriminant of a second-degree polynomial, decide if the zeros are
- (A) real and distinct,
- (B) real and equal,
- (C) complex conjugates.

VI. Factor a second-degree polynomial using the quadratic formulas.

VII. Given a quadratic function,
- (A) decide if it opens upward or downward,
- (B) find its x-intercepts,
- (C) graph the function.

POLYNOMIALS OF THE FIRST DEGREE

67. In this chapter we shall discuss polynomials of the first degree. A *polynomial of the first degree* is of the form $P(x) = ax + b$ where $a \neq 0$. Which of the following expressions are first-degree polynomials?
- (a) $5x^2 - 3$
- (b) $4x + 2$
- (c) $\frac{1}{2}x - \sqrt{2}$
- (d) $4x^{-1} - 3$
- (e) $\sqrt{3}x + 6$

67. (b), (c), and (e)

EXAMPLE 1

68. We shall call the equation $ax + b = 0$ a **linear** equation. Which of the following expressions are linear equations?

- (a) $6x - \frac{1}{5} = 0$
- (b) $x^2 - 1 = 0$
- (c) $5x + 6$

68. (a)
 NOTE: $5x + 6$ is a first-degree polynomial but not an equation.

69. A **zero** of a polynomial $P(x)$ is a solution of the equation $P(x) = 0$. Thus a zero of $P(x) = 4x - 8$ is $x =$ ___ .

---

69. 2
(since if $x = 2$, then
$P(x) = 4x - 8 = 0$)

70. The zeros of the polynomial $P(x) = x^2 - 1$ are

$x =$ _____ .

---

70. $+1$ and -1

71. The equation $ax + b = 0$ has the one solution $x =$ _____ .

Hence the polynomial $P(x) = ax + b$ has one zero, $x =$ _____ .

---

71. $-\dfrac{b}{a}$;

$-\dfrac{b}{a}$

72. We now prove a simple result that will be generalized later.

THEOREM 1. If $P(x) = ax + b$ and r is the zero of $P(x)$, then $P(x) = a(x - r)$.

Proof: If r is the zero of $P(x) = ax + b$, then $r =$ _____ .

---

72. $-\dfrac{b}{a}$

73. If $P(x) = ax + b$, we can factor out a and get

$P(x) = ax + b = a\ ($ _____ $)$.

---

73. $x + \dfrac{b}{a}$

74. We can write $x + \dfrac{b}{a}$ as $x - \left(-\dfrac{b}{a}\right)$ and get

$$P(x) = ax + b = a\left(x + \dfrac{b}{a}\right) = a\left(x - \left(-\dfrac{b}{a}\right)\right).$$

Since $-\dfrac{b}{a} =$ ____ ,

we get $P(x) = ax + b = a\left(x - \left(-\dfrac{b}{a}\right)\right) =$ _____ .

---

74. r;
$a(x - r)$

75. Thus $P(x) = ax + b = a(x - r)$ where $r =$ _____ .

---

75. $-\dfrac{b}{a}$

Theorem 1

If $P(x) = ax + b$ and r is the zero of $P(x)$, then $P(x) = a(x - r)$.

Proof: If $P(x) = ax + b$, we can factor out a and get

$$P(x) = ax + b = a\left(x + \frac{b}{a}\right)$$

$$= a\left(x - \left(-\frac{b}{a}\right)\right).$$

And, since $r = -\dfrac{b}{a}$,

$$P(x) = ax + b = a\left(x + \frac{b}{a}\right)$$

$$= a\left(x - \left(-\frac{b}{a}\right)\right)$$

$$= a(x - r).$$

Thus we have shown that

$$P(x) = ax + b = a(x - r) \qquad \text{where } r = -\frac{b}{a}.$$

EXAMPLE 2

76. Find the zero of $P(x) = 3x - 5$ and write $P(x)$ in the form $P(x) = a(x - r)$. _____

76. $P(x) = 3\left(x - \frac{5}{3}\right)$

(since $3x - 5 = 0$ implies $x = \frac{5}{3}$)

77. If the rule of a function $f : R \rightarrow$ is given by a first-degree polynomial $f(x) = mx + b$, with m and b real, f is called a **linear function** in x. Which of the following functions are linear functions?

(a) $f(x) = 7x - 5$

(b) $f(x) = 4x^2 + 2$

(c) $f(x) = \sqrt{3x + 2}$

(d) $f(x) = \frac{1}{2}x + \sqrt{2}$

(e) $f(x) = 4^x + 1$

---

77. (a) and **(d)**

78. If we represent linear functions by $y = mx + b$, we can graph them on a two-dimensional rectangular coordinate system. Graph $y = 2x + 1$ by plotting a few points and connecting them.

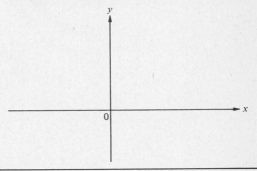

78.

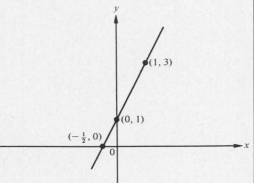

If you had difficulty, see frames 447 to 450, Chapter 12, Volume I.

79. We drew a straight line to connect the three points that satisfy $y = 2x + 1$.

   We shall now prove that the graph of a linear function $f(x) = mx + b$ is, in fact, a straight line.

If we take any three real numbers, x_1, x_2, and x_3, then the points $P(x_1, mx_1 + b)$, $Q(x_2, mx_2 + b)$, and $R(x_3, mx_3 + b)$ lie on the graph of $y = mx + b$ as shown in the figure. Hence the graph of $y = mx + b$ will be a straight line if and only if the slope of the line between P and Q is equal to the slope of the line between _____ .

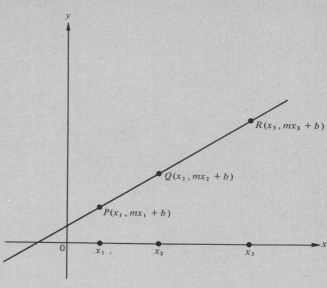

---

79. Q and R

80. The slope of the line between P and Q is

_____ .

---

80. $\dfrac{(mx_2 + b) - (mx_1 + b)}{x_2 - x_1}$.

If you had difficulty, see Chapter 9, Volume I.

81. But, by combining terms, we see that the slope between P and Q,

$$\frac{(mx_2 + b) - (mx_1 + b)}{x_2 - x_1} = \underline{\qquad} = \underline{\qquad} = \underline{\quad}.$$

---

81. $\dfrac{mx_2 - mx_1}{x_2 - x_1} \; ; m\left(\dfrac{x_2 - x_1}{x_2 - x_1}\right) \; ; m$

82. The slope between Q and R is

_____ .

---

82. $\dfrac{(mx_3 + b) - (mx_2 + b)}{x_3 - x_2}$

83. And by combining terms, we see that the slope between Q and R,

$$\frac{(mx_3 + b) - (mx_2 + b)}{x_3 - x_2} = \underline{\qquad}.$$

---

83. $\dfrac{mx_3 - mx_2}{x_3 - x_2} = m\left(\dfrac{x_3 - x_2}{x_3 - x_2}\right) = m$

	84. Thus the slope between P and Q equals the slope between Q and R equals ___ , Thus $y = mx + b$ is the equation of a straight line with slope ___ .
84. m; m	**85.** The slope of the line given by the equation $y = 5x - 3$ is ___ .
85. 5	**86.** The x-intercept of the line given by $y = 5x - 3$ is ___ .
86. $\frac{3}{5}$	**87.** In general the line given by the equation $y = mx + b$ has slope ___ and x-intercept ___ .
87. m; $-\dfrac{b}{m}$	**88.** Since the x-intercept is the x-value that makes $mx + b = $ **(a)** ___ , $-\dfrac{b}{m}$ is a solution of the equation **(b)** ___ and hence a zero of the polynomial **(c)** ___ .
88. (a) 0, **(b)** $mx + b = 0$, **(c)** $P(x) = mx + b$	**89.** That is, the zero of $mx + b$ is the ___ of the graph of $y = mx + b$.
89. x-intercept	**90.** The zero of $\frac{1}{2}x + 3$ is ___ .
90. -6	**91.** The line, given by the equation $y = \frac{1}{2}x + 3$, has slope ___ and x-intercept ___ .
91. $\frac{1}{2}$; -6	**92.** We see further that if $x = 0$ in $y = mx + b$, then $y = $ ___ .
92. b	**93.** Thus the y-intercept of the line given by $y = mx + b$ is ___ .
93. b	**94.** The line given by $y = 2x - 6$ has slope **(a)** ___ , x-intercept **(b)** ___ , and y-intercept **(c)** ___ .
94. (a) 2, **(b)** 3, **(c)** -6	

137

EXAMPLE 3

95. If $m = 0$, then the linear function $f(x) = mx + b$ becomes $f(x) = b$ or $y = b$, the constant function. Graph $y = 5$ on the axes below.

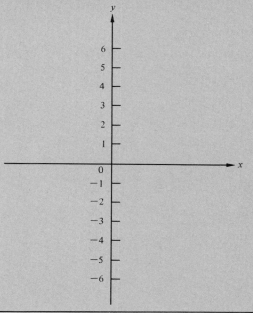

95.

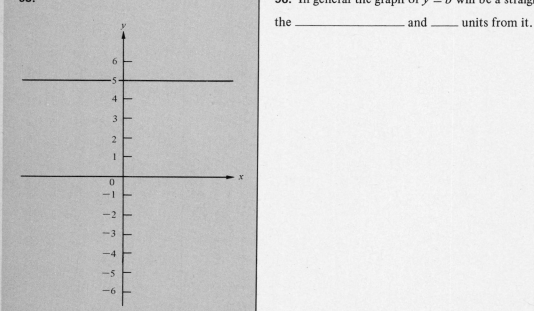

96. In general the graph of $y = b$ will be a straight line parallel to

the _____ and _____ units from it.

96. x-axis; b

EXAMPLE 4

97. Find the slope, x-intercept, and y-intercept, and graph the function $y = 3x - 6$.

Slope is **(a)** ___ .

x-intercept is **(b)** ___ .

y-intercept is **(c)** ___ .

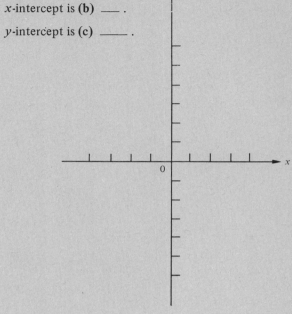

97. (a) 3,
(b) 2,
(c) -6

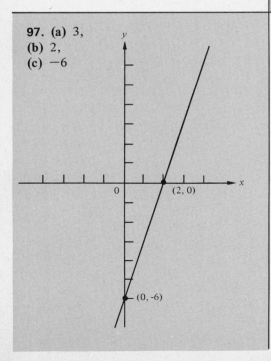

EXAMPLE 5

98. The zero of the polynomial $P(x) = \frac{1}{3}x + 1$ is _____ .

98. -3.
If you had difficulty, see frames 69 to 76.

EXAMPLE 6

99. Find the slope, x-intercept, and y-intercept, and graph the function $y = -2x + 8$.

Slope is **(a)** _____ .

x-intercept is **(b)** _____ .

y-intercept is **(c)** _____ .

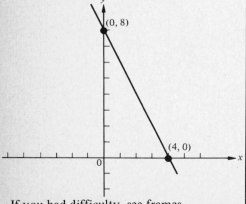

99. (a) -2, **(b)** 4, **(c)** 8.

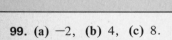

If you had difficulty, see frames 78 to 98.

100. A polynomial of the second degree is of the form $P(x) = ax^2 + bx + c$ where $a \neq 0$. Which of the following expressions are second-degree polynomials?

(a) $6x^2 + 3$

(b) $5x - 2$

(c) $x^{-2} + x^{-1} - 6$

(d) $4x^2 - ix + \sqrt{3}$

(e) $\frac{1}{2}x^2 + \frac{2}{3}x$

---

100. (a), (d), and (e)

EXAMPLE 7

101. We shall call the equation $ax^2 + bx + c = 0$, $a \neq 0$, a **quadratic equation**. Which of the following are quadratic equations?

(a) $6x - 5 = 0$

(b) $\frac{2}{3}x^2 - \frac{5}{8}x + 2 = 0$

(c) $x^2 - x + 2$

(d) $x^2 + 3x^{1/2} + 4 = 0$

(e) $x^2 - \sqrt{2}x + i = 0$

---

101. (b) and (e).

NOTE: (c) is not an equation.

102. The zeros of $P(x) = ax^2 + bx + c$ will be the solutions of the equation _____ .

---

102. $P(x) = ax^2 + bx + c = 0$

103. Thus, the zeros of the polynomial

$$P(x) = x^2 - x - 2 = (x + 1)(x - 2) \text{ are } x = \underline{\hspace{2cm}} .$$

---

103. -1 and 2

104. Finding the solutions of $ax^2 + bx + c = 0$ is straight-forward if we can recognize the factors of $ax^2 + bx + c$. For example, to find the zeros of $P(x) = 2x^2 + 5x - 3$, we solve

the equation _____ .

---

104. $2x^2 + 5x - 3 = 0$

105. Factoring $2x^2 + 5x - 3$, we get

$$2x^2 + 5x - 3 = (\underline{\hspace{1.5cm}})(\underline{\hspace{1.5cm}}) = 0.$$

---

105. $2x - 1; x + 3$

106. But the product of two factors is zero if and only if one or both of the factors is zero. That is, $(2x - 1)(x + 3) = 0$ if and only if either _____ $= 0$ or _____ $= 0$ or both.

---

106. $2x - 1; x + 3$

107. Therefore, since $x = \frac{1}{2}$ is a solution of $2x - 1 = 0$, it is also a solution of _____ .

---

107. $(2x - 1)(x + 3) = 0$

108. Similarly, since $x =$ ____ is a solution of $x + 3 = 0$, it is a solution of _____ .

---

108. -3;
$(2x - 1)(x + 3) = 0$

109. In fact, the solution set of $(2x - 1)(x + 3) = 0$ is the _____ of the two solution sets of the two factors
(union, intersection)
$(2x - 1) = 0$ and $(x + 3) = 0$.

---

109. union

110. That is, the solution set of
$2x^2 + 5x - 3 = (2x - 1)(x + 3) = 0$ is $\{$_____$\}$.

---

110. $\frac{1}{2}, -3$

111. Hence the zeros of $P(x) = 2x^2 + 5x - 3$ are ____ and ____ .

---

111. $\frac{1}{2}; -3$

EXAMPLE 8
112. The zeros of $P(x) = x^2 - x - 6$ are $x =$ _____ .

---

112. -2 and 3.
If you had difficulty,
go on to the next frame.
If not, skip to frame 120.

113. To find the zeros of $P(x) = x^2 - x - 6$ we must find the solutions of the equation _____ .

---

113. $x^2 - x - 6 = 0$

114. Factoring $x^2 - x - 6$, we get
$x^2 - x - 6 = ($_____$)($_____$) = 0$.

---

114. $x + 2; x - 3$

	115. But $(x + 2)(x - 3) = 0$ if and only if either _____ or _____ or both.
115. $x + 2 = 0$; $x - 3 = 0$	**116.** Therefore, since $x =$ ____ is a solution of $x + 2 = 0$, it is also a solution of _____ .
116. -2; $(x + 2)(x - 3) = 0$	**117.** Similarly, since $x =$ ____ is a solution of $x - 3 = 0$, it is a solution of _____ .
117. 3; $(x + 2)(x - 3) = 0$	**118.** Thus the solution set of $x^2 - x - 6 = (x + 2)(x - 3) = 0$ is $\{$_____$\}$.
118. $-2, 3$	**119.** Hence the zeros of $P(x) = x^2 - x - 6$ are ____ and ____ .
119. -2; 3	**EXERCISE 1** **120.** The zeros of $P(x) = x^2 + 3x - 4$ are _____ .
120. 1 and -4. If you had difficulty, see frames 102 to 119.	**EXAMPLE 9** **121.** If we cannot easily recognize the factors of $ax^2 + bx + c = 0$, we can use a process known as **completing the square**. Find the zeros for the second-degree polynomial $P(x) = x^2 + 4x - 2$ by completing the square. _____
121. $-2 + \sqrt{6}$ and $-2 - \sqrt{6}$. If you had difficulty, go on to the next frame. If not, skip to frame 134.	**122.** To find the zeros of $P(x) = x^2 + 4x - 2$, we want to solve the equation _____ by completing the square.
122. $x^2 + 4x - 2 = 0$	**123.** We first put the constant term on the right-hand side of the equation and we obtain the equation _____ .
123. $x^2 + 4x = 2$	

124. We now want to put $x^2 + 4x$ in the form $(x + h)^2 - k$ for some numbers h and k. If we take h to be half the coefficient of the x term, then $h =$ ___ and we form $(x +$ ___$)^2$.

---

124. $2; 2$

125. Multiplying out $(x + 2)^2$ gives us the two terms $x^2 + 4x$ that we want, but it also gives us the constant term ___ that we do not want.

---

125. 4

126. Therefore, we must subtract ___ from $(x + 2)^2$ to get the equality $x^2 + 4x =$ _____.

---

126. $4; (x + 2)^2 - 4$

127. Thus by completing the square, we can replace $x^2 + 4x$ by _____ in the equation $x^2 + 4x = 2$.

---

127. $(x + 2)^2 - 4$

128. We get _____.

---

128. $(x + 2)^2 - 4 = 2$

129. Collecting the constants on the right gives

_____.

---

129. $(x + 2)^2 = 6$

130. Hence $x + 2 =$ _____ or _____.

---

130. $\sqrt{6}; -\sqrt{6}$

131. That is, $x =$ _____ or _____.

---

131. $-2 + \sqrt{6}; -2 - \sqrt{6}$

132. Thus the solutions of the equation $x^2 + 4x - 2 = 0$ are

_____.

---

132. $-2 + \sqrt{6}$ and $-2 - \sqrt{6}$

133. Hence the zeros of $P(x) = x^2 + 4x - 2$ are

_____.

---

133. $-2 + \sqrt{6}$ and $-2 - \sqrt{6}$

EXAMPLE 10

134. Find the zeros of $P(x) = x^2 - 6x + 2$ by completing the square. _____

---

134. $3 + \sqrt{7}$ and $3 - \sqrt{7}$.
If you had difficulty, see frames 121 to 133.

135. We now find the zeros for the general second-degree polynomial $P(x) = ax^2 + bx + c$. To do this, we shall find the solutions of the general quadratic equation _____ by completing the square.

---

135. $ax^2 + bx + c = 0$

136. Since $a \neq 0$, we can divide $ax^2 + bx + c = 0$ by a and put the constant term on the right-hand side of the equation. We get

(1) _____ + _____ = _____ .

---

136. $x^2; \dfrac{b}{a}x \quad -\dfrac{c}{a}$

137. We now want to put $x^2 + \dfrac{b}{a}x$ in the form $(x + h)^2 - k$ for some numbers h and k. If we take $\dfrac{1}{2}\left(\dfrac{b}{a}\right)$, which is half the coefficient of the x term, and form $\left(x + \dfrac{b}{2a}\right)^2$ we get, on multiplying,

$$\left(x + \frac{b}{2a}\right)^2 = \underline{\hspace{4cm}} .$$

---

137. $x^2; +\dfrac{b}{a}x; +\dfrac{b^2}{4a^2};$

138. This gives us the two terms $x^2 + \dfrac{b}{a}x$ that we want, but it also gives the constant term $\dfrac{b^2}{4a^2}$ that we do not need. Therefore, we must subtract _____ form $\left(x + \dfrac{b}{2a}\right)^2$ to get the desired equality $x^2 + \dfrac{b}{a}x =$

$$\underline{\hspace{5cm}} .$$

---

138. $\dfrac{b^2}{4a^2};$

$\left(x + \dfrac{b}{2a}\right) - \dfrac{b^2}{4a^2}$

139. Thus completing the square, enables us to replace $x^2 + \dfrac{b}{a}x$ by

_____ in the equation

(1) $x^2 + \dfrac{b}{a}x = -\dfrac{c}{a}$, and get

$$\underline{\hspace{5cm}} .$$

---

139. $\left(x + \dfrac{b}{2a}\right)^2 - \dfrac{b^2}{4a^2};$

$\left(x + \dfrac{b}{2a}\right)^2 - \dfrac{b^2}{4a^2} = -\dfrac{c}{a}$

140. Collecting the constant terms on the right gives

_____ .

---

140. $\left(x + \dfrac{b}{2a}\right)^2 = \dfrac{b^2}{4a^2} - \dfrac{c}{a}$

141. And putting the right-hand side of the equation over a common denominator gives _____ .

---

141. $\left(x + \dfrac{b}{2a}\right)^2 = \dfrac{b^2 - 4ac}{4a^2}$

142. Finally, if $\left(x + \dfrac{b}{2a}\right)^2 = \dfrac{b^2 - 4ac}{4a^2}$, then $\left(x + \dfrac{b}{2a}\right) =$

_____ or _____ .

---

142. $\dfrac{-\sqrt{b^2 - 4ac}}{2a}$;

$\dfrac{+\sqrt{b^2 - 4ac}}{2a}$.

143. That is, $x =$ _____ or

_____ .

---

143. $\dfrac{-b - \sqrt{b^2 - 4ac}}{2a}$;

$\dfrac{-b + \sqrt{b^2 - 4ac}}{2a}$

144. We have started with the general quadratic equation $ax^2 + bx + c = 0$, completed the square, and shown that the solutions of $ax^2 + bx + c = 0$ are $x =$ _____

and $x =$ _____ .

---

144. $\dfrac{-b - \sqrt{b^2 - 4ac}}{2a}$;

$\dfrac{-b + \sqrt{b^2 - 4ac}}{2a}$

145. Thus the zeros of the general second-degree polynomial $P(x) = ax^2 + bx + c$ are _____

and _____ .

---

145. $\dfrac{-b - \sqrt{b^2 - 4ac}}{2a}$;

$\dfrac{-b + \sqrt{b^2 - 4ac}}{2a}$

146. We state as a theorem the result that we have just proved.

THEOREM 2. The second-degree polynomial $ax^2 + bx + c$ has two zeros, which may be equal;

$x_1 =$ _____

and $x_2 =$ _____ .

---

146. $\dfrac{-b - \sqrt{b^2 - 4ac}}{2a}$;

$\dfrac{-b + \sqrt{b^2 - 4ac}}{2a}$

Theorem 2

The second-degree polynomial $ax^2 + bx + c$ has two zeros, which may be equal.

$$x_1 = \frac{-b - \sqrt{b^2 - 4ac}}{2a} \quad \text{and} \quad x_2 = \frac{-b + \sqrt{b^2 - 4ac}}{2a}$$

Proof: To find the zeros of $ax^2 + bx + c$, we must find the solutions of the equation

$$ax^2 + bx + c = 0.$$

Since $a \neq 0$, we can divide by a and put the constant term on the right-hand side of the equation. We get

$$(1) \quad x^2 + \frac{b}{a}x = -\frac{c}{a}.$$

Completing the square of $x^2 + \frac{b}{a}x$, we get $x^2 + \frac{b}{a}x = \left(x + \frac{b}{2a}\right)^2 - \frac{b^2}{4a^2}$.

And substituting in (1) gives $\left(x + \frac{b}{2a}\right)^2 - \frac{b^2}{4a^2} = -\frac{c}{a}$.

Collecting the constant terms on the right gives $\left(x + \frac{b}{2a}\right)^2 = \frac{b^2}{4a^2} - \frac{c}{a}$,

and putting the right-hand side of the equation over a common denominator gives

$$\left(x + \frac{b}{2a}\right)^2 = \frac{b^2 - 4ac}{4a^2}$$

Hence $\left(x + \frac{b}{2a}\right) = \frac{-\sqrt{b^2 - 4ac}}{2a}$ or $\left(x + \frac{b}{2a}\right)^2 = \frac{+\sqrt{b^2 - 4ac}}{2a}$.

That is, $x = \frac{-b - \sqrt{b^2 - 4ac}}{2a}$ or $x = \frac{-b + \sqrt{b^2 - 4ac}}{2a}$.

We have started with $ax^2 + bx + c = 0$, completed the square, and shown that the solutions of $ax^2 + bx + c = 0$ are

$$x = \frac{-b - \sqrt{b^2 - 4ac}}{2a} \quad \text{and} \quad x = \frac{-b + \sqrt{b^2 - 4ac}}{2a}$$

Thus the zeros of the general second-degree polynomial $P(x) = ax^2 + bx + c$ are

$$\frac{-b - \sqrt{b^2 - 4ac}}{2a} \quad \text{and} \quad \frac{-b + \sqrt{b^2 - 4ac}}{2a}$$

147. These formulas are called the **quadratic formulas**. They are

often written $x = \dfrac{-b + \sqrt{b^2 - 4ac}}{2a}$. They give the zeros of

_____ in terms of a, b, and c.

---

147. $ax^2 + bx + c$

EXAMPLE 11

148. To find the zeros of the polynomial $P(x) = x^2 - 3x + 1$, we

must solve the quadratic equation _____ .

---

148. $x^2 - 3x + 1 = 0$

149. In the polynomial $x^2 - 3x + 1$

$a = $ (a) ____ , $b = $ (b) ____ , and $c = $ (c) ____ .

---

149. $1, -3, 1$

150. Thus by the quadratic formulas, $x_1 = $

_____

and $x_2 = $

_____ .

---

150. $\dfrac{3 - \sqrt{9 - 4}}{2}$; $\dfrac{3 + \sqrt{9 - 4}}{2}$

$\left(\text{or } x_1 = \dfrac{3 - \sqrt{5}}{2} \text{ and } x_2 = \dfrac{3 + \sqrt{5}}{2}\right)$

151. That is, _____ and _____ are the

zeros of $P(x) = x^2 - 3x + 1$.

---

151. $\dfrac{3 - \sqrt{5}}{2}$; $\dfrac{3 + \sqrt{5}}{2}$

EXAMPLE 12.

152. Find the zeros of the polynomial $Q(x) = x^2 - 4x + 4$;

$x = $ ____

---

152. 2. $\left(\text{The two zeros are equal.}\right)$
If you had difficulty, go on to the
next frame. If not, skip to frame 156.

153. To find the zeros of the polynomial $Q(x) = x^2 - 4x + 4$, we

must solve the quadratic equation _____ .

---

153. $x^2 - 4x + 4 = 0$

154. Since $a = $ **(a)** ___ , $b = $ **(b)** ___ , and $c = $ **(c)** ___ , we have by the quadratic formulas $x_1 = $ **(d)** _____

and $x_2 = $ **(e)** _____ .

---

154. (a) 1, **(b)** −4, **(c)** 4,

(d) $\dfrac{4 - \sqrt{16 - 16}}{2}$, **(e)** $\dfrac{4 + \sqrt{16 - 16}}{2}$

$\left(\text{or } x_1 = \dfrac{4 - \sqrt{0}}{2} = 2\right.$

and $\left. x_2 = \dfrac{4 + \sqrt{0}}{2} = 2\right)$

155. Thus the two solutions are the same, and the zero of $Q(x) = x^2 - 4x + 4$ is ___ .

---

155. 2

EXAMPLE 13

156. Use the quadratic formulas to find the zeros of the polynomial $R(x) = 2x^2 + 3x + 3$. _____

_____

---

156. $\dfrac{-3 - \sqrt{15}\, i}{4}$ and $\dfrac{-3 + \sqrt{15}\, i}{4}$.

If you had difficulty, go on to the next frame. If not, skip to frame 162.

157. Since $a = $ **(a)** ___ , $b = $ **(b)** ___ , and $c = $ **(c)** ___ , we have by the quadratic formulas $x = $ **(d)** _____

or **(e)** _____ .

---

157. (a) 2, **(b)** 3, **(c)** 3,

(d) $\dfrac{-3 - \sqrt{9 - 24}}{4}$, **(e)** $\dfrac{-3 + \sqrt{9 - 24}}{4}$

158. And combining the numbers under the radicals we get

$x = $ or

_____   _____ .

---

158. $\dfrac{-3 - \sqrt{-15}}{4}$; $\dfrac{-3 + \sqrt{-15}}{4}$

159. But $\sqrt{-15} = \sqrt{15}\,\sqrt{-1} = $ _____ .

---

159. $\sqrt{15}\, i$

160. Hence, we have $x = $ or

_____

_____ .

---

160. $\dfrac{-3 - \sqrt{15}\, i}{4}$; $\dfrac{-3 + \sqrt{15}\, i}{4}$

161. Thus the zeros of $R(x) = 2x^2 + 3x + 3$ are

_____ .

---

161. $\dfrac{-3 - \sqrt{15}\,i}{4}$ and $\dfrac{-3 + \sqrt{15}\,i}{4}$

162. We see in the preceding examples that $P(x) = x^2 - 3x + 1$ has two distinct real zeros, $Q(x) = x^2 - 4x + 4$ has equal real zeros, and $R(x) = 2x^2 + 3x + 3$ has distinct complex zeros that are complex conjugates.

The nature of the zeros can be determined by examining the

quadratic formulas $x =$ _____ and

_____ .

---

162. $\dfrac{-b + \sqrt{b^2 - 4ac}}{2a}$;

$\dfrac{-b - \sqrt{b^2 - 4ac}}{2a}$

163. In fact, the nature of the zeros can be determined by examining the terms under the radical $b^2 - 4ac$. If a, b, and c are all real numbers, then $b^2 - 4ac$ is called the **discriminant** of the quadratic polynomial $ax^2 + bx + c$.

If $b^2 - 4ac > 0$, then $\sqrt{b^2 - 4ac}$ will be _____ .
(real, complex, zero)

---

163. Real.
(The positive square root of a positive real number is a positive real number.)

164. Thus, if $b^2 - 4ac > 0$, then $\sqrt{b^2 - 4ac}$ will be real and

$x = \dfrac{-b + \sqrt{b^2 - 4ac}}{2a}$ and $x = \dfrac{-b - \sqrt{b^2 - 4ac}}{2a}$

will be **(a)** real and distinct, **(b)** real and equal, **(c)** complex and distinct.

---

164. (a)

165. If $b^2 - 4ac = 0$, then $\sqrt{b^2 - 4ac}$ will be _____ .

---

165. zero

166. And the zeros $x = \dfrac{-b + \sqrt{b^2 - 4ac}}{2a}$ and

$x = \dfrac{-b - \sqrt{b^2 - 4ac}}{2a}$ will be _____ .

---

166. real and equal
$\left(\text{Since } \dfrac{-b + 0}{2a} = \dfrac{-b - 0}{2a}\right)$

167. Finally, if $b^2 - 4ac < 0$, then $\sqrt{b^2 - 4ac}$ will be

_____ .

---

167. complex (or imaginary)

---

168. And the zeros $x =$ **(a)** _____

and $x =$ **(b)** _____

will be **(c)** _____ .

---

168. (a) $\dfrac{-b + \sqrt{b^2 - 4ac}}{2a}$,

(b) $\dfrac{-b - \sqrt{b^2 - 4ac}}{2a}$,

(c) complex and distinct.
(In fact they are complex
conjugates.)

169. If a, b, and c are real numbers, then $b^2 - 4ac$ is called the

_____ of the quadratic polynomial

$ax^2 + bx + c$.

---

169. discriminant

170. If $b^2 - 4ac > 0$, then the zeros of $ax^2 + bx + c$ are

_____ .

---

170. real and distinct

171. If $b^2 - 4ac = 0$, then the zeros of $ax^2 + bx + c$ are

_____ .

---

171. real and equal

172. And if $b^2 - 4ac < 0$, then the zeros of $ax^2 + bx + c$ are

_____ .

---

172. distinct complex conjugates

SUMMARY

We summarize the relation between the discriminant $b^2 - 4ac$ and the zeros of $ax^2 + bx + c$ in the following table.

Let $P(x) = ax^2 + bx + c$ with a, b, and c real.

$b^2 - 4ac$	zeros of $P(x) = ax^2 + bx + c$
positive	real and unequal
zero	real and equal
negative	complex conjugates

NOTE: The relation between the discriminant $b^2 - 4ac$ and the zeros of $ax^2 + bx + c$ holds only if the coefficients a, b, and c are real.

EXAMPLE 14

173. If the coefficients of a second-degree polynomial are complex numbers we can still find the zeros by factoring, by completing the square, or by using the quadratic formulas.

Use the quadratic formulas to find the zeros of the polynomial $P(x) = x^2 - 2ix + 3$.

$x =$ _____

---

173. $-i$ and $x = 3i$.
If you had difficulty,
go on to the next frame.
If not, skip to frame 176.

174. Since $a =$ **(a)** ___, $b =$ **(b)** _____, and $c =$ **(c)** ___ , we have

by the quadratic formulas $x =$ **(d)** _____

or **(e)** _____ .

---

174. (a) 1, **(b)** $-2i$, **(c)** 3,

(d) $\dfrac{2i - \sqrt{-4 - 12}}{2}$,

(e) $\dfrac{2i + \sqrt{-4 - 12}}{2}$

175. But $\sqrt{-4-12} = \sqrt{-16} =$ **(a)** _____ . Thus, the zeros of $x^2 - 2ix + 3$ are **(b)** _____ and

(c) _____ .

---

175. (a) $4i$,

(b) $\dfrac{2i - 4i}{2} = -i$,

(c) $\dfrac{2i + 4i}{2} = 3i$

EXAMPLE 15

176. The zeros of the polynomial $P(x) = ix^2 + 2x + 3i$ are

_____ .

---

176. $-\dfrac{3}{i}$ and $\dfrac{1}{i}$.

If you had difficulty, see frames 173 to 175.

177. Earlier in the section we proved a theorem that states that if $P(x) = ax + b$ is a first-degree polynomial and r is a zero of $P(x)$, then we can write $P(x) =$

_____ .

---

177. $a(x - r)$ where $r = -\dfrac{b}{a}$.

If you had difficulty, see frames 72 to 75.

178. We now look at some preliminary material that will lead to a similar result for polynomials of the second degree.

If r_1 and r_2 are the two zeros of the second-degree polynomial $P(x) = ax^2 + bx + c$, we see by the quadratic formulas that

$r_1 =$ _____ and $r_2 =$ _____ .

---

178. $\dfrac{-b - \sqrt{b^2 - 4ac}}{2a}$;

$\dfrac{-b + \sqrt{b^2 - 4ac}}{2a}$

179. Adding these two expressions we see that $r_1 + r_2 =$

_____ .

---

179. $\dfrac{-b - \sqrt{b^2 - 4ac}}{2a} + \dfrac{-b + \sqrt{b^2 - 4ac}}{2a} =$

$\dfrac{-2b}{2a} = \dfrac{-b}{a}$

180. And multiplying them gives $r_1 \cdot r_2 =$

_____

_____ .

---

180. $\dfrac{-b - \sqrt{b^2 - 4ac}}{2a} \cdot \dfrac{-b + \sqrt{b^2 - 4ac}}{2a} =$

$\dfrac{b^2 - (b^2 - 4ac)}{4a^2} = \dfrac{c}{a}$

181. We can state this result as a lemma.

LEMMA. If r_1 and r_2 are the zeros (either real or complex) of the second-degree polynomial $P(x) = ax^2 + bx + c$, then

(i) $r_1 + r_2 = $ _____ and (ii) $r_1 \cdot r_2 = $ _____ .

---

181. $\dfrac{-b}{a}$; $\dfrac{c}{a}$

SUMMARY

Lemma

If r_1 and r_2 are the zeros (either real or complex) of the second-degree polynomial

$P(x) = ax^2 + bx + c$, then (i) $r_1 + r_2 = \dfrac{-b}{a}$ and (ii) $r_1 \cdot r_2 = \dfrac{c}{a}$.

Proof: If r_1 and r_2 are the zeros of $ax^2 + bx + c$, then by the quadratic formulas,

$$r_1 = \frac{-b - \sqrt{b^2 - 4ac}}{2a} \text{ and } r_2 = \frac{-b + \sqrt{b^2 - 4ac}}{2a} .$$

(i) Adding these two expressions we see that

$$r_1 + r_2 = \frac{-b - \sqrt{b^2 - 4ac}}{2a} + \frac{-b + \sqrt{b^2 - 4ac}}{2a} = \frac{-2b}{2a} = \frac{-b}{a} .$$

(ii) And multiplying them gives

$$r_1 \cdot r_2 = \left(\frac{-b - \sqrt{b^2 - 4ac}}{2a}\right) \cdot \left(\frac{-b + \sqrt{b^2 - 4ac}}{2a}\right) = \frac{b^2 - (b^2 - 4ac)}{4a^2} = \frac{c}{a} .$$

---

182. THEOREM 3. If r_1 and r_2 are the zeros (either real or complex) of the second-degree polynomial $P(x) = ax^2 + bx + c$, then $P(x) = a(x - r_1)(x - r_2)$.

Proof: Consider the polynomial $a((x - r_1)(x - r_2))$. Multiplying out the product $(x - r_1)(x - r_2)$ we get (1) $a((x - r_1)(x - r_2)) = a(\underline{\hspace{4cm}})$.

---

182. $x^2 - (r_1 + r_2)x + r_1 \cdot r_2$

	183. But by the preceding lemma, $r_1 + r_2 =$ _____ and $r_1 \cdot r_2 =$ _____ .
183. $-\dfrac{b}{a}$; $\dfrac{c}{a}$	**184.** Substituting these for $r_1 + r_2$ and $r_1 \cdot r_2$ in (1) we get $a((x-r_1)(x-r_2)) = a(\underline{\hspace{4cm}})$.
184. $x^2 - (-\dfrac{b}{a})x + \dfrac{c}{a}$	**185.** And on multiplying through by a we get $a((x-r_1)(x-r_2)) = \underline{\hspace{4cm}}$.
185. $ax^2 + bx + c$	**186.** But $ax^2 + bx + c = P(x)$. Thus we have shown that $P(x) = ax^2 + bx + c$ can be written as $P(x) = \underline{\hspace{3cm}}$.
186. $a(x-r_1)(x-r_2)$	

SUMMARY

Theorem 3

If r_1 and r_2 are the zeros (either real or complex) of the second-degree polynomial $P(x) = ax^2 + bx + c$, then $P(x) = a(x-r_1)(x-r_2)$.

Proof: Consider the polynomial $a((x-r_1)(x-r_2))$.

Multiplying out the product $(x-r_1)(x-r_2)$ we get

(1) $a((x-r_1)(x-r_2)) = a(x^2 - (r_1 + r_2)x + r_1 \cdot r_2)$.

But, by the preceding lemma, $r_1 + r_2 = -\dfrac{b}{a}$ and $r_1 \cdot r_2 = \dfrac{c}{a}$.

Substituting these for $r_1 + r_2$ and $r_1 \cdot r_2$ in (1) gives

$a((x-r_1)(x-r_2)) = a\left[x^2 - \left(-\dfrac{b}{a}\right)x + \dfrac{c}{a}\right]$ and on multiplying through by a we get

$a((x-r_1)(x-r_2)) = ax^2 + bx + c = P(x)$.

Thus we have shown that $P(x) = ax^2 + bx + c$ can be written as $P(x) = a(x-r_1)(x-r_2)$ as required.

187. Thus we have shown that if r_1 and r_2 are the zeros of

$P(x) = ax^2 + bx + c$, we can write $P(x) =$ _____ .

---

187. $a(x - r_1)(x - r_2)$

EXAMPLE 16

188. Use the quadratic formulas to factor the polynomial

$P(x) = 2x^2 + 4x - 6.$ $P(x) =$ _____

---

188. $2(x + 3)(x - 1)$.

If you had difficulty, go on to the next frame. If not, skip to frame 191.

189. Since $a = $ **(a)** ___ , $b = $ **(b)** ___ , and $c = $ **(c)** ___ , we see by the quadratic formulas that the zeros of $P(x)$ are

$r_1 = $ **(d)** _____

and $r_2 = $ **(e)** _____ .

---

189. (a) 2, (b) 4, (c) −6,

(d) $\dfrac{-4 - \sqrt{16 + 48}}{4}$,

(e) $\dfrac{-4 + \sqrt{16 + 48}}{4}$

$\left(\text{or } r_1 = \dfrac{-4 - 8}{4} = -3 \text{ and } r_2 = \dfrac{-4 + 8}{4} = 1\right)$

190. Hence by the preceding theorem, we can write $P(x) =$

$P(x) =$ _____ .

---

190. $2(x + 3)(x - 1)$

EXAMPLE 17

191. Factor the polynomial $P(x) = x^2 - 4x + 5.$

$P(x) =$ _____ .

---

191. $(x - (2 - i))(x - (2 + i))$.

If you had difficulty, go on to the next frame. If not, skip to frame 194.

192. Since $a = $ **(a)** ___ , $b = $ **(b)** ___ , and $c = $ **(c)** ___ , we see by the quadratic formulas that the zeros of $P(x) = x^2 - 4x + 5$ are

$r_1 = $ **(d)** _____ and

$r_2 = $ **(e)** _____ .

---

192. (a) 1, (b) −4, (c) 5,

(d) $\dfrac{4 - \sqrt{16 - 20}}{2}$, **(e)** $\dfrac{4 + \sqrt{16 - 20}}{2}$

$\left(\text{or } r_1 = \dfrac{4 - \sqrt{-4}}{2} = 2 - i \text{ and } r_2 = \dfrac{4 + \sqrt{-4}}{2} = 2 + i\right)$

193. Hence by theorem 3,

$P(x) = $ _____ .

---

193. $(x - (2 - i))(x - (2 + i))$

EXAMPLE 18

194. Factor the polynomial $P(x) = x^2 + ix + 2$.

$P(x) = $ _____

---

194. $(x + 2i)(x - i)$.

If you had difficulty,
see frames 188 to 193.

GRAPHS OF POLYNOMIALS OF THE SECOND DEGREE

195. If the rule of a function $f: R \to R$ is given by a second-degree polynomial, $f(x) = ax^2 + bx + c$, with a, b, and c real coefficients and $a \neq 0$, f is called **quadratic function** in x. Which of the following are quadratic functions $f: R \to R$?
(a) $f(x) = 4x + 3$
(b) $f(x) = 7x^2 - \sqrt{2}$
(c) $f(x) = 3x^2 - ix + 2$
(d) $f(x) = 4x^{-2} - x^{-1} - 6$
(e) $f(x) = \frac{1}{2}x^2 - 3x + \sqrt{7}$

---

195. (b) and (e).
NOTE: $3x^2 - ix + 2$ is not a function
from R to R since the coefficient
for x is not real.

196. As in the case of linear functions, the zeros of the polynomial

$ax^2 + bx + c$ are the _____ of the
graph of the function $f(x) = ax^2 + bx + c$.

---

196. x-intercepts

197. Thus if $f(x) = x^2 - x - 2 = (x + 1)(x - 2)$ then the x-intercepts of the graph of $f(x)$ are _____ .

---

197. -1 and 2

EXAMPLE 19

198. Graph the quadratic function $f(x) = x^2 - 6x + 8$ by plotting the five points whose first elements are 1, 2, 3, 4, 5 and by connecting these points with a smooth curve.

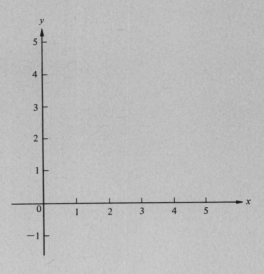

198.

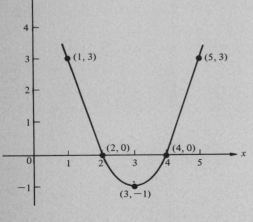

199. The zero(s) of $f(x) = x^2 - 6x + 8$ are _____ .

199. 2 and 4
(since $f(x) = x^2 - 6x + 8 =$
$(x - 2)(x - 4)$)

EXAMPLE 20

200. The graph of $g(x) = x^2 - 6x + 9$ is shown below.

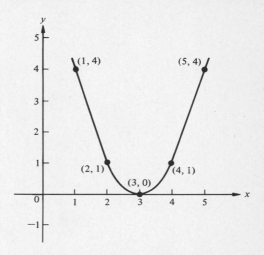

The zero(s) of $g(x) = x^2 - 6x + 9$ are ___ .

200. 3
(since $g(x) = x^2 - 6x + 9 =$
$(x - 3)(x - 3)$)

EXAMPLE 21

201. Finally, the graph of $h(x) = x^2 - 6x + 10$ is shown.

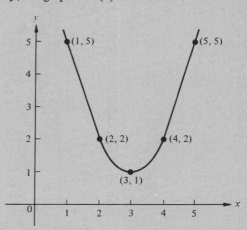

The zero(s) of $h(x) = x^2 - 6x + 10$ are _____ .

201. There are no real zeros.

202. $f(x) = x^2 - 6x + 8$ in frame 198 has _____ real zero(s)

(two, one, no)

since the discriminant $b^2 - 4ac$ _____ .

---

202. two; > 0

203. Hence the graph of $f(x) = x^2 - 6x + 8$ has _____

(how many?)

x-intercept(s).

---

203. two

204. $g(x) = x^2 - 6x + 9$ in frame 200 has _____

zero(s), since the discriminant _____ .

---

204. one real;
$b^2 - 4ac = 0$

205. And the graph of $g(x) = x^2 - 6x + 9$ has _____
x-intercept(s).

---

205. one

206. Finally, $h(x) = x^2 - 6x + 10$ in frame 201 has _____

zero(s), since _____

_____ .

---

206. no real;
the discriminant $b^2 - 4ac < 0$
(and the zeros will be complex
conjugates)

207. And the graph of $h(x) = x^2 - 6x + 10$ has _____
x-intercept(s).

---

207. no

EXAMPLE 22

 208. How many x-intercepts does the graph of the function

$f(x) = x^2 - 2x + 5$ have? _____

---

208. None.

If you had difficulty, go on to
the next frame. If not, skip to
frame 211.

209. Since the discriminant $b^2 - 4ac$ _____ , $f(x) =$

$f(x) = x^2 - 2x + 5$ has _____ real zero(s).

---

209. < 0; no
no

210. Hence the graph of $f(x) = x^2 - 2x + 5$ has _____
x-intercept(s).

---

210. no

211. The graph of the function $g(x) = x^2 - 2x + 1$ has _____ x-intercept(s).

---

211. One.

If you had difficulty, go on to the next frame. If not, skip to frame 214.

212. Since the discriminant _____ , $g(x) = x^2 - 2x + 1$ has _____ real zero(s).

---

212. $b^2 - 4ac = 0$; one

213. Hence the graph of $g(x) = x^2 - 2x + 1$ has _____ x-intercept(s).

---

213. one

EXAMPLE 23

214. The graph of the function $h(x) = x^2 - 2x - 3$ has _____ x-intercept(s).

---

214. two
(since the discriminant $b^2 - 4ac > 0$).

If you had difficulty, see frames 202 to 213.

EXAMPLE 24

215. Graph the quadratic function $f(x) = -x^2 + 2x + 3$ by plotting the five points whose first elements are $-2, -1, 1, 3, 4$ and by connecting these points with a smooth curve.

215.

216. The graph of every quadratic $ax^2 + bx + c$ with real coefficients has the same general shape as the graphs in frames 198, 200, 201, and 215. This shape is called a **parabola**. It can be shown that if $a > 0$, as in the examples in frames 198, 200, and 201, then

the graph opens _____ .
(upward, downward)

---

216. upward

217. If $a < 0$, as in the example in frame 215, then the graph opens

_____ .

---

217. downward

EXAMPLE 25

218. State whether the graph of each of the following quadratic functions opens upward or downward.
(a) $f(x) = x^2 - 3x + 4$
(b) $f(x) = -2x^2 - 4x + 5$
(c) $f(x) = -x^2 + 5x - 2$
(d) $f(x) = \frac{1}{2}x^2 + x - 8$

(e) $f(x) = -\frac{1}{3}x^2 + 2x + 3$

---

218. (a) upward,
(b) downward,
(c) downward,
(d) upward,
(e) downward

219. $f(x) = x^2 - 3x + 4$ has _____ x-intercept(s).
(how many?)

---

219. no
(since $b^2 - 4ac = 9 - 16 = -7 < 0$)

220. $f(x) = -2x^2 - 4x + 5$ has _____ x-intercept(s).

---

220. two
(since $b^2 - 4ac = 16 + 40 = 56 > 0$)

EXAMPLE 26

221. Find the x-intercepts (if there are any) of $f(x) = -x^2 + 6x - 5$ and graph the function. x-intercepts: _____

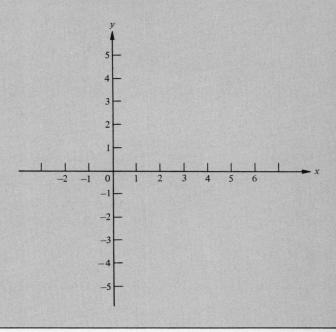

221. 1 and 5.

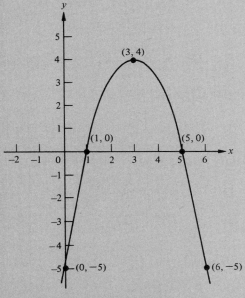

If you had difficulty, go on to the next frame. If not, skip to frame 228.

163

	222. Since the coefficient a of x^2 is negative the graph will open _____ .
222. downward	**223.** And since $b^2 - 4ac$ _____ , there will be _____ x-intercept(s).
223. $= 36 - 20 = 16 > 0$; two	**224.** We can factor $-x^2 + 6x - 5 = 0$ and obtain $-x^2 + 6x - 5 = -($_____$)($_____$) = 0$.
224. $x - 1; x - 5$	**225.** Thus the zeros of $-x^2 + 6x - 5$ are ___ and ___ .
225. 1; 5	**226.** Hence the x-intercepts are ___ and ___ .
226. 1; 5	

227. Thus we know that the graph opens downward and has two *x*-intercepts, 1 and 5. Graph the function by plotting the points whose *x*-values are 0, 1, 3, 5, 6 and by connecting these points with a smooth curve.

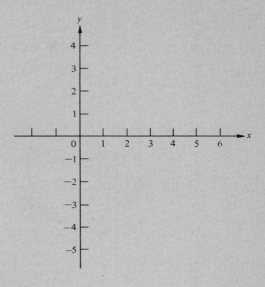

227.

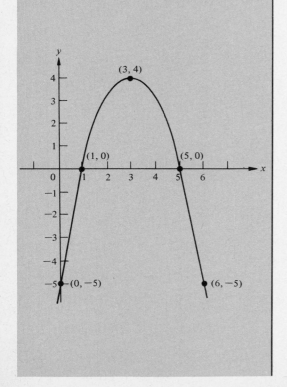

EXERCISE 2

228. The function $f(x) = 4x + 2$ is called a _____ function.

---

228. linear.

If you had difficulty, see frame 77.

EXERCISE 3

229. The function $f(x) = 3x^2 - 5x + 4$ is called a

_____ function.

---

229. quadratic.

If you had difficulty, see frame 195.

EXERCISE 4

230. Find the slope, x-intercept, y-intercept, and graph of the function $y = \frac{1}{2}x - 2$.

Slope is **(a)** _____ .

x-intercept is **(b)** _____ .

y-intercept is **(c)** _____ .

---

230. **(a)** $\frac{1}{2}$, **(b)** 4, **(c)** -2.

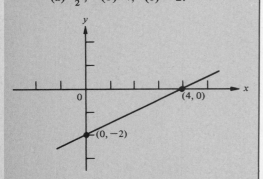

If you had difficulty, see frames 78 to 99.

	EXERCISE 5
	231. Find the zeros of $f(x) = x^2 + 2x - 8$ by factoring.
	$x = $ _____ and _____
231. -4; 2 (since $x^2 + 2x - 8 = (x + 4)(x - 2)$)	**EXERCISE 6** **232.** Find the zeros of $f(x) = x^2 - 4x - 1$ by completing the square. $x = $ _____ and _____
232. $2 + \sqrt{5}$; $2 - \sqrt{5}$ If you had difficulty, see frames 121 to 133.	**EXERCISE 7** **233.** Use the quadratic formulas to find the zeros of $f(x) = 2x^2 + 3x - 5$. $x = $ _____ and _____
233. $-\frac{5}{2}$; 1. If you had difficulty, see frames 147 to 161.	**EXERCISE 8** **234.** Factor $f(x) = 2x^2 + 3x - 5$, the equation in the preceding frame. $f(x) = $ _____
234. $2(x + \frac{5}{2})(x - 1)$. If you had difficulty, see frames 177 to 194.	**EXERCISE 9** **235.** Find the zeros of $P(x) = ix^2 - 4x + 3i$. $x = $ _____ and _____
235. $\dfrac{2 + \sqrt{7}}{i}$; $\dfrac{2 - \sqrt{7}}{i}$ If you had difficulty, see frames 173 to 175.	**EXERCISE 10** **236.** Use the discriminant to determine the number of x-intercepts of $f(x) = x^2 - 5x + 6$. _____
236. two. If you had difficulty, see frames 163 to 172 and the summary on page 152.	**EXERCISE 11** **237.** The graph of $f(x) = x^2 - 5x + 6$ opens _____ .
237. upward. If you had difficulty, see frames 216 and 217.	

EXERCISE 12

238. The x-intercept(s) of $f(x) = x^2 - 5x + 6$ are _____ .

238. 2 and 3.

If you had difficulty,
see frames 195 to 213.

EXERCISE 13

239. Graph the function $f(x) = x^2 - 5x + 6$.

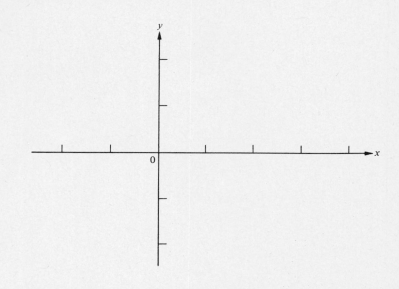

239.

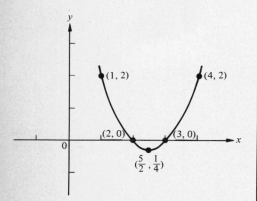

If you had difficulty,
see frames 195 to 227.

PROBLEMS

1. Solve the following equations by factoring.

(a) $x^2 + x - 2 = 0$

(b) $x^2 - 2x - 3 = 0$

(c) $x^2 + 8x = -12$

(d) $x^2 - 3x = 3x - 8$

(e) $2x^2 + x - 6 = 0$

(f) $2x^2 + 2x - 4 = 0$

2. Solve the following equations by completing the square.

(a) $x^2 + 4x = 1$

(b) $x^2 - 6x - 5 = 0$

(c) $x^2 + 2x + 4 = 0$

(d) $2x^2 - x + 2 = 0$

3. Use the quadratic formulas to solve the following equations.

(a) $x^2 + 3x - 1 = 0$

(b) $x^2 - 4x + 2 = 0$

(c) $2x^2 - x + 4 = 0$

(d) $x^2 - 2x + 1 = 0$

(e) $x^2 + 8x + 16 = 0$

(f) $3x^2 + 2x + 2 = 0$

4. Solve the following equations.

(a) $x^2 - ix + 2 = 0$

(b) $x^2 + (2 - i)x - 2i = 0$

(c) $ix^2 + 2x + 3i = 0$

(d) $2x^2 + 3ix - 1 = 0$

5. Determine the number of zeros for each of the following polynomials by calculating the discriminant.

(a) $P(x) = x^2 - 5x + 3$

(b) $P(x) = x^2 - 6x + 9$

(c) $P(x) = 3x^2 - 4x + 2$

(d) $P(x) = 2x^2 + 3x - 6$

6. Find the sum and product of the solutions of the following quadratic equations.

(a) $x^2 - 3x + 5 = 0$

(b) $2x^2 + 4x - 9 = 0$

(c) $3x^2 + 5x + 12 = 0$

(d) $x^2 - 11x - 17 = 0$

7. Use theorem (3) to factor the following polynomials.

(a) $2x^2 - 3x - 2$

(b) $3x^2 - 2x - 1$

(c) $12x^2 - 7x + 1$

(d) $2x^2 - ix + 1$

(e) $x^2 - 6x + 10$

(f) $2x^2 - 5x + (4 - 3i)$

8. Graph the following quadratic functions.

(a) $f(x) = x^2 + x - 2$ (d) $f(x) = 2x^2 - x + 4$

(b) $f(x) = x^2 - 2x + 1$ (e) $f(x) = -x^2 - 8x - 16$

(c) $f(x) = -x^2 - 8x - 12$ (f) $f(x) = x^2 - 4x + 2$

9. (a) The product of two consecutive positive integers is 90. Find the integers.

 (b) The product of two consecutive positive integers is 870. Find the integers.

10. (a) The product of two consecutive even integers is 360. Find the integers.

 (b) The product of two consecutive even integers is 224. Find the integers.

Answers are at end of book.

QUIZ

If you cannot answer the following questions correctly, review the appropriate frames.

1. Which of the following expressions are polynomials of first degree?

(a) $5x^2 + 1$ (d) $\frac{1}{2}x - \sqrt{2}$
(b) $3x - 9$
(c) $2x^{-1} + 6$ (e) $\sqrt{x - 6}$

2. The zero of the polynomial $P(x) = \frac{1}{4}x - 1$ is _____ .

3. Find the slope, x-intercept, and y-intercept and graph the function $y = -3x + 6$.

4. Find the zeros of the following second-degree polynomials.

(a) $P(x) = x^2 + x - 6$
(b) $R(x) = 2x^2 - 3x - 1$

5. Given the following second-degree polynomials, and by looking at the discriminant, decide if the zeros are

(a) real and distinct
(b) real and equal
(c) complex conjugates

(i) $x^2 - 6x + 9$
(ii) $x^2 - 6x - 9$
(iii) $x^2 + 4x + 9$

6. The graph of $f(x) = -x^2 + 2x + 3$ opens _____ .
$\qquad\qquad\qquad\qquad\qquad\qquad\qquad$ (upward, downward)

7. Graph the function $f(x) = -x^2 + 2x + 3$.

Answers are at end of book.

12 Equations in Quadratic Form

Upon completing this chapter you should be able to

I. Solve equations of the form $au^2 + bu + c = 0$ where $u = x^r$.

II. Solve equations of the form $ax + b = \sqrt{cx + d}$.

III. Solve equations of the form $a \sin^2 x + b \sin x + c = 0$.

---

240. In this chapter we discuss equations of the form $au^2 + bu + c = 0, a \neq 0$, where u is a function of another variable x.

$au^2 + bu + c = 0$ is a _____ equation in u.

---

240. quadratic
(or second-degree)

241. Thus we can solve $au^2 + bu + c = 0$ for u by **(a)** factoring,

(b) _____ , or

(c) _____ as we
did in the preceding chapter.

---

241. (b) completing the square,
(c) using the quadratic formula

EXAMPLE 1

242. We say that $au^2 + bu + c = 0$ is in **quadratic form**. To find the solutions of the equation $x^4 + x^2 - 2 = 0$, we must convert the equation to the form $au^2 + bu + c = 0$ for some u.

If we let $u = x^2$, $x^4 + x^2 - 2 = 0$ becomes _____ .

---

242. $u^2 + u - 2 = 0$

243. Now we must solve the equation $u^2 + u - 2 = 0$ for u. Factoring we get $u^2 + u - 2 = ($_____$)($_____$) = 0$.

---

243. $u - 1$; $u + 2$

244. Hence $u = $_____ or _____ .

---

244. 1; -2

245. Since $u = x^2$ we have $x^2 = $_____ or $x^2 = $_____ .

---

245. 1; -2

246. And $x = $_____ or _____ .

---

246. $+1, -1$;
$+\sqrt{2}i, -\sqrt{2}i$

247. That is, the solution set of $x^4 + x^2 - 2 = 0$ is

{_____}.

---

247. $1, -1, \sqrt{2}i - \sqrt{2}i$

248. You can check that these are the solutions by substituting them into $x^4 + x^2 - 2 = 0$. We see that the fourth-degree equation $x^4 + x^2 - 2 = 0$ has _____ solutions.
<u>(how many?)</u>

---

248. four

EXAMPLE 2

249. Find the solution set of the equation $2x^{2/3} + 4x^{1/3} - 6 = 0$.

{_____}

---

249. $-27, 1$.

If you had difficulty,
go on to the next frame.
If not, skip to frame 256.

250. $2x^{2/3} + 4x^{1/3} - 6 = 0$ is a _____ form.

---

250. quadratic

251. $x^{1/3}$;
$2u^2 + 4u - 6 = 0$

251. For if we let $u =$ _____ , we get the quadratic equation in

u, _____ $= 0$.

252. $\dfrac{-4 - \sqrt{16 + 48}}{4}$; $\dfrac{-4 + \sqrt{16 + 48}}{4}$

(or $u = -3$ or 1)

252. Using the quadratic formulas to solve $2u^2 + 4u - 6 = 0$ for u,

we get $u =$ _____ or _____ .

253. -3; 1

253. Since $u = x^{1/3}$, $x^{1/3} =$ _____ or ___ .

254. -27; 1

254. And $x =$ _____ or _____ .

255. -27, 1

255. That is, the solution set of $2x^{2/3} + 4x^{1/3} - 6 = 0$ is $\{$ _____ $\}$. Again we can check that these are the solutions by substituting them into the equation.

EXAMPLE 3

256. Find the solution set of the equation $x^{2/5} - 2x^{1/5} - 3 = 0$.

$\{$ _____ $\}$

256. 243, -1

If you had difficulty,
see frames 249 to 255.

257. In solving an equation we often perform algebraic operations to obtain a new equation. In doing so we must always check that the resulting equation has the same set of solutions as the original equation. If the two equations have the same solution set, they are said to be **equivalent**.

Are the equations $x^2 + x - 2 = 0$ and $x^2 + 2x - 3 = 0$ equivalent?

_____

257. no

258. The solutions of $x^2 + x - 2 = 0$ are _____ and _____ .

258. 1; -2
(since $x^2 + x - 2 = (x - 1)(x + 2)$)

259. And the solutions of $x^2 + 2x - 3 = 0$ are _____ and _____ .

---

259. 1; -3 (since
$x^2 + 2x - 3 = (x-1)(x+3)$)

260. Are the equations $x^2 + \frac{2}{3}x - \frac{1}{3} = 0$ and $3x^2 + 2x - 1 = 0$ equivalent? _____

---

260. yes (since
$3x^2 + 2x - 1 = 3(x^2 + \frac{2}{3}x - \frac{1}{3}) = 0$
if and only if $x^2 + \frac{2}{3}x - \frac{1}{3} = 0$)

261. If we form a new equation that has solutions that are not solutions of the original equation, these new solutions are said to be **extraneous solutions**. For example, the equation $x = 1$ obviously has one solution $x = 1$. However, if we square both sides of $x = 1$, we get $x^2 = 1$, which has as its solution(s) _____ .

---

261. 1 and -1

262. Thus _____ is an extraneous solution.

---

262. -1

263. Therefore, whenever we perform an algebraic operation on an equation that we are trying to solve, we must always check to see that we have not introduced any _____ solutions in the process.

---

263. extraneous

EXAMPLE 4

264. We now want to find the solutions of equations of the form
(1) $x = \sqrt{2x + 3}$. If we square both sides of (1), we get
$x^2 =$ _____ or _____ $= 0$.

---

264. $2x + 3$;
$x^2 - 2x - 3$

265. $x^2 - 2x - 3 = 0$ is a _____ equation.

---

265. quadratic

266. And factoring gives
$x^2 - 2x - 3 = ($_____$)($_____$) = 0$.

---

266. $x + 1; x - 3$

267. Hence _____ and _____ are the solutions of $x^2 - 2x - 3 = 0$.

---

267. $-1; 3$

---

268. We must now check to see if -1 and 3 are solutions of our original equation (1) $x = \sqrt{2x + 3}$. Substituting -1 and 3 in (1) we see that -1 _____ a solution and 3 _____ a solution of

(is, is not)   (is, is not)
$x = \sqrt{2x + 3}$.

---

268. is not (since
$\sqrt{2(-1) + 3} = 1 \neq -1$);
is

269. Thus ____ is an extraneous solution and ____ is the only solution of $x = \sqrt{2x + 3}$.

---

269. -1; 3

EXAMPLE 5
270. Find the solution set of the equation $x - 2 = \sqrt{x - 2}$.
$\{$ _____ $\}$

---

270. 2, 3.

If you had difficulty,
go on to the next frame.
If not, skip to frame 276.

271. Squaring both sides of $x - 2 = \sqrt{x - 2}$, we get

_____ = _____ or

_____ = 0.

---

271. $(x - 2)^2$; $x - 2$;
$x^2 - 5x + 6$

272. Factoring gives

$x^2 - 5x + 6 = ($ _____ $)($ _____ $) = 0$.

---

272. $x - 2$; $x - 3$

273. Hence ____ and ____ are the solutions of $x^2 - 5x - 6 = 0$.

---

273. 2; 3

274. Checking if 2 and 3 are solutions of our original equation $x - 2 = \sqrt{x - 2}$, we see that 2 _____ a solution and 3

(is, is not)
_____ a solution.

(is, is not)

---

274. is; is

275. Thus $\{$ _____ $\}$ is the solution set of $x - 2 = \sqrt{x - 2}$.

---

275. 2, 3

EXAMPLE 6

276. Find the solution set of the equation $x - 1 = \sqrt{x + 5}$.

$\{\underline{\hspace{2em}}\}$

---

276. 4.

NOTE: -1 is an extraneous solution. Remember that $\sqrt{x + 5}$ means the positive square root of $x + 5$.

If you had difficulty, see frames 264 to 275.

EXAMPLE 7

277. In Volume II, the chapter on trigonometric equations contains equations such as $\cos^2 x - \cos x - 2 = 0$. Since

$\cos^2 x - \cos x - 2 = 0$ is in quadratic form we can let

$u = \underline{\hspace{4em}}$, and get a quadratic equation in u,

$\underline{\hspace{8em}} = 0$.

---

277. $\cos x$;
$u^2 - u - 2$

278. Since $u^2 - u - 2 = 0$ is a quadratic equation, we can use any method for solving quadratic equations to solve for u. This time we can factor.

We get $u^2 - u - 2 = (\underline{\hspace{4em}})(\underline{\hspace{4em}}) = 0$

---

278. $u - 2$; $u + 1$

279. Thus $u = \underline{\hspace{2em}}$ or $\underline{\hspace{2em}}$.

---

279. $2; -1$

280. Since $u = \cos x$, we have $\cos x = \underline{\hspace{2em}}$ or $\underline{\hspace{2em}}$.

---

280. $2; -1$

281. Since $-1 \leqslant \cos x \leqslant 1$, $\cos x$ can never equal $\underline{\hspace{2em}}$.

---

281. 2

282. Thus $\cos x = -1$ and $x = \underline{\hspace{2em}}$ for $0 \leqslant x < 2\pi$.

---

282. π

283. Hence $\underline{\hspace{2em}}$ is the only solution of the equation $\cos^2 x - \cos x - 2 = 0$ in the interval $0 \leqslant x \leqslant 2\pi$. That is, the solution set of $\cos^2 x - \cos x - 2 = 0$ is $\{\underline{\hspace{2em}}\}$.

---

283. π;
π

EXAMPLE 8

284. Solve the equation

$2 \sin^2 x - 7 \sin x + 3 = 0$ for $x, 0 \leqslant x < 2\pi$.

$\{$ _____ $\}$

---

284. $\frac{\pi}{6}(30°)$, $\frac{5\pi}{6}(150°)$.

If you had difficulty, go on to the next frame. If not skip to frame 290.

285. If we let $u =$ _____ , we get a quadratic equation in u,

_____ $= 0$.

---

285. $\sin x$;

$2u^2 - 7u + 3$

286. And from the quadratic formulas we see that

$u =$ _____ or _____ .

---

286. $\dfrac{+7 - \sqrt{49 - 24}}{4}$; $\dfrac{+7 + \sqrt{49 - 24}}{4}$

(or $u = \frac{1}{2}$ or 3)

287. Since $u = \sin x$, we have $\sin x =$ ____ or ____ .

---

287. $\frac{1}{2}$; 3

288. But $-1 \leqslant \sin x \leqslant 1$, hence $\sin x$ cannot equal ____ .

---

288. 3

289. Hence $\sin x = $ **(a)** ____ and **(b)** _____
are the solutions in the interval $0 \leqslant x < 2\pi$. That is, the solution

set of $2 \sin^2 x - 7 \sin x + 3 = 0$ is **(c)** $\{$ _____ $\}$.

---

289. (a) $\frac{1}{2}$,

(b) $\frac{\pi}{6}(30°)$ or $\frac{5\pi}{6}(150°)$,

(c) $\frac{\pi}{6}$, $\frac{5\pi}{6}$

EXERCISE 1

290. Find the solution set of the equation $x^4 - 5x^2 + 6 = 0$.

$\{$ _____ $\}$

---

290. $\sqrt{2}, -\sqrt{2}, \sqrt{3}, -\sqrt{3}$.

If you had difficulty, see frames 242 to 255.

EXERCISE 2

291. Find the solution set of the equation $x + 2 = \sqrt{5x + 16}$.

{_____}

291. 4

(−3 is an extraneous solution).

If you had difficulty,
see frames 264 to 275.

EXERCISE 3

292. Solve the equation

$2\cos^2 x - 11\cos x - 6 = 0$ for $x, 0 \leqslant x < 2\pi$.

{_____}

292. $\frac{2\pi}{3}(120°)$ $\frac{4\pi}{3}(240°)$.

If you had difficulty,
see frames 277 to 289.

PROBLEMS

Find the zeros of each of the following.

1. $x^4 + 6x^2 + 8 = 0$

2. $x^4 - 2x^2 - 3 = 0$

3. $12x^4 - 7x^2 + 1 = 0$

4. $2x^4 - 3x^2 + 1 = 0$

5. $\sin^2 x + \sin x - 2 = 0, 0 = x < 2\pi$

6. $2\cos^2 x + \cos x - 1 = 0, 0 \leqslant x < 2\pi$

7. $x^{2/3} + 4x^{1/3} - 21 = 0$

8. $2x + \sqrt{x} - 6 = 0$

9. $2x^{2/5} + 2x^{1/5} - 4 = 0$

10. $x^{4/7} - 5x^{2/7} + 6 = 0$

11. $2x^{-2} - 3x^{-1} - 2 = 0$

12. $3x^3 - 2x^{3/2} - 1 = 0$

13. $x + 3 = \sqrt{9x + 19}$

14. $(x + 1) - \sqrt{2 + 2x} = 0$

15. $x + 4 = 2\sqrt{x + 7}$

16. $x - 2 = \sqrt{2x + 11}$

Answers are at end of book.

If you cannot answer the following questions correctly, review the appropriate frames.

Solve the following equations.

1. $x^{4/5} - 5x^{2/5} + 4 = 0$

2. $x + 2 = \sqrt{5 + 4x}$

Answers are at end of book.

13   Remainder and Factor Theorems

Upon completing this chapter, you should be able to

I. Use the remainder theorem to find the remainder obtained by dividing a polynomial $P(x)$ by a linear factor $x - a$.

II. Find a polynomial $P(x)$ whose zeros are $r_1, r_2, \ldots, r_n$.

III. Find the zeros of polynomials of the form
$P(x) = (x - d)(ax^2 + bx + c)$.

IV. Use synthetic division to divide a polynomial $P(x)$ by a linear factor $x - a$.

V. Given a polynomial $P(x)$, use synthetic division to calculate $P(a)$.

VI. Find upper and lower bounds of the set of real zeros of a polynomial $P(x)$ by synthetic division.

---

293. We now turn our attention to the problem of finding the zeros of polynomials of degree greater than two. To find the zeros of a polynomial $P(x) = a_n x^n + \ldots + a_1 x + a_0$, we find the solutions of the equation _____ .

293. $P(x) = a_n x^n + \ldots + a_1 x + a_0 = 0$

294. Theorem 1 of Chapter 10 stated that is $P(x)$ and $D(x)$ are polynomials, then there exist polynomials $Q(x)$ and $R(x)$ such that $P(x) = $ _____ and the degree of $R(x)$ is less than the degree of $D(x)$.

294. $D(x) \cdot Q(x) + R(x)$.
If you had difficulty, see frames 30 to 34 of Part II.

295. $Q(x)$ is called the _____

and $R(x)$ is called the _____ .

---

295. quotient; remainder.
If you had difficulty, see frames 30 to 34 of Part II.

296. It was further stated that either $R(x) = 0$ or the degree of $R(x)$ is less than the degree of $D(x)$.

Thus if $P(x)$ is any polynomial and $D(x) = x - a$, then

$R(x) = 0$ or $R(x)$ must be of degree _____ .

---

296. zero

297. That is, $R(x)$ must be a _____ .

And we can write $P(x) = (x - a) Q(x) + R$, where $R = 0$ or

R is _____ .

---

297. number (or coefficient);
a number (or of degree zero)

298. $P(x) = (x - a)Q(x) + R$ is an identity and is true for all x. In particular it is true for $x = a$, in which case

$P(a) = $ _____ .

---

298. $(a - a)Q(x) + R$

299. But $(a - a)Q(x) = $ _____ , thus $P(a) = $ _____ , and we have proved the following theorem.

---

299. $0; R$

EXAMPLE 1

300. THEOREM 1 (The Remainder Theorem). If a polynomial $P(x)$ is divided by $x - a$, where a is any complex number, until a remainder R is obtained, then $R = P(a)$.

Thus the remainder R obtained by dividing $P(x) = 2x^4 - x^3 + 2x - 5$ by $D(x) = x - 1$ is given by

$R = $ _____

---

300. $P(1)$

301. On substituting, we see that

$P(1) = $ _____ .

---

301. $2 - 1 + 2 - 5 = -2$

302. Hence the remainder $R = $ _____

---

302. -2

EXAMPLE 2

303. The remainder R obtained by dividing
$P(x) = 4x^3 - 2x^2 + 5x - 7$ by $P(x) = x + 2$ is _____ .

---

303. -57.

If you had difficulty, go on to the next frame. If not, skip to frame 307.

304. By the remainder theorem, the remainder R is given by _____ .

---

304. $P(-2)$

305. On substituting, we see that $P(-2) =$

_____ .

---

305. $4(-8) - 2(4) + 5(-2) - 7$

306. Hence the remainder $R =$ _____ .

---

306. -57.

EXAMPLE 3

307. The remainder R obtained by dividing
$P(x) = x^5 + 2x^3 - 4x^2 - 6x - 5$ by $x - 2$ is _____ .

---

307. 15.

If you had difficulty, see frames 300 to 306.

SUMMARY

Theorem 1 (The Remainder Theorem)

If a polynomial $P(x)$ is divided by $x - a$, where a is any complex number, until a remainder R is obtained, then $R = P(a)$.

Proof: By theorem 1 of Chapter 10, there exists a polynomial and a complex number R such that

$$P(x) = (x - a)Q(x) + R.$$

This is an identity and is true for all x. In particular it is true for $x = a$. We get

$$P(a) = (a - a)Q(a) + R = 0 \cdot Q(a) + R = R.$$

That is, $P(a) = R$.

	308. If a polynomial $P(x)$ is divided by $x - a$, then by theorem 1 of chapter 9, $P(x) = $ _____ .
308. $(x-a)Q(x) + R$	**309.** If $x - a$ is a factor of $P(x)$, then $P(x) = (x-a)Q(x)$ and $P(a) = $ _____ .
309. $(a-a)Q(a) = 0$	**310.** That is, if $x - a$ is a factor of $P(x)$, then $P(a) = $ _____ .
310. 0	**311.** Conversely, if $P(a) = 0$, then by the remainder theorem there exists a polynomial $Q(x)$ such that $P(x) = $ **(a)** _____ , since $R = $ **(b)** _____ . Hence **(c)** _____ is a factor of $P(x)$.
311. (a) $(x-a)Q(x)$, **(b)** $P(a) = 0$, **(c)** $x-a$	**312.** That is, if $P(x)$ is any polynomial and $P(a) = 0$, then _____ .
312. $x - a$ is a factor of $P(x)$	**313.** We have proved the following theorem. **THEOREM 2** (Factor Theorem). $x - a$ is a factor of a polynomial $P(x)$ if and only if _____ .
313. $P(a) = 0$	

SUMMARY

Theorem 2 (Factor Theorem)

$x - a$ is a factor of a polynomial $P(x)$ if and only if $P(a) = 0$.

Proof: If $x - a$ is a factor of $P(x)$, then
$$P(x) = (x-a)Q(x) \text{ and}$$
$$P(a) = (a-a)Q(x) = 0.$$
Conversely, if $P(a) = 0$, then by the remainder theorem
$$P(x) = (x-a)Q(x) \text{ since } R = P(a) = 0.$$
Hence $x - a$ is a factor of $P(x)$.

314. An alternative statement of the factor theorem is:

$x - a$ is a factor of $P(x)$ if and only if a is a zero of $P(x)$.

The two statements are equivalent since a is a zero of $P(x)$

if and only if _____ .

---

314. $P(a) = 0$

315. The factor theorem does not, however, tell us if polynomials have any zeros. But we saw earlier that first-degree

polynomials have _____ zero(s) and polynomials of degree
<u>(how many?)</u>

two have _____ zero(s).
<u>(how many?)</u>

---

315. one;

two (which may be equal)

316. The next two theorems do not help us find the zeros of a polynomial, but they assure us of the existence of zeros.

The proof of the first of these theorems, the fundamental theorem of algebra, is beyond the scope of this book. Therefore, we state it without proof.

THEOREM 3 (Fundamental Theorem of Algebra). If $P(x)$ is a polynomial of degree ≥ 1 with real or complex coefficients, then $P(x)$ has at least one zero, which may be either real or complex. That is, given any polynomial $P(x)$, there exists at least one number r

such that $P(r) = $ _____ .

---

316. 0

317. In Chapter 10, we proved that every linear polynomial

$P(x) = ax + b$ can be factored as $P(x) = ax + b = $ _____ where r
is the zero of $P(x)$.

---

317. $a(x - r)$

318. We also proved that every polynomial of degree two, can be

factored as $P(x) = ax^2 + bx + c = $ _____
where r_1 and r_2 are the zeros of $P(x)$.

---

318. $a(x - r_1)(x - r_2)$

319. We now generalize these results for polynomials of degree $n \geq 1$.

Suppose $P(x) = a_n x^n + \ldots + a_1 x + a_0$ is a polynomial of degree $n, n \geq 1$. By the fundamental theorem of algebra, $P(x)$ has at least one zero, say r_1. That is, $P(r_1) = $ ___ .

---

319. 0

320. Since $P(r_1) = 0$, by the factor theorem _____ is a factor of $P(x)$.

---

320. $x - r_1$

321. Thus, there is a polynomial $Q_1(x)$ of degree $n - 1$, whose leading coefficient is also a_n, such that $P(x) =$ _____ .

---

321. $(x - r_1)Q_1(x)$

322. If $n - 1 \geqslant 1$, then $Q_1(x)$ is a polynomial of degree $\geqslant 1$, and we can repeat the steps in frames 319 to 321 for $Q_1(x)$. That is, we can apply the fundamental theorem of algebra and the factor theorem to $Q_1(x)$. Thus $Q_1(x)$ has at least one zero, say r_2, and there exists a polynomial $Q_2(x)$ of degree $n - 2$, whose leading coefficient is a_n, such that $Q_1(x) =$ _____ .

---

322. $(x - r_2)Q_2(x)$

323. Therefore we can write $P(x)$ as $P(x) =$ _____ .

---

323. $(x - r_1)(x - r_2)Q_2(x)$

324. If $n - 2 \geqslant 1$, $Q_2(x)$ has a zero, say r_3, and there exists a polynomial Q_3 of degree _____ , and we can write $Q_2(x) =$

_____ .

---

324. $n - 3$;
$(x - r_3)Q_3(x)$

325. Again $Q_3(x)$ has a_n as its leading coefficient, and we can write $P(x) =$ _____ .

---

325. $(x - r_1)(x - r_2)(x - r_3)Q_3(x)$

326. We can repeat the process n times until the degree of $Q_n(x)$ is _____ .

---

326. $n - n = 0$

327. We then have $P(x) =$ _____ .

327.
$(x - r_1)(x - r_2)(x - r_3) \ldots (x - r_n)Q_n(x)$

328. And, since $Q_n(x) = a_n x^{n-n} = a_n$, we have

$P(x) =$ _____ .

328.
$a_n(x - r_1)(x - r_2)(x - r_3) \ldots (x - r_n)$

329. Since $P(x)$ has exactly _____ factors, by the factor
(how many?)
theorem it must have exactly _____ zeros.
(how many?)

---

329. n; n

	330. By the factor theorem $x - r$ is a factor of $P(x)$ if and only if _____ .
330. $P(r) = 0$ (or r is a zero of $P(x)$)	**331.** That is, we have shown that if $P(x)$ is a polynomial of degree n, $n \geqslant 1$, then $P(x)$ has exactly ___ zero(s). The numbers $r_1, r_2 \ldots, r_n$ need not all be distinct.
331. n	**332.** We have proved the following theorem. **THEOREM 4:** If $P(x)$ is a polynomial of degree n, $n \geqslant 1$, with real or complex coefficients, then $P(x)$ has exactly ___ zeros (which need not be distinct).
332. n	

SUMMARY

Theorem 4

If $P(x)$ is a polynomial of degree n, $n \geqslant 1$, with real or complex coefficients, then $P(x)$ has exactly n zeros (which need not be distinct).

Proof: Suppose $P(x) = a_n x^n + \ldots + a_1 x + a_0$, $a_n \neq 0$ is a polynomial of degree n, $n \geqslant 1$. By the fundamental theorem of algebra, $P(x)$ has at least one zero, say r_1. That is, $P(r_1) = 0$ and by the factor theorem $x - r_1$ is a factor of $P(x)$. We can write $P(x) = (x - r_1)Q_1(x)$ where $Q_1(x)$ is a polynomial of degree $n - 1$, whose leading coefficient is also a_n.

If $n - 1 \geqslant 1$, then $Q_1(x)$ is a polynomial of degree $\geqslant 1$ and we can apply the fundamental theorem of algebra and the factor theorem to $Q_1(x)$. Thus $Q_1(x)$ has at least one zero, say r_2, and there exists a polynomial $Q_2(x)$ of degree $n - 2$ whose leading coefficient is a_n such that $Q_1(x) = (x - r_2)Q_2(x)$. Therefore, we can write

$$P(x) \text{ as } P(x) = (x - r_1)(x - r_2)Q_2(x).$$

If $n - 2 \geqslant 1$, $Q_2(x)$ has a zero, say r_3, and there exists a polynomial $Q_3(x)$ of degree $n - 3$, whose leading coefficient is again a_n such that $Q_2(x) = (x - r_3)Q_3(x)$.

We can write $P(x) = (x - r_1)(x - r_2)(x - r_3)Q_3(x)$. We can repeat the process n times until the degree of $Q_n(x)$ is $n - n = 0$, and $Q_n(x) = a_n x^{n-n} = a_n$. We have

$$P(x) = (x - r_1)(x - r_2)(x - r_3) \ldots (x - r_n)Q_n(x).$$

That is, since $Q_n(x) = a_n$, we have

$$P(x) = a_n(x - r_1)(x - r_2)(x - r_3) \ldots (x - r_n).$$

Since $P(x)$ has exactly n factors, it must have exactly n zeros by the factor theorem. And our proof is complete.

333. If a number r_i appears m times in $P(x) =$
$P(x) = a_n (x - r_i)(x - r_2) \ldots (x - r_n)$, we say that r_i is a **zero of multiplicity m**. For example, if
$P(x) = 4(x - 1)^4 (x - 2)^3 (x - 3)^2 (x - 4)(x - 5)$, then $P(x)$ is
a polynomial of degree _____ .

---

333. 11

334. 1 is a zero of multiplicity _____ ;

2 is a zero of multiplicity _____ .

---

334. 4;
3

335. We also say the 2 is a **triple zero**. 3 is a zero of multiplicity
____ or a _____ zero.

---

335. 2; double

336. 4 and 5 are also zeros, making eleven zeros in all if 1 is
counted **(a)** _____ times, 2 is counted **(b)** _____ times, 3 is
counted **(c)** _____ times, and 4 and 5 are counted once each.

---

336. (a) four,
(b) three,
(c) two

EXAMPLE 4
337. Find a polynomial $P(x)$ of degree three whose zeros are 1,
-2, and 4. $P(x) =$ _____ .

---

337. $(x - 1)(x + 2)(x - 4)$.

If you had difficulty, go on to the next
frame. If not, skip to frame 341.

338. Since $1, -2$, and 4 are zeros, $P(x)$ has factors (_____),
(_____), and (_____) by the factor theorem.

---

338. $x - 1$;
$x + 2$; $x - 4$

339. $P(x)$ can be written as
$P(x) = a_n ($_____$)($_____$)($_____$), a_n \neq 0.$

---

339. $x - 1$;
$x + 2$; $x - 4$

340. Since a_n may be any number, we choose $a_n = 1$ and get
$P(x) =$ _____ .

---

340. $(x - 1)(x + 2)(x - 4)$

EXAMPLE 5

341. Find a polynomial $P(x)$ of degree 5 that has 1 as a triple zero and 2 as a double zero. $P(x) = $ _____

341. $(x-1)^3(x-2)^2$.

If you had difficulty, go on to the next frame. If not, skip to frame 345.

342. Since 1 is a triple zero and 2 is a double zero, $P(x)$ has _____ factors $(x-1)$ and _____ factors $(x-2)$.
(how many?)

342. three; two

343. Thus $P(x)$ can be written as $P(x) = a_n$ _____ .

343. $(x-1)^3(x-2)^2$

344. If we choose $a_n = 1$, we get

$P(x) = $ _____ .

344. $(x-1)^3(x-2)^2 = $
$x^5 - 7x^4 + 19x^3 - 25x^2 + 16x - 4$

EXAMPLE 6

345. Find the zeros of $P(x) = (x-2)(x^2 + x - 2)$.

$x = $ _____

345. $2, 1, -2$.

If you had difficulty, go on to the next frame. If not, skip to frame 349.

346. Factoring $x^2 + x - 2$, we get $x^2 + x - 2 = ($_____$)($_____$)$.

346. $x-1$; $x+2$

347. Hence $P(x) = $ _____ .

347. $(x-2)(x-1)(x+2)$

348. Hence ___ , ___ , and ___ are the zeros of $P(x)$.

348. $2; 1; -2$

EXAMPLE 7

349. Find the zeros of $P(x) = (x+3)(x^2 - 2x - 35)$.

$x = $ _____

349. $-3, -5, 7$.

If you had difficulty, see frames 345 to 348.

SYNTHETIC DIVISION

350. We have shown that a polynomial $P(x)$ of degree n has exactly ___ zeros.

---

350. n

351. We have also shown that r is a zero of $P(x)$ — (That is, $P(r) =$ ___). if and only if _____ is a factor of $P(x)$.

---

351. $0; x - r$

352. If we divide $P(x)$ by $x - r$, the remainder $R = P(r)$. Hence $x - r$ will be a factor of $P(x)$ if and only if $R =$ _____ .

---

352. 0.

EXAMPLE 8

353. We now discuss a shorter process for dividing a polynomial $P(x)$ by $x - a$ called **synthetic division.** We shall illustrate the process by means of an example. If we divide
$P(x) = 2x^3 - 7x^2 + 9$ by $x - 2$ by long division, we get

$$x - 2 \overline{\smash{\big)}\ 2x^3 - 7x^2 + 0x + 9} \ .$$

353.
$$
\begin{array}{r}
2x^2 - 3x \ -6 \\
x-2 \overline{\smash{\big)}\ 2x^3 - 7x^2 + 0x + 9} \\
\underline{2x^3 - 4x^2} \\
-3x^2 + 0x \\
\underline{-3x^2 + 6x} \\
-6x + \ 9 \\
\underline{-6x + 12} \\
-3
\end{array}
$$

If you had difficulty, see frames 35 to 48 of Part II.

354. Thus the quotient $Q(x) =$ _____ and the remainder $R =$ _____..

---

354. $2x^2 - 3x - 6$; -3.

If you had difficulty, see frames 30 to 34 of Part II.

355. Hence by theorem 1 of Chapter 10, we can write
$P(x) = 2x^3 - 7x^2 + 9 =$ _____

---

355. $(x - 2)(2x^2 - 3x - 6) - 3$

356. In the long-division process in the answer to frame 353, the powers of x, x^2, x^3, etc. serve only to keep the coefficients in order. Therefore we may drop the powers of x if we write the coefficients of each power in a separate vertical column. If we drop the powers of x, the long division

$$
\begin{array}{r}
2x^2 - 3x\ -6 \\
x - 2 \overline{\smash{\big)}\ 2x^3 - 7x^2 + 0x + 9} \\
\underline{2x^3 - 4x^2} \\
-3x^2 + 0x \\
\underline{-3x^2 + 6x} \\
-6x + 9 \\
\underline{-6x + 12} \\
-3
\end{array}
$$

becomes

$$
1 - 2 \overline{\smash{\big)}\ 2 \quad -7 \quad 0 \quad 9}
$$

$$\overline{}$$

$$\overline{}$$

$$\overline{}\ .$$

We have been careful to write the coefficients 1 and 0.

356.
$$
\begin{array}{r}
2 - 3 - 6 \\
1 - 2 \overline{\smash{\big)}\ 2 - 7 - 0 \quad 9} \\
\underline{2 - 4} \\
-3 \quad 0 \\
\underline{-3 \quad 6} \\
-6 \quad 9 \\
-6 \quad 12 \\
\underline{} \\
-3
\end{array}
$$

357. We see that the bottom number of each column (except the extreme right column) is a repetition of the number above it. Thus we can simplify the expression still further by omitting these bottom numbers. We get

$$
1-2 \overline{\smash{\big)}\,2-7\quad 0\quad 9}
$$

$$
\underline{}
$$

$$
\underline{}
$$

$$
\underline{}\,-3\,.
$$

357.
$$
\begin{array}{r}
2-3-6 \\
1-2 \overline{\smash{\big)}\,2-7\quad 0\quad 9} \\
-4 \\
\overline{-3\quad 0} \\
6 \\
\overline{-6\quad 9} \\
12 \\
\overline{-\ 3}
\end{array}
$$

---

358. If we move the remaining numbers up to fill in the gaps, we get four horizontal rows as follows.

$$
\overline{} \overline{\smash{\big)}\,2-7\quad 0\quad 9}
$$
$$
\underline{}\ 6\quad 12
$$
$$
\overline{}\ \overline{}\ \overline{}
$$

358.
$$
\begin{array}{r}
2-3-6 \\
1-2 \overline{\smash{\big)}\,2-7\quad 0\quad 9} \\
-4\quad 6\quad 12 \\
\overline{-3-6-\ 3}
\end{array}
$$

359. Since synthetic division applies only if the coefficient of x in the divisor is 1, we may drop the 1 in the divisor. And if we write the leading 2 of the first two rows in the fourth row, we get

---

359.

$$\begin{array}{r} \;2-3-6 \\ -2\,\overline{)\,2-7\quad 0\quad 9} \\ \,-4\quad 6\;\;12 \\ \hline \,2-3-6-3 \end{array}$$

---

360. We see that the first three numbers of the bottom row are the coefficients of the quotient polynomial in their proper order and the last number, -3, is the _____ obtained when $P(x) = 2x^3 - 7x^2 + 9$ is divided by $x - 2$.

---

360. Remainder.

If you had difficulty, see frames 353 and 354.

---

361. Thus we may omit the top line and get the compact form

361.

$$\begin{array}{r} -2\,\overline{\;\;|\;\;2-7\quad 0\quad 9} \\ \,-4\quad 6\;\;12 \\ \hline \,2-3-6-3 \end{array}$$

---

362. In this form, we see that any number on the second row can be obtained by multiplying the divisor, -2, by the number in the third row in the column preceding the desired number. That is, $-4 = -4 = 2 \cdot (-2)$ as shown.

Similarly, $6 = \underline{} \cdot (-2)$ and $12 = \underline{} \cdot (-2)$.

---

362. $-3;\ -6$

etc.

363. Any number in the third row can be obtained by subtracting the number in row two from the number in the first row of the same column. Thus starting with

$$\underline{-2}\,\rvert\;2\;-7\quad 0\quad 9,$$

we copy the leading coefficient in row three and then determine alternately the numbers in rows two and three as follows.

$$\underline{-2}\,\rvert\;2\;-7\quad 0\quad 9$$

---

363. 2

364.
$$\underline{-2}\,\rvert\;2\;-7\quad 0\quad 9$$
$$\overline{}$$
$$2$$

---

364. -4

365.
$$\underline{-2}\,\rvert\;2\;-7\quad 0\quad 9$$
$$-4$$
$$\overline{2\;\underline{}}$$

---

365. -3

366.
$$\underline{-2}\,\rvert\;2\;-7\quad 0\quad 9$$
$$-4\;\underline{}$$
$$\overline{2\;-3}$$

---

366. 6

367.
$$\underline{-2}\,\rvert\;2\;-7\quad 0\quad 9$$
$$-4\quad 6$$
$$\overline{2\;-3\;\underline{}}$$

---

367. -6

368.
$$\underline{-2}\,\rvert\;2\;-7\quad 0\quad 9$$
$$-4\quad 6\;\underline{}$$
$$\overline{2\;-3\;-6}$$

---

368. 12

369. And, finally,
$$\underline{-2}\,\rvert\;2\;-7\quad 0\quad 9$$
$$-4\quad 6\quad 12$$
$$\overline{2\;-3\;-6\;\underline{}}$$

---

369. -3

370. We can then read immediately that the quotient

$Q(x) =$ _____ and the remainder $R =$ ___ .

---

370. $2x^2 - 3x - 6$;
-3

EXAMPLE 9

371. It is customary to make one final change before we obtain the process known as synthetic division.

If we change the sign of the divisor and proceed as before, we get a second row of opposite sign and can **add** rows 1 and 2 instead of subtracting.

We get

$$
\begin{array}{r}
2 \,\underline{|\; 2 - 7 \quad 0 \quad 9} \\
4 - 6 - 12 \\
\hline
2 - 3 - 6 - \ 3,
\end{array}
$$

which gives the same result.

Given

$$
\begin{array}{r}
3 \,\underline{|\; 1 - 5 \quad 4 \quad 2} \\
 \\
\hline

\end{array}
$$

find the first number in row three and the first number in row two.

---

371. 3;
1

---

372. Now find the next number in rows three and two.

$$
\begin{array}{r}
3 \,\underline{|\; 1 - 5 \quad 4 \quad 2} \\
3 \ \rule{1em}{0.4pt} \\
\hline
1 \ \rule{1em}{0.4pt}
\end{array}
$$

---

372. -6;
-2

---

373. Now complete the synthetic division.

$$
\begin{array}{r}
3 \,\underline{|\; 1 - 5 \qquad 4 \qquad 2} \\
3 \quad -6\ \textbf{(b)}\rule{2em}{0.4pt} \\
\hline
1 - 2\ \textbf{(a)}\rule{1em}{0.4pt}\ \textbf{(c)}\rule{1em}{0.4pt}
\end{array}
$$

---

373. (a) -2, (b) -6
(c) -4

---

374. Thus, if we divide $P(x) = x^3 - 5x^2 + 4x + 2$ by $x - 3$, the quotient $Q(x) =$ _____ and the remainder

$R =$ ___ .

---

374. $x^2 - 2x - 2$;
-4

375. Recall that in frame 374 we changed the sign of the divisor; thus

$$-4 \,\rvert\, 2-7 \quad 1-5$$
_____

means that we are dividing $P(x) = 2x^3 - 7x^2 + x - 5$ by _____ .

---

375. $x + 4$

376. And

$$4 \,\rvert\, 2-7 \quad 1-5$$
_____

means that we are dividing by _____ .

---

376. $x - 4$

EXAMPLE 10

377. Complete the synthetic division.

$$4 \,\rvert\, 2-7 \quad 1-5$$
_____

---

377. 8   4   20
   2 1   5   15.

If you had difficulty, see frames 371 to 373.

EXAMPLE 11

378. Complete the synthetic division.

$$3 \,\rvert\, 4-10-7 \quad 7$$
_____

---

378.   12   6   −3
   4   2   −1   4

379. The statement $-4 \,\rvert\, \quad 2 \quad -7 \quad 1 \quad -5$
_____

means that we are dividing the polynomial

$P(x) =$ _____ by

_____ by synthetic division.

---

379. $2x^3 - 7x^2 + x - 5$;
$x + 4$

EXAMPLE 12

380. Use synthetic division to divide
$P(x) = 3x^4 + 8x^3 + 4x - 7$ by $x + 3$.

$Q(x) =$ _____

$R =$ _____

---

380. $3x^3 - x^2 + 3x - 5$;
8.

If you had difficulty, go on to the next frame. If not, skip to frame 384.

381. Since $x + 3 = x - (-3)$ and there is no x^2 term, we have

$$\underline{\quad}\big) \quad 3 \quad\quad 8 \quad\quad 0 \quad\quad 4 \quad\quad -7$$

---

381. -3

382. And completing the synthetic division, we get

$$-3\big) \quad 3 \quad\quad 8 \quad\quad 0 \quad\quad 4 \quad\quad -7$$

382.
	-9	3	-9	15
3	-1	3	-5	8

383. Thus, the first four numbers are the coefficients of the quotient and the last number is the remainder. We have

$Q(x) = \underline{\hspace{4cm}}$ and

$R = \underline{\quad}$.

---

383. $3x^3 - x^2 + 3x - 5$;
8

384. Hence we can write

$P(x) = 3x^4 + 8x^3 + 4x - 7 =$

$(\underline{\hspace{2cm}}) (\underline{\hspace{3cm}}) + \underline{\quad}$

---

384. $x + 3; 3x^3 - x^2 + 3x - 5; 8$

385. Since $R = 8$, when we divide

$P(x) = 3x^4 + 8x^3 + 4x - 7$, then

$P(-3) = \underline{\quad}$ by the remainder theorem.

---

385. 8

EXAMPLE 13

386. Divide $P(x) = 2x^4 - 7x^3 + 16x - 8$ by $x - 2$.

$Q(x) = \underline{\hspace{4cm}}$

$R = \underline{\quad}$

---

386. $2x^3 - 3x^2 - 6x + 4$;
0.

If you had difficulty, go on to the next frame. If not, skip to frame 390.

387. We set up the problem for synthetic division and get

$$\underline{\quad}\big)$$

387.
2	2	-7	0	16	-8

388. And carrying out the synthetic division gives

$$2\big) \quad 2 \quad\quad -7 \quad\quad 0 \quad\quad 16 \quad\quad -8$$

388.
	4	-6	-12	8	
2	-3	-6	4	0	

	389. Thus the quotient $Q(x) = $ _____ , and the remainder $R = $ ____ .
389. $2x^3 - 3x^2 - 6x + 4$; 0	**390.** Since $R = 0, P(2) = $ ___ .
390. 0	**391.** Hence $x - 2$ is a _____ of $P(x)$, and 2 is a _____ of $P(x)$.
391. factor; zero zero	**392.** We can write $P(x) = 2x^4 - 7x^3 + 16x - 8 = $ _____ _____ .
392. $(x - 2)(2x^3 - 3x^2 - 6x + 4)$	**EXAMPLE 14** **393.** Divide $P(x) = 4x^4 - 10x^3 + 6x^2 + 2x - 2$ by $x + \frac{1}{2}$. $Q(x) = $ _____ $R = $ ____
393. $4x^3 - 12x^2 + 12x - 4$; 0. If you had difficulty, see frames 380 to 392.	**394.** Since $R = 0, x + \frac{1}{2}$ is a _____ of $P(x)$ and $-\frac{1}{2}$ is a _____ of $P(x)$.
394. factor; zero	**395.** We can write $P(x) = 4x^4 - 10x^3 + 6x^2 + 2x - 2 = $ _____ .
395. $(x + \frac{1}{2})(4x^3 - 12x^2 + 12x - 4)$	**396.** By the remainder theorem _____ , when we divide $P(x)$ by $x - a$.
396. $P(a) = R$, the remainder	

EXAMPLE 15

397. Therefore we can use synthetic division to determine $P(a)$ for a given polynomial $P(x)$.

If $P(x) = x^4 + 2x^3 - 3x^2 + 5x - 4$, then $P(-3) = $ _____ .

---

397. -19.

If you had difficulty, go on to the next frame. If not, skip to frame 401.

398. Dividing $P(x) = x^4 + 2x^3 - 3x^2 + 5x - 4$ by $x + 3$ using synthetic division, we get

_____

_____ .

398.

$$
\begin{array}{r|rrrrr}
-3 & 1 & 2 & -3 & 5 & -4 \\
   &   & -3 & 3 & 0 & -15 \\
\hline
   & 1 & -1 & 0 & 5 & -19
\end{array}
$$

399. Thus the remainder is _____ .

---

399. -19

400. And by the remainder theorem, $P(-3) = $ _____ .

---

400. -19

EXAMPLE 16

401. Let $P(x) = x^4 - 4x^3 - 2x + 5$. Use synthetic division to find $P(4)$.

$P(4) = $ _____

---

401. -3.

If you had difficulty, go on to the next frame. If not, skip to frame 404.

402. Dividing $P(x) = x^4 - 4x^3 - 2x + 5$ by $x - 4$ using synthetic division, we get

_____

_____ .

402.

$$
\begin{array}{r|rrrrr}
4 & 1 & -4 & 0 & -2 & 5 \\
  &   & 4 & 0 & 0 & -8 \\
\hline
  & 1 & 0 & 0 & -2 & -3
\end{array}
$$

NOTE: We must indicate the $0x^2$ term by 0.

403. Thus the remainder is ____ , and by the remainder theorem $P(4) = $ ____ .

---

403. $-3; -3$

EXAMPLE 17

404. Let $P(x) = 6x^3 - 7x^2 + x - 5$. Use synthetic division to find $P(2)$. $P(2) =$ _____

---

404. 17.

If you had difficulty, see frames 396 to 403.

405. We can use synthetic division to determine upper and lower bounds for the real zeros of a polynomial. This will be very useful in determining the set of real zeros of a polynomial.

---

405. Go on to the next frame.

406. Let $P(x)$ be a polynomial with real coefficients and degree $\geqslant 1$. If we divide $P(x)$ by $x - r$, using synthetic division, we get a

polynomial $Q(x)$ called the _____ and a _____ R.

---

406. quotient;
remainder

407. We can write $P(x) =$ _____ ,
where the degree of $Q(x)$ is one less than the degree of $P(x)$.

---

407. $(x - r)Q(x) + R$

408. Since R is zero, or of degree less than the divisor,

R is _____ .

---

408. a number, possibly zero

409. Now suppose that upon dividing $P(x)$ by $x - r$, by synthetic division, every number in the third row has the same sign or is zero.

That is, the coefficients of _____ and _____ all have the same sign.

---

409. $Q(x); R$

410. Thus for any $x > 0$, the numbers $Q(x)$ and R _____

_____ .

---

410. will have the same sign

411. For example, if we divide
$P(x) = x^3 - 2x^2 + 2x - 12$ by $x - 3$, and get

$$3 \underline{\smash{\big)}\ \begin{array}{rrrr} 1 & -2 & 2 & -12 \\ & 3 & 3 & 15 \\ \hline 1 & 1 & 5 & 3 \end{array}} \ .$$

Then $Q(x) =$ _____ and $R =$ ___ .

---

411. $x^2 + x + 5; 3$

412. And for any number $x > 0$, $Q(x)$ and R are both

_____ 0.
(>, <)

---

412. >

413. In general, if we divide $P(x)$ by $x - r$, using synthetic division, and get all positive numbers in the third row, then for all $x > 0$, $Q(x)$ and R will both be _____ .

---

413. positive (or > 0)

414. If all the numbers in the third row are negative, then for all $x > 0$, $Q(x)$ and R _____ .

---

414. will both be negative

415. If the degree of $P(x)$ is $\geqslant 2$, and $P(x) = (x - r)Q(x)$, then the degree of $Q(x)$ is $\geqslant$ ___ .

---

415. 1

416. That is, $Q(x)$ must have at least one non-zero coefficient. Thus if $x > 0$, then $Q(x)$ cannot be zero. If all the numbers in the third row are positive, or zero, then for all $x > 0$, $Q(x)$ will be _____ and R will either be zero or _____ .

---

416. positive; positive

417. If all the numbers in the third row are negative or zero, then for all $x > 0$, $Q(x)$ will be _____ and R will either be zero or _____ .

---

417. negative; negative

418. Moreover if $r \geqslant 0$, and $x > r$, then $(x - r) > 0$, and $(x - r)Q(x)$ will be _____ if $Q(x)$ is positive and R is
(positive, negative)

positive or zero, and $(x - r)Q(x)$ will be _____ if $Q(x)$
(positive, negative)

is negative and R is negative or zero.

---

418. positive; negative

419. That is, $(x - r)Q(x)$ and R will have _____ sign(s)
unless $R = 0$.
(the same, different)

---

419. the same

420. And in either case, since $(x-r)Q(x)$ and R have the same sign, or $R = 0$,

$$|P(x)| = |(x-r)Q(x) + R| = |(x-r)Q(x)| + |R| \geqslant |(x-r)Q(x)|.$$

And since $Q(x) \neq 0$, $(x-r)Q(x) \neq 0$, and hence $P(x)$ _____ .

---

420. $\neq 0$

421. That is, if $r \geqslant 0$, and upon dividing $P(x)$ by $x-r$, using synthetic division, all the terms in the third row have the same sign, or are zero, then any $x > r$ cannot be a _____ of $P(x)$.

---

421. zero

422. We have proved the following result.

THEOREM 5 (Upper Bound). Let $P(x)$ be a polynomial with real coefficients and degree $\geqslant 2$. If $r \geqslant 0$, and upon dividing $P(x)$ by $x-r$, using synthetic division, all the numbers in the third row have the same sign (with 0 being given the appropriate sign), then r is an upper bound for the set of all real zeros of $P(x)$.

---

422. Go on to the summary.

SUMMARY

Theorem 5 (Upper Bound)

Let $P(x)$ be a polynomial with real coefficients and degree $\geqslant 2$. If $r \geqslant 0$, and upon dividing $P(x)$ by $x-r$, using synthetic division, all the numbers in the third row have the same sign (with 0 being given the appropriate sign), then r is an upper bound for the set of all zeros of $P(x)$.

Proof: We can write

$$P(x) = (x-r)Q(x) + R$$

where $Q(x)$ is the quotient polynomial and the remainder R is a number (possibly zero). Since the numbers in the third row all have the same sign, the coefficients of $Q(x)$ and R will have the same sign. And since $Q(x)$ has degree $\geqslant 1$, $Q(x) \neq 0$.

Thus for any $x > 0$, the numbers $Q(x)$ and R will have the same sign. Moreover, if $x > r$, then $(x-r) > 0$ and $(x-r)Q(x)$ and R will have the same sign. Thus

$|P(x)| = |(x-r)Q(x) + R| = |(x-r)Q(x)| + |R| \geqslant |(x-r)Q(x)|.$ That is,

That is, $|P(x)| \geqslant |(x-r)Q(x)|$.

And since $Q(x \neq 0, (x-r)Q(x) \neq 0$ and hence $P(x) \neq 0$.

Therefore, if $x > r$, x cannot be a zero of $P(x)$. That is, r is an upper bound of the set of real zeros of $P(x)$.

423. upper bounds

EXAMPLE 18

424. In fact there are an infinite number of upper bounds to the set.

Let $P(x) = x^3 - 4x^2 + 2x - 30$. Below are the synthetic divisions obtained by dividing $P(x)$ by $x - 1, x - 2, x - 3, x - 4, x - 5,$ and $x - 6$.

$$
\begin{array}{r|rrrr}
1 & 1 & -4 & 2 & -30 \\
  &   & 1 & -3 & -1 \\
\hline
  & 1 & -3 & -1 & -31 \\
\end{array}
$$

$$
\begin{array}{r|rrrr}
2 & 1 & -4 & 2 & -30 \\
  &   & 2 & -4 & -4 \\
\hline
  & 1 & -2 & -2 & -34 \\
\end{array}
$$

$$
\begin{array}{r|rrrr}
3 & 1 & -4 & 2 & -30 \\
  &   & 3 & -3 & -3 \\
\hline
  & 1 & -1 & -1 & -33 \\
\end{array}
$$

$$
\begin{array}{r|rrrr}
4 & 1 & -4 & 2 & -30 \\
  &   & 4 & 0 & 8 \\
\hline
  & 1 & 0 & 2 & -22 \\
\end{array}
$$

$$
\begin{array}{r|rrrr}
5 & 1 & -4 & 2 & -30 \\
  &   & 5 & 5 & 35 \\
\hline
  & 1 & 1 & 7 & 5 \\
\end{array}
$$

$$
\begin{array}{r|rrrr}
6 & 1 & -4 & 2 & -30 \\
  &   & 6 & 12 & 84 \\
\hline
  & 1 & 2 & 14 & 54 \\
\end{array}
$$

Which of the six numbers 1, 2, 3, 4, 5, 6, if any, are upper bounds for the set of real zeros of $P(x) = x^3 - 4x^2 + 2x - 30$?

_____

424. 5 and 6.

If you had difficulty, go on to the next frame. If not, skip to frame 428.

425. Since the third rows obtained by dividing $P(x)$ by $x - 1$, $x - 2, x - 3$, and $x - 4$ have both positive and negative numbers, _____ do not satisfy the theorem and hence we have not shown that they are upper bounds.

---

425. $1, 2, 3, 4$

426. However, the third rows obtained by dividing $P(x)$ by $x - 5$ and $x - 6$ have numbers that all have _____ .

---

426. the same sign

427. Thus by theorem 5, 5 and 6 are _____ for the set of real zeros of $P(x) = x^3 - 4x^2 + 2x - 30$.

---

427. upper bounds

428. Furthermore, 7, 8, 10, and 99 are also _____ for the set of real zeros of $P(x)$.

---

428. upper bounds

EXAMPLE 19

429. Let $P(x) = -x^3 + 3x^2 - 2x + 20$. Below are the synthetic divisions obtained by dividing $P(x)$ by $x - 1, x - 2, x - 3, x - 4$, and $x - 5$.

```
 1 │ -1     3    -2    20
   │        -1    2     0
   ────────────────────────
     -1     2     0    20

 2 │ -1     3    -2    20
   │        -2    2     0
   ────────────────────────
     -1     1     0    20

 3 │ -1     3    -2    20
   │        -3    0    - 6
   ────────────────────────
     -1     0    -2    14

 4 │ -1     3    -2    20
   │        -4   -4   -24
   ────────────────────────
     -1    -1    -6    - 4

 5 │ -1     3    - 2    20
   │        -5   -10   -60
   ────────────────────────
     -1    -2   -12   -40
```

Which of the five numbers $1, 2, 3, 4, 5$, if any, are upper bounds for the set of real zeros of $P(x) = -x^3 + 3x^2 - 2x + 20$? _____

---

429. 4 and 5.

If you had difficulty, see frames 405 to 428.

430. We now consider the problem of finding lower bounds for the set of real zeros of polynomials. If r is any number and $P(x)$ is divided by $x - r$, we can write $P(x) = $ _____ .

---

430. $(x - r)Q(x) + R$

431. Where $Q(x)$ is the _____ and the remainder R is a _____ .

---

431. quotient; number

432. This time suppose that upon dividing $P(x)$ by $x - r$, by synthetic division, the numbers in the third row have alternating signs. That is, the coefficients of $Q(x)$ will have _____ signs, and the constant term a_0 of $Q(x)$ and R will have

_____ signs.
(the same, different)

---

432. alternating; different

433. Thus if $Q(x) = a_3x^3 + a_2x^2 + a_1x + a_0$ and R is positive, then a_0 is **(a)** _____ a_1 is **(b)** _____ ,
(positive, negative)'

a_2 is **(c)** _____ , and a_3 is **(d)** _____ .

---

433. (a) negative,
(b) positive,
(c) negative,
(d) positive

434. And if $x < 0$, a_1x will be **(a)** _____ , a_2x^2 will be
(positive, negative)

(b) _____ , and a_3x^3 will be **(c)** _____ .

---

434. (a) negative,
(b) negative,
(c) negative

435. Thus, if $x < 0$ and R is positive, $Q(x)$ will be _____ .

---

435. negative (since a_0, a_1x, a_2x^2, and a_3x^3 are all negative)

436. In fact, if $Q(x) = a_nx^n + ... + a_0$, $x < 0$ and R is positive, each of the terms $a_0, a_1x^1, a_2x^2, ..., a_nx^n$ will be _____ and hence $Q(x)$ will be _____ .

---

436. negative; negative

437. On the other hand, if $x < 0$ and R is negative, then a_0 will be

(a) _____ , $a_1 x$ will be **(b)** _____ ,

$a_2 x^2$ will be **(c)** _____ , $a_3 x^3$ will be **(d)** _____ ,

etc.

---

437. (a) positive, **(b)** positive, **(c)** positive, **(d)** positive

438. Hence $Q(x)$ will be _____ .

---

438. positive

439. Thus, in either case, if the numbers in the third line alternate signs (with zero being given the appropriate sign), and $x < 0$, then $Q(x)$ and R will have _____ sign(s).
(the same, different)

---

439. different

440. Moreover, if $r \leqslant 0$, and $x < r$, then $(x - r) < 0$ and $(x - r)Q(x)$ will be _____ if R is positive and $(x - r)Q(x)$ will be _____ if R is negative.

---

440. positive (since the product of $(x - r)$ and $Q(x)$, which are both negative, will be positive); negative

441. That is, $(x - r)Q(x)$ and R will have _____ sign(s).
(the same, different)

---

441. the same

442. Thus, as in the case for upper bounds, since $(x - r)Q(x)$ and R have the same sign, or $R = 0$, and $P(x) = (x - r)Q(x) + R$,

$|P(x)| =$ _____

_____ .

---

442. $|(x - r)Q(x) + R| =$ $|(x - r)Q(x)| + |R| \geqslant |(x - r)Q(x)|$

443. That is, $|P(x)| \geqslant$ _____ .

---

443. $|(x - r)Q(x)|$

444. And since $Q(x) \neq 0$, $(x - r)Q(x) \neq 0$ and hence $P(x)$ _____ .

---

444. $\neq 0$

	445. Therefore, if $x < r$, x cannot be a _____ of $P(x)$, since $P(x) \neq 0$.
445. zero	**446.** That is, if $r \leq 0$, and upon dividing $P(x)$ by $x - r$, using synthetic division, the terms in the third row alternate signs (with zero being given the appropriate sign), then any $x < r$ cannot be a _____ of $P(x)$.
446. zero	**447.** Hence such an r will be a _____ of the set of real zeros of $P(x)$.
447. lower bound	**448.** We have proved the following result. **THEOREM 6** (Lower Bound). Let $P(x)$ be a polynomial with real coefficients and degree ≥ 2. If $r \leq 0$, and upon dividing $P(x)$ by $x - r$, using synthetic division, the numbers in the third row alternate signs (with zero being given the appropriate sign), then r is a _____ for the set of real zeros of $P(x)$.
448. lower bound	

SUMMARY

Theorem 6 (Lower Bound)

Let $P(x)$ be a polynomial with real coefficients and degree ≥ 2. If $r \leq 0$, and upon dividing $P(x)$ by $x - r$, using synthetic division, the numbers in the third row alternate signs (with zero being given the appropriate sign), then r is a lower bound for the set of real zeros of $P(x)$.

Proof: We can write

$$P(x) = (x - r)Q(x) + R$$

where $Q(x)$ is the quotient polynomial and the remainder R is a number. Since the numbers in the third row have alternating signs, the coefficients of $Q(x)$ will have alternating signs and the constant term a_0 of $Q(x)$ and R will have different signs. Thus if $x < 0$, the numbers $Q(x)$ and R will have different signs. Moreover if $x < r$, then $(x - r) < 0$ and $(x - r)Q(x)$ and R will have the same sign. Therefore, as before,

$$|P(x)| = |(x - r)Q(x) + R| = |(x - r)Q(x)| + |R| \geq |(x - r)Q(x)|.$$

That is, $|P(x)| \geq |(x - r)Q(x)|$
and since $Q(x) \neq 0$, $(x - r)Q(x) \neq 0$ and hence $P(x) \neq 0$. Hence if $x < r$, x cannot be a zero of $P(x)$. That is, r is a lower bound of the set of real zeros of $P(x)$.

449. Again we note that a lower bound obtained by synthetic division is not unique. For if −2 is a lower bound

of a set, then −3, −4, −5, −9, −1762 are all _____ of that set.

---

449. lower bounds

EXAMPLE 20

450. In fact there are an infinite number of lower bounds of the set.

Let $P(x) = 2x^3 + 8x^2 - 9x + 4$. Below are the synthetic divisions obtained by dividing $P(x)$ by $x + 1, x + 2, x + 3, x + 4, x + 5,$ and $x + 6$.

$$
\begin{array}{r|rrrr}
-1 & 2 & 8 & -9 & 4 \\
   &   & -2 & -6 & 15 \\
\hline
   & 2 & 6 & -15 & 19
\end{array}
$$

$$
\begin{array}{r|rrrr}
-2 & 2 & 8 & -9 & 4 \\
   &   & -4 & -8 & 34 \\
\hline
   & 2 & 4 & -17 & 38
\end{array}
$$

$$
\begin{array}{r|rrrr}
-3 & 2 & 8 & -9 & 4 \\
   &   & -6 & -6 & 45 \\
\hline
   & 2 & 2 & -15 & 49
\end{array}
$$

$$
\begin{array}{r|rrrr}
-4 & 2 & 8 & -9 & 4 \\
   &   & -8 & 0 & 36 \\
\hline
   & 2 & 0 & -9 & 40
\end{array}
$$

$$
\begin{array}{r|rrrr}
-5 & 2 & 8 & -9 & 4 \\
   &   & -10 & 10 & -5 \\
\hline
   & 2 & -2 & 1 & -1
\end{array}
$$

$$
\begin{array}{r|rrrr}
-6 & 2 & 8 & -9 & 4 \\
   &   & -12 & 24 & -90 \\
\hline
   & 2 & -4 & 15 & -86
\end{array}
$$

Which of the six numbers −1, −2, −3, −4, −5, −6, if any, are lower bounds for the set of real zeros of
$P(x) = 2x^3 + 8x^2 - 9x + 4?$ _____

---

450. −5 and −6.

If you had difficulty, go on to the next frame. If not, skip to frame 454.

451. Since the numbers in the third rows obtained by dividing $P(x)$ by $x + 1, x + 2, x + 3$, and $x + 4$ do not have _____ _____ , the theorem does not apply, and we do not know that $-1, -2, -3$, and -4 are lower bounds.

451. alternating signs

452. However, the numbers in the third rows obtained by dividing $P(x)$ by $x + 5$ and $x + 6$ do have _____ .

452. alternating signs

453. Hence by theorem 6, -5 and -6 are _____ for the set of real zeros of $P(x) = 2x^3 + 8x^2 - 9x + 4$.

453. lower bounds

454. Furthermore, $-7, -8, -9$, and -713 are also _____ _____ of the set of real zeros for $P(x)$.

454. lower bounds

EXAMPLE 21

455. Let $P(x) = x^4 + 2x^3 - 3x^2 + 4x + 10$. Below are the synthetic divisions obtained by dividing $P(x)$ by $x + 1, x + 2, x + 3, x + 4$, and $x + 5$.

$$
\begin{array}{r|rrrrr}
-1 & 1 & 2 & -3 & 4 & 10 \\
   &   & -1 & -1 & 4 & -8 \\
\hline
   & 1 & 1 & -4 & 8 & 2
\end{array}
$$

$$
\begin{array}{r|rrrrr}
-2 & 1 & 2 & -3 & 4 & 10 \\
   &   & -2 & 0 & 6 & -20 \\
\hline
   & 1 & 0 & -3 & 10 & -10
\end{array}
$$

$$
\begin{array}{r|rrrrr}
-3 & 1 & 2 & -3 & 4 & 10 \\
   &   & -3 & 3 & 0 & -12 \\
\hline
   & 1 & -1 & 0 & 4 & -2
\end{array}
$$

$$
\begin{array}{r|rrrrr}
-4 & 1 & 2 & -3 & 4 & 10 \\
   &   & -4 & 8 & -20 & 64 \\
\hline
   & 1 & -2 & 5 & -16 & 74
\end{array}
$$

$$
\begin{array}{r|rrrrr}
-5 & 1 & 2 & -3 & 4 & 10 \\
   &   & -5 & 15 & -60 & 280 \\
\hline
   & 1 & -3 & 12 & -56 & 290
\end{array}
$$

Which of the five numbers $-1, -2, -3, -4, -5$, if any, are lower bounds of the set of real zeros of $P(x) = x^4 + 2x^3 - 3x^2 + 4x + 10$?

_____

455. -4 and -5.

If you had difficulty, see frames 430 to 454.

EXAMPLE 22

456. Is 4 an upper bound of the set of real zeros of the polynomial
$P(x) = x^3 - 2x^2 - 5x + 6$? _____

456. Yes.

If you had difficulty, go on to the next frame. If not, skip to frame 459.

457. Dividing $P(x) = x^3 - 2x^2 - 5x + 6$ by $x - 4$, we get

$$\underline{} \Big|$$

_____

457.

$$
\begin{array}{r|rrrr}
4 & 1 & -2 & -5 & 6 \\
  &   & 4 & 8 & 12 \\
\hline
  & 1 & 2 & 3 & 18
\end{array}
$$

458. Thus 4 is an upper bound of the set of real zeros of

$P(x) = x^3 - 2x^2 - 5x + 6$, since _____

_____ .

---

458. all the numbers in the third row of the synthetic division have the same sign

EXAMPLE 23

459. Is −1 a lower bound of the set of real zeros of

$P(x) = x^3 - 2x^2 - 5x + 6$? _____

---

459. no.

If you had difficulty, go on to the next frame. If not, skip to frame 462.

460. Dividing $P(x) = x^3 - 2x^2 - 5x + 6$ by $x + 1$ we get

$\underline{\quad}\rfloor$

_____

460.

$$
\begin{array}{r|rrrr}
-1 & 1 & -2 & -5 & 6 \\
   &   & -1 & 3 & 2 \\
\hline
   & 1 & -3 & -2 & 8
\end{array}
$$

461. Thus −1 is not a lower bound of the set of zeros of

$P(x) = x^3 - 2x^2 - 5x + 6$ since _____

_____ .

---

461. the numbers in the third row do not have alternating signs

EXAMPLE 24

462. Is −3 a lower bound of the set of real zeros of

$P(x) = x^3 - 2x^2 - 5x + 6$? _____

---

462. Yes.

If you had difficulty, see frames 459 to 461.

463. Since −1 is not a lower bound of the set of real zeros of $P(x) = x^3 - 2x^2 - 5x + 6$, and −3 is a lower bound, there must be a zero of $P(x)$ in the interval ____ $< x <$ ____ .

---

463. −3; −1

464. Divide $P(x) = x^3 - 2x^2 - 5x + 6$ by $x + 2$. What conclusion do you draw?

$$\underline{\quad\quad}\rfloor$$

464.

$$
\begin{array}{r|rrrr}
-2 & 1 & -2 & -5 & 6 \\
   &   & -2 & 8 & -6 \\
\hline
   & 1 & -4 & 3 & 0 \\
\end{array}
$$

-2 is a zero of $P(x)$ since $R = 0$. Moreover, it is a lower bound of the zeros, since the numbers in the third row alternate signs.

EXAMPLE 25

465. Find an upper and a lower bound of the set of real zeros of $P(x) = x^3 + 2x^2 - 6x - 3$.

upper bound _____

lower bound _____

---

465. 2 or any number larger than 2; -4 or any number smaller than -4.

If you had difficulty, see frames 424 to 464.

EXERCISE 1

466. Find the remainder obtained by dividing $P(x) = x^4 - 4x^3 - 6x^2 + 5x + 2$ by $x - 3$.

$R =$ _____

---

466. -64.

If you had difficulty, see frames 293 to 306.

EXERCISE 2

467. Find a polynomial $P(x)$ with leading coefficient 1, whose zeros are $3, -2$, and i.

$P(x) =$ _____

---

467. $(x - 3)(x + 2)(x - i)$.

If you had difficulty, see frames 337 to 344.

EXERCISE 3

468. Determine the polynomial with leading coefficient 1, whose zeros are 4 as a double zero, -3 as a triple zero, and 2 as a single zero.

$P(x) =$ _____

---

468. $(x - 4)^2(x + 3)^3(x - 2)$.

If you had difficulty, see frames 333 to 344.

EXERCISE 4

469. Find the zeros of $P(x) = (x - 2)(x^2 + 3x - 28)$.

$x =$ _____

---

469. $2, 4, -7$.

If you had difficulty, see frames 345 to 348.

EXERCISE 5

470. Use synthetic division to divide

$P(x) = x^4 - 2x^3 - 9x^2 + 12$ by $x - 4$.

$P(x) = (x - 4)\,($ _____ $) +$ _____ .

---

470. $x^3 + 2x^2 - x - 4; -4$

If you had difficulty, see frames 350 to 392.

EXERCISE 6

471. Is $x + 3$ a factor of $P(x) = x^4 + 5x^3 + 4x^2 - 7x - 3$?

_____

---

471. yes.

If you had difficulty, see frames 386 to 395.

EXERCISE 7

472. If $P(x) = x^3 + 6x^2 + 3x - 8$, then $P(-5) =$ ___ .

---

472. 2.

If you had difficulty, see frames 396 to 404.

EXERCISE 8

473. Find an upper bound of the set of zeros of

$P(x) = -x^3 + 2x^2 + 6x + 3.$ _____

_____

---

473. 4, or any number greater than 4.

If you had difficulty, see frames 424 to 428.

EXERCISE 9

474. Find a lower bound of the set of zeros of

$P(x) = -x^3 + 2x^2 + 6x + 3.$ _____

_____

---

474. -2, or any number less than -2.

If you had difficulty, see frames 449 to 455.

PROBLEMS

1. Use synthetic division to divide
   $P(x) = 5x^4 - 2x^3 - 4x^2 - 3x + 4$ by
   (a) $x + 1$ (c) $x + 2$
   (b) $x - 1$ (d) $x - 2$

2. Use synthetic division to divide
   $P(x) = 3x^4 + 5x^3 - 30x - 44$ by
   (a) $x + 1$ (c) $x + 2$
   (b) $x - 1$ (d) $x - 2$

3. Use synthetic division to divide
   $P(x) = 9x^4 - 10x^2 + 1$ by
   (a) $x + \frac{1}{2}$ (c) $x - \frac{1}{3}$
   (b) $x + \frac{1}{3}$ (d) $x - \frac{1}{2}$

4. Use synthetic division to divide
   $P(x) = x^4 - 4x^3 - x^2 + 16x - 12$ by
   (a) $x + 2$ (c) $x - \frac{1}{2}$
   (b) $x + 1$ (d) $x - 3$

5. If $P(x) = x^3 + 4x^2 - 2x - 3$, use synthetic division to find
   (a) $P(-3)$ (c) $P(1)$
   (b) $P(-1)$ (d) $P(2)$

6. If $P(x) = 3x^4 - 7x^2 + 4x - 5$, use synthetic division to find
   (a) $P(-2)$ (c) $P(1)$
   (b) $P(-1)$ (d) $P(2)$

7. If $P(x) = 4x^5 - 3x^3 + 12$, use synthetic division to find
   (a) $P(-\frac{1}{2})$ (c) $P(\frac{1}{3})$
   (b) $P(-\frac{1}{3})$ (d) $P(\frac{1}{2})$

8. Use synthetic division to show that 2 is an upper bound and -2 is a lower bound of the set of real zeros of $P(x) = 9x^4 - 10x^2 + 1$.

9. Use synthetic division to show that 5 is an upper bound and -3 is a lower bound of the set of real zeros of $P(x) = x^4 - 4x^3 - x^2 + 16x - 12$.

10. Given $P(x) = x^3 - 4x^2 + x - 5$ use synthetic division to find an upper bound and a lower bound of the set of real zeros.

11. Given $P(x) = x^4 - 4x^3 - 4x^2 + 16x + 1$ use synthetic division to find an upper bound and a lower bound of the set of real zeros.

12. In each of the following, determine if $D(x)$ is a factor of the polynomial $P(x)$.

   (a) $P(x) = x^4 + 3x^3 + x^2 - 5$, $\quad D(x) = x - 3$

   (b) $P(x) = x^3 - x^2 - 4x + 4$, $\quad D(x) = x + 2$

   (c) $P(x) = 3x^3 - 17x^2 + 11x - 5$, $\quad D(x) = x - 5$

   (d) $P(x) = 2x^3 + 17x^2 + 32x + 12$, $\quad D(x) = x + \frac{1}{2}$

   (e) $P(x) = 4x^3 - 2x^2 + 5x + 3$, $\quad D(x) = x - 2$

   (f) $P(x) = 3x^4 + 13x^3 + 7x^2 + 11x - 4$, $\quad D(x) = x + 4$

13. Show that $x - 1$ is a factor of

   (a) $x^3 - 1$ (c) $x^5 - 1$ (e) $x^7 - 1$

   (b) $x^4 - 1$ (d) $x^6 - 1$ (f) $x^8 - 1$

14. Show that $x - a$ is a factor of

   (a) $x^4 - a^4$ (c) $x^6 - a^6$

   (b) $x^5 - a^5$ (d) $x^7 - a^7$

15. Show that $x + 1$ is a factor of

   (a) $x^3 + 1$ (c) $x^7 + 1$

   (b) $x^5 + 1$ (d) $x^9 + 1$

16. Show that $x + a$ is a factor of

   (a) $x^3 + a^3$

   (b) $x^5 + a^5$

   (c) $x^7 + a^7$

17. Show that $x + a$ is not a factor of

   (a) $x^2 + a^2$

   (b) $x^4 + a^4$

   (c) $x^6 + a^6$

18. Determine the polynomial of lowest degree and leading coefficient 1 that has the following zeros.

   (a) $1, 2, -4$ (c) $-1, \frac{1}{2}, 3$ (e) $1, i, -2i$

   (b) $-1, -2, 2$ (d) $-3, -1, 1, 2$ (f) $1 - i, 1 + i, -1, 4$

19. Determine the polynomial of lowest degree and leading coefficient 1 that has the following zeros.

(a) 1 is double zero, 2 is a single zero.

(b) -2 is a triple zero, 1 and 3 are single zeros.

(c) 2 has multiplicity 4, -1 has multiplicity 2, and 3 is a single zero.

(d) $\frac{1}{3}$ is a double zero, $-\frac{1}{2}$ is a double zero, and -1 is a single zero.

20. Find the real zeros in each of the following.

(a) $P(x) = (x - 3)^2 (x + 2)^3$

(b) $P(x) = (x + \frac{1}{2})^4 (x - 2)$

(c) $P(x) = (3x + 1)^3 (x - 1)^2$

(d) $P(x) = (2x - 3)^2 (x - 1)(x + 2)$

(e) $(x - 1)^2 (2x^2 - 3x - 2)$

(f) $(x + \frac{1}{2})(x^2 + 8x + 12)$

(g) $(x + 1)(x^2 - 6x + 8)$

(h) $(x - 2)(2x^2 - 5x + 2)$

21. Given $P(x) = x^4 + 3x^3 - 7x^2 - 27x - 18$, use synthetic division to find

(a) the smallest integer that is an upper bound of the set of real zeros,

(b) the largest integer that is a lower bound of the set of real zeros,

(c) the real roots.

22. Given $P(x) = x^4 - 2x^3 - 13x^2 + 14x + 24$ use synthetic division to find

(a) the smallest integer that is an upper bound of the set of real zeros,

(b) the largest integer that is a lower bound of the set of real zeros,

(c) the real roots.

Answers are at end of book.

QUIZ

If you cannot answer the following questions correctly, review the appropriate frames.

1. Use the remainder theorem to find the remainder obtained by dividing
$P(x) = x^4 - 5x^3 + 6x^2 - 3x + 4$ by $x - 2$.

2. Find a polynomial $P(x)$ with leading coefficient 1, whose zeros are 4, -6, and $2i$.

3. Find the zeros of the polynomial $P(x) = (x + i)(x^2 - 2x - 8)$.

4. Given $P(x) = x^4 + 4x^3 - 7x^2 - 2x - 5$, use synthetic division to

   (a) divide $P(x)$ by $x - 1$

   (b) find $P(2)$

   (c) find the upper bound of the set of zeros of $P(x)$.

Answers are at end of book.

14 Zeros of Polynomials with Real Coefficients

Upon completing this chapter you should be able to

I. Given a complex zero of $P(x)$ of degree 4 or less, find the remainder of the zeros.

II. Factor polynomials of the form $P(x) = ax^3 + bx^2 + cx + d$ into linear and quadratic factors.

III. Use Descartes' rule of signs to investigate the number of positive and negative real zeros, and hence the number of complex zeros, of a polynomial $P(x)$.

In this chapter we turn our attention to the problem of finding zeros of polynomials with real coefficients. This is, in general, a very difficult problem. However, we shall discuss three results that will give us information about the number of zeros a polynomial with real coefficients will have and shall explain the nature of those zeros rather than discussing the ways of finding them.

475. We first show that complex zeros come in pairs.

Let r be a zero of $P(x)$, a polynomial with real coefficients, thus $P(r) = $ ___ .

---

475. 0

476. Since $P(r) = a_n r^n + \cdots + a_1 = 0$, we can take the complex conjugate of both sides of the equation and get

$$\overline{a_n r^n + \cdots + a_0} = \underline{\hspace{2cm}} .$$

---

476. $\overline{0} = 0$

477. But theorem (1) in the chapter on complex numbers in Volume III states that the conjugate of a sum is the same as the sum of the conjugates. Thus $0 = \overline{a_n r^n + \cdots + a_0} = $ _____ .

---

477. $\overline{a_n r^n} + \cdots + \overline{a_0}$

478. Moreover, the same theorem states that the conjugate of a product is the product of the conjugates. Thus $\overline{a_n r^n} = $ _____ , $\overline{a_{n-1} r^{n-1}} = $ _____ , etc.

---

478. $\overline{a_n r^n} = \overline{a_n}\,\overline{r^n}$; $\overline{a_{n-1}} \overline{r^{n-1}}$

479. And $0 = \overline{a_n r^n} + \cdots + \overline{a_0} = $ _____ .

---

479. $\overline{a_n}\,\overline{r^n} + \cdots + \overline{a_0}$

480. Finally, if the coefficients $a_n, a_{n-1}, \ldots, a_0$ are all real, then (a) $\overline{a_n} = $ ____ , (b) $\overline{a_{n-1}} = $ _____ , $\ldots$, (c) $\overline{a_0} = $ ____ .

---

480. (a) a_n, (b) a_{n-1}, (c) a_0

481. And we get $0 = \overline{a_n}\,\overline{r}^n + \cdots + \overline{a_0} = $ _____ .

---

481. $a_n \overline{r}^n + \cdots + a_0$

482. That is, $P(\overline{r}) = a_n \overline{r}^n + \cdots + a_0 = $ ____ .

---

482. 0

483. Hence $\overline{r}$ is _____ .

---

483. a zero of $P(x)$

484. Thus we have proved the following result.

THEOREM 1. Let $P(x) = a_n x^n + \cdots + a_0$ be a polynomial of degree $n \geqslant 1$ with real coefficients. Then if r is a zero of $P(x)$, so is

_____ .

---

484. its complex conjugate, $\overline{r}$

Theorem 1

Let $P(x) = a_n x^n + \cdots + a_0$ be a polynomial of degree $n \geqslant 1$ with real coefficients. Then if r is a zero of $P(x)$, so is its complex conjugate $\bar{r}$.

Proof: Let r be a zero of $P(x)$, then $P(r) = a_n r^n + \cdots + a_0 = 0$. Taking the conjugate of both sides of the equation, we get

$$\overline{a_n r^n + \cdots + a_0} = \bar{0} = 0.$$

But theorem 1 in the chapter on complex numbers in Volume III states that the conjugate of a sum is the same as the sum of the conjugates. Thus we have

$$\overline{a_n r^n} + \cdots + \overline{a_0} = 0.$$

Moreover, the same theorem states that the conjugate of a product is the product of the conjugates. Thus

$$\overline{a_n r^n} = \overline{a_n}\,\overline{r}^n, \overline{a_{n-1} r^{n-1}} = \overline{a_{n-1}}\,\overline{r}^{n-1}, \text{etc.},$$

and we have $\overline{a_n}\,\overline{r}^n + \cdots + \overline{a_0} = 0.$

Finally, since the coefficients are all real,

$$\overline{a_n} = a_n, \overline{a_{n-1}} = a_{n-1}, \dots, \overline{a_0} = a_0, \quad \text{and}$$

$a_n \bar{r}^n + \cdots + a_0 = 0.$

That is,

$$P(r) = a_n \bar{r}^n + \cdots + a_0 = 0,$$

and $\bar{r}$ is a real zero of $P(x)$.

---

	485. If r is a real zero of $P(x)$, then $\bar{r} = \underline{\quad}$. Hence $\bar{r}$ is clearly a zero.
485. r	**486.** On the other hand, the theorem states that complex zeros of a polynomial $P(x)$ with real coefficients appear in pairs. That is, if $r = a + bi$ is a zero of $P(x)$, then so is $\underline{\hspace{3cm}}$.
486. $\bar{r} = a - bi$. If you had difficulty, see the chapter on complex numbers in Volume III.	

EXAMPLE 1

487. If $3i$ and $2 - i$ are two zeros of
$P(x) = x^4 - 4x^3 + 14x^2 - 36x + 45$, then by theorem 1 their conjugates are also zeros. That is, _____ and _____ are also zeros.

---

487. $-3i$; $2 + i$

488. $3i, 2 - i, -3i$ and $2 + i$ are *all* the zeros, since the polynomial
$P(x) = x^4 - 4x^3 + 14x^2 - 36x + 45$ of degree ____ has exactly
_____ zeros.

---

488. 4; four

EXAMPLE 2

489. $-2i$ and $1 + i$ are two zeros of
$P(x) = x^4 - 2x^3 + 6x^2 - 8x + 8$. Find the remaining zeros of
$P(x)$. _____ .

---

489. $2i$ and $1 - i$.

If you had difficulty, see
frames 485 to 488.

EXAMPLE 3

490. $-i$ is one zero of $P(x) = x^4 - 5x^3 + 7x^2 - 5x + 6$.

Find the remaining three zeros. _____

---

490. i, 2, and 3.

If you had difficulty, go on to the next
frame. If not, skip to frame 497.

491. Since $-i$ is a zero its complex conjugate ____ must also be a
zero.

---

491. i

492. Thus we can write
$x^4 - 5x^3 + 7x^2 - 5x + 6 = $ _____ $Q(x)$.

---

492. $(x - i)(x + i)$

493. But $(x - i)(x + i) = $ _____ . Thus
$x^4 - 5x^3 + 7x^2 - 5x + 6 = $ _____ $Q(x)$.

---

493. $x^2 + 1$;
$x^2 + 1$

494. And dividing $x^4 - 5x^3 + 7x^2 - 5x + 6$ by $x^2 + 1$, we see that
$x^4 - 5x^3 + 7x^2 - 5x + 6 = (x^2 + 1)($ _____ $)$.

---

494. $x^2 - 5x + 6$

495. Finally, we can factor $x^2 - 5x + 6$

as $x^2 - 5x + 6 = ($ _____ $)($ _____ $)$.

---

495. $x - 2;\ x - 3$

496. Hence { _____ } is the set of zeros of $x^4 - 5x^3 + 7x^2 - 5x + 6$.

---

496. $-i, i, 2$, and 3

497. Since we have developed methods for determining the zeros of polynomials of degree 1 and 2, we can find the zeros of any polynomial $P(x)$ if we can write it as the product of _____

_____ and _____

factors.

---

497. linear (or first degree); quadratic (or second degree)

498. We are now ready to prove that we can, in fact, write any polynomial with real coefficients as the product of linear and quadratic factors that have real coefficients.

---

498. Go on to the next frame.

499. By the factor theorem, if r is a real zero of $P(x)$, then $P(r) = $ ___ .

---

499. 0

500. And by the factor theorem we can write $P(x) = $ _____ , since $R = $ _____ .

---

500. $(x - r)Q(x); P(r) = 0$

501. On the other hand, if r is a complex zero, then _____

_____ is also a zero.

---

501. its complex conjugate $\bar{r}$

502. And we can write $P(x) = ($ _____ $)($ _____ $)Q(x)$.

---

502. $x - r;\ x - \bar{r}$

503. But by multiplying we get $(x - r)(x - \bar{r}) = x^2 + bx + c$ for some real b and c, and we can write $P(x) = $ _____ .

---

503. $(x^2 + bx + c)Q(x)$, b and c real

	504. We can apply the same reasoning to the polynomial $Q(x)$ to factor it. That is, if r_1 is a real zero of $Q(x)$, then
	$Q(x) = \underline{\hspace{2cm}} Q_1(x).$
504. $(x - r_1)$	505. If r_1 is a complex zero of $Q(x)$, then so is $\underline{\hspace{3cm}}$ $\underline{\hspace{4cm}}$, and we can write $$Q(x) = (\underline{\hspace{5cm}}) Q_1(x).$$
505. its complex conjugate $\bar{r}_1$; $(x - r_1)(x - \bar{r}_1)$ $= (x + b_1 x + c_1)Q_1(x),$ b_1 and c_1 real	506. We can apply the process to $Q_1(x)$ etc. until we have $$P(x) = a_n(x - r_1)\cdots(x - r_k)(x^2 + b_1 x + c_1)\cdots(x^2 + b_m + c_m)$$ with $b_1, b_2, \ldots, b_m$, and $c_1, c_2, \ldots, c_m$ all real. Thus we have written $P(x)$ as a product of k $\underline{\hspace{2cm}}$ factors and m $\underline{\hspace{2cm}}$ factors that have real coefficients.
506. linear; quadratic	507. We have proved the following result. **Theorem 2.** Let $P(x) = a_n x^n + \cdots + a_0$ be a polynomial of degree $n \geqslant 1$ with real coefficients. Then $P(x)$ can be written as a_n times a product of factors with real coefficients each of which has the form $\underline{\hspace{2cm}}$ or $\underline{\hspace{2cm}}$.
507. $x - r; x^2 + bx + c$ $x^2 + bx + c$	

SUMMARY

Theorem 2

Let $P(x) = a_n x^n + \cdots + a_0$ be a polynomial of degree $n \geqslant 1$ with real coefficients. Then $P(x)$ can be written as a_n times a product of factors with real coefficients each of which has the form $x - r$ or $x^2 + bx + c$.

Proof: By the factor theorem, if r is a real zero of $P(x)$, we can write

$$P(x) = (x - r)Q(x)$$

for some polynomial $Q(x)$. If r is a complex zero, then its conjugate $\bar{r}$ is also a zero and we can write

$$P(x) = (x - r)(x - \bar{r})Q(x).$$

But $(x - r)(x - \bar{r}) = x^2 + bx + c$, b and c real, and we can write

$$P(x) = (x^2 + bx + c)Q(x)$$

for some polynomial $Q(x)$. We can apply the same reasoning to $Q(x)$ to factor it, and so on until we have

$$P(x) = a_n(x - r_1) \cdots (x - r_k)(x^2 + b_1 x + c_1) \cdots (x^2 + b_m x + c_m)$$

with $b_1, b_2, \ldots, b_m$ and $c_1, c_2 \ldots, c_m$ real, and our proof is complete.

EXAMPLE 4

508. Let 1 be a zero of $P(x) = 2x^3 - 5x^2 + x + 2$. Then we know that _____ is a linear factor of $P(x)$.

---

508. $x - 1$

509. And synthetic division by $x - 1$ gives

_____ .

509.

$$\begin{array}{r|rrrr} 1 & 2 & -5 & 1 & 2 \\ & & 2 & -3 & -2 \\ \hline & 2 & -3 & -2 & 0 \end{array}$$

510. Hence we can write $P(x)$ as

$2x^3 - 5x^2 + x + 2 =$ _____ .

---

510. $(x - 1)(2x^2 - 3x - 2)$

511. But factoring out a 2 gives

$2x^2 - 3x - 2 = 2 ($ _____ $)$.

---

511. $x^2 - \frac{3}{2}x - 1$

512. Thus we can write $P(x)$ as

$2x^3 - 5x^2 + x + 2 = 2 ($ _____ $)($ _____ $)$, two times a product of linear and quadratic factors.

---

512. $x - 1$; $x^2 - \frac{3}{2}x - 1$

EXAMPLE 5

513. Factor the polynomial $P(x) = x^3 - 5x^2 + 2x + 8$ into linear and quadratic factors. -1 is a zero of $P(x)$.

$P(x) = $ _____

---

513. $(x + 1)(x^2 - 6x + 8)$.

If you had difficulty, go on to the next frame. If not, skip to frame 517.

514. Since -1 is a zero of $P(x)$, _____ is a factor of $P(x)$.

---

514. $x + 1$

515. Synthetic division of $P(x)$ by $x + 1$ gives

⌐

_____ .

515.

$$
\begin{array}{r|rrrr}
-1 & 1 & -5 & 2 & 8 \\
   &   & -1 & 6 & -8 \\
\hline
   & 1 & -6 & 8 & 0 \\
\end{array}
$$

516. Hence we can write $P(x)$ as

$x^3 - 5x^2 + 2x + 8 = $ _____ .

---

516. $(x + 1)(x^2 - 6x + 8)$

EXAMPLE 6

517. Factor the polynomial $P(x) = x^4 - 1$ into linear and quadratic factors with real coefficients.

$x^4 - 1 = $ _____

---

517. $(x - 1)(x + 1)(x^2 + 1)$.

If you had difficulty, go on to the next frame. If not, skip to frame 526.

518. To find the zeros of $x^4 - 1$ we must solve the equation

_____ .

---

518. $x^4 - 1 = 0$

519. $x^4 - 1 = 0$ is in quadratic form. If we let $u = $ _____ ,

---

519. x^2

520. $x^4 - 1 = 0$ becomes _____ .

---

520. $u^2 - 1 = 0$

521. $(u-1)(u+1)=0$

522. 1; 0

523. 1; 0

524. ±1

525. $(x-1)(x+1)(x^2+1)$

526. $(x-2)(x^2+1)$.

If you had difficulty, see
frames 508 to 516.

527. Go on to the next frame.

528. two.

If you had difficulty, go on to the
next frame. If not, skip to frame 532.

529. $1, -3, -4, 4$

---

521. And factoring we get _____ .

522. Thus $u =$ ___ and $u + 1 =$ ___ .

523. Since $u = x^2$, we have $x^2 =$ ___ and $x^2 + 1 =$ ___ .

524. And $x =$ _____ and $x^2 + 1 = 0$.

525. Therefore, $x^4 - 1 =$ _____ .

EXAMPLE 7

526. Factor the polynomial $P(x) = x^3 - 2x^2 + x - 2$ into linear
and quadratic factors. 2 is a zero of $P(x)$.

$P(x) =$ _____

527. Unfortunately, there is no procedure that allows us to
actually factor a polynomial into linear and quadratic factors, even
though, by theorem 2, we know such factors exist. However, we
shall state, without proof, one final result, Descartes' rule of signs,
which will give us some information about the number of positive
real zeros possessed by a polynomial.

528. A polynomial $P(x) = a_n x^n + a_{n-1} x^{n-1} + \cdots + a_0$, written
in order of descending powers of x, with all 0 terms omitted, is
said to have a **variation of sign** when two adjacent coefficients have
opposite signs. For example, $x^4 - 3x^2 + 4x - 5$ has three variations
in sign, while $x^4 - 3x^2 - 4x + 4$ has _____ variations in sign.

529. The coefficients of $x^4 - 3x^2 - 4x + 4$ are in order

_____ .

530. Thus one variation is sign occurs between 1 and −3 and the only other variation in sign occurs between _____ and _____ .

---

530. −4; 4

531. Thus $x^4 - 3x^2 - 4x + 4$ has _____ variations in sign.

---

531. two

532. $P(x) = x^4 - 3x^2 - 4x - 5$ has _____ variation(s) in sign.

---

532. one

533. We now state Descartes' rule of signs without proof.

THEOREM 3 (Descartes Rule of Signs). The number or positive real zeros of a polynomial $P(x) = a_n x^n + \cdots + a_0$ is either
(i) equal to the number of variations in sign or
(ii) less than the number of variations by a positive even integer.

Thus if a polynomial $P(x)$ has four variations in sign, $P(x)$ will have

(a) _____ , (b) _____ , or (c) _____ positive real zeros.

---

533. (a) four, (b) two, (c) no

534. If a polynomial $P(x)$ has five variations in sign, $P(x)$ will have _____ positive real zeros.

---

534. five, three, or one

535. If $P(x)$ has one variation is sign, $P(x)$ will have _____ positive real zero(s).

---

535. one

536. And if $P(x)$ has no variation in sign, $P(x)$ will have _____ positive real zero(s).

---

536. no

537. The theorem applies to _____ real zeros.
(all, positive, negative)

---

537. positive

538. In order to investigate the number of **negative** real zeros of $P(x)$, we must apply Descartes' rule of signs to $P(-x)$.

If $P(x) = x^3 - 3x^2 + 4x - 5$, then we get $P(-x)$ by replacing x in the equation by _____ .

---

538. −x

539. We get $P(-x) =$ _____ .

---

539. $-x^3 - 3x^2 - 4x - 5$

540. If $P(x) = x^4 - x^3 - 4x^2 + 5x - 7$,

$P(-x) =$ _____ .

---

540. $x^4 + x^3 - 4x^2 - 5x - 7$.
If you had difficulty, see
frames 538 and 539.

541. Let $r < 0$. If r is a zero of $P(x) = a_n x^n + \cdots + a_0$, then

$P(r) = $ ___ .

---

541. 0

542. And $P(r) = 0$ if and only if $P(-(-r)) = $ ___ , since
$P(x) = P(-(-x))$).

---

542. 0

543. That is, r is a zero of $P(x)$ if and only if $-r$ is a zero of _____ .

---

543. $P(-x)$

544. And since r is negative, $-r$ is a _____ zero of $P(-x)$ and
we can apply Descartes' rule of signs to $P(-x)$ to find the number of

negative real zeros of _____ .

---

544. positive; $P(x)$

EXAMPLE 8

545. To find the number of negative real zeros of
$P(x) = x^4 + 4x^3 - 2x^2 - x + 7$, we first find $P(-x)$.

$P(-x) =$ _____ .

---

545. $x^4 - 4x^3 - 2x^2 + x + 7$

546. $P(-x)$ has _____ variation(s) in sign.

---

546. two

547. Thus by Descartes' rule of signs, $P(-x)$ has _____

(how many?)

_____ real zero(s).
(positive, negative)

---

547. two or no; positive

548. Hence $P(x)$ has _____ real zero(s).

---

548. two or no negative

EXAMPLE 9

549. Now consider the new polynomial
$P(x) = x^4 - 7x^3 + 4x^2 + 5x + 6$.

$P(x)$ has _____ negative real zero(s).

---

549. two or no.

If you had difficulty, go on to the next frame. If not, skip to frame 554.

550. To find the number of negative zeros of $P(x)$ we must apply Descartes' rule of signs to _____ .

---

550. $P(-x)$

551. $P(-x) = $ _____

---

551. $x^4 + 7x^3 + 4x^2 - 5x + 6$

552. Thus $P(-x)$ has _____ variation(s) in sign and hence

_____ real zero(s).

---

552. two; two or no positive

553. Thus $P(x)$ has _____ real zero(s).

---

553. two or no negative

EXAMPLE 10

554. $P(x) = x^4 + 3x^3 + 4x^2 + 5x + 6$ has _____ negative real zero(s).

---

554. four, two, or no.

If you had difficulty, see frames 545 to 553.

EXAMPLE 11

555. We can use Descartes' rule of signs to investigate the nature of the zeros of $P(x) = x^5 + 3x^4 - 3x^3 - 5x + 2$. Since $P(x)$ has

_____ variation(s) in sign, there are _____ positive real zero(s).

---

555. two; two or no

556. To investigate the number of negative real zeros, we apply Descartes' rule of signs to _____ .

---

556. $P(-x)$

557. $P(-x) = $ _____

---

557. $-x^5 + 3x^4 + 3x^3 + 5x + 2$

558. $P(-x)$ has _____ variation(s) in sign.

Thus $P(x)$ has _____ negative real zero(s).

---

558. one;
one

559. Thus $P(x)$ has _____ positive real zero(s) and

_____ negative real zero(s).

---

559. two or no; one

560. That is, $P(x)$ has at most _____ real zero(s) and at least

_____ real zero(s).

---

560. three; one

561. But, since $P(x) = x^5 + 3x^4 - 3x^3 - 5x + 2$ is of

degree ___ , $P(x)$ has exactly _____ real or complex zero(s).

---

561. 5; five

562. Hence $P(x)$ has at least _____ complex zero(s) and at

most _____ complex zero(s).

---

562. two; four

563. Thus there are two possibilities for the zeros of $P(x)$. Either $P(x)$ has

(i) _____ positive real zero(s), _____ negative real zero(s)

and _____ pair(s) of complex conjugates or

(ii) _____ positive real zero(s), _____ negative real zero(s),

and _____ pair(s) of complex conjugates.

In either case the total number of zeros is _____ .

---

563. (i) two, one, one;
(ii) no, one, two;
five

EXAMPLE 12

564. Use Descartes' rule of signs to investigate the nature of the zeros of the polynomial $P(x) = x^4 - 3x^3 + 5x^2 - 2x + 3$. List the possible combinations of zeros below.

_____

_____

_____

_____

_____

_____

---

564. (i) four positive real zeros, no negative real zeros, and no pairs of complex conjugates;
(ii) two positive real zeros, no negative real zeros, and one pair of complex conjugates;
(iii) no positive real zeros, no negative real zeros, and two pairs of complex conjugates.

If you had difficulty, go on to the next frame. If not, skip to frame 572.

565. $P(x)$ has _____ variation(s) in sign. Thus $P(x)$ has

_____ positive real zero(s).

---

565. four; four, two, or no

566. $P(-x)$ has _____ variation(s) in sign.
Hence $P(x)$ has _____ negative real zero(s).

---

566. no
(since $P(-x) = x^4 + 3x^3 + 5x^2 + 2x + 3$);
no

567. Thus $P(x)$ has _____ positive real zero(s) and
_____ negative real zero(s).

---

567. four, two, or no; no

568. But $P(x)$ has exactly _____ zero(s).

---

568. four (since $P(x)$ is of degree 4)

569. Thus $P(x)$ could have _____ pair(s) of complex conjugates as zeros.

---

569. two, one, or no

---

570. Thus there are three possibilities for zeros of $P(x)$. $P(x)$ has

(i) _____ positive real zero(s), _____ negative real zero(s), and _____ pair(s) of complex conjugates;

(ii) _____ positive real zero(s), _____ negative real zero(s), and _____ pair(s) of complex conjugates;

(iii) _____ positive real zero(s), _____ negative real zero(s), and _____ pair(s) of complex conjugates.

---

570. (i) four, no, no;
(ii) two, no, one;
(iii) no, no, two

571. In each case the total number of zeros is _____ .

---

571. four

EXAMPLE 13

572. Use Descartes' rule of signs to investigate the nature of the zeros of the polynomial $P(x) = x^5 - x^4 - x^3 + x^2 - 1$. List the possible combinations of zeros below.

_____

_____

_____

_____

_____

_____

---

572. (i) three positive real zeros, two negative real zeros, and no pairs of complex zeros;
(ii) three positive, no negative, and one pair of complex conjugates;
(iii) one positive, two negative, and one pair of complex conjugates;
(iv) one positive, no negative, and two pairs of complex conjugates.

If you had difficulty, see frames 555 to 571.

573. Finally, we note the following result. If $P(x)$ is a polynomial with an odd degree and real coefficients, then $P(x)$ has at least one real zero. A polynomial of odd degree has an _____ number of zeros.
(even, odd)

---

573. odd (since a polynomial of degree n has n zeros)

574. Moreover, we have shown that complex zeros occur in pairs. That is, every polynomial with real coefficients has an _____ number of complex zeros.
(even, odd)

---

574. even

575. Therefore, every polynomial with real coefficients of odd degree must have at least one _____ zero.

---

575. real

EXAMPLE 14

576. Which of the following polynomials must have at least one real zero? _____
(a) $P(x) = x^5 - 3x^2 + 2$
(b) $P(x) = x^4 - 4x^3 + 6x^2 - 9$
(c) $P(x) = x^6 + 3x^4 + 2x^2 - 5$
(d) $P(x) = 3x^3 - 4x^2 + 6x - 7$

---

576. (a) and **(d)** (since they have an odd degree)

EXERCISE 1

577. If $3 - i$ is a zero of $P(x) = x^3 - 3x^2 - 8x + 30$, find the remaining zeros of $P(x)$. _____ .

---

577. $3 + i; -3.$
If you had difficulty, see frames 485 to 496.

EXERCISE 2

578. If -2 is a zero of $P(x) = x^3 - 4x^2 - 2x + 20$, factor $P(x)$ into linear and quadratic factors with real coefficients.

$P(x) =$ _____

---

578. $(x + 2)(x^2 - 6x + 10).$
If you had difficulty, see frames 508 to 516.

579. **(i)** three positive real zeros, one negative real zero, and no pairs of complex conjugates;
(ii) one positive real zero, one negative real zero, and one pair of complex conjugates.

If you had difficulty, see frames 545 to 571.

PROBLEMS

1. Determine the polynomial $P(x)$, with real coefficients, of lowest degree and leading coefficient 1 that has the following zeros as some, but not necessarily all, of its zeros.

   (a) $\{1, i, 2 - i\}$ **(c)** $\{3 - i, 4i\}$

   (b) $\{3, -5, \sqrt{2}i + 3\}$ **(d)** $\{2, 2 - \sqrt{2}i, \sqrt{2} + i\}$

2. Factor the following polynomials into linear and quadratic factors with real coefficients. One zero is given in each problem.

   (a) $x^4 + x^3 - x^2 + x - 2;$ $r = i$

   (b) $x^4 - 2x^3 - 6x - 9;$ $r = \sqrt{3}i$

   (c) $x^3 - 2x^2 - 2x + 12;$ $r = 2 - \sqrt{2}i$

   (d) $x^3 - 3x^2 - 8x + 30;$ $r = 3 + i$

   (e) $x^4 - 4x^3 - 16x^2 + 76x - 17;$ $r = 4 - i$

3. Find the set of zeros for the polynomials in problem 2. One zero r is given in each problem.

4. Use Descartes' rule of signs to investigate the nature of the zeros of the following polynomials $P(x)$.

(a) $P(x) = x^4 - 3x^3 + x - 7$

(b) $P(x) = x^4 + 4x^3 + 2x - 9$

(c) $P(x) = x^5 + 5x^4 - 3x^3 - x^2 - 6$

(d) $P(x) = x^5 - 2x^4 - 4x^3 + 3x^2 + x - 8$

(e) $P(x) = 7x^3 - 3x^2 + x - 9$

(f) $P(x) = x^6 - 3x^5 + 4x^4 - 2$

Answers are at end of book.

QUIZ

If you cannot answer the following questions correctly, review the appropriate frames.

1. If $2 + i$ is a zero of $P(x) = x^3 - 3x^2 + x + 5$, find the remaining zeros of $P(x)$.

2. Factor $P(x) = x^3 - 3x^2 + x + 5$ into real linear and quadratic factors.

3. Use Descartes' rule of signs to investigate the nature of the zeros of the polynomial

$$P(x) = x^4 + 3x^3 + 8x^2 - 6x - 7$$

List the possible combinations of zeros.

Answers are at end of book.

15 Rational Zeros of Polynomials With Rational Coefficients

Upon completing this chapter, you should be able to

I. Given a polynomial $P(x)$ whose coefficients are integers,

   (A) find the set of possible rational zeros of $P(x)$,
   (B) determine the set of rational zeros of $P(x)$.

II. Given a polynomial $P(x)$ with rational coefficients,

   (A) find the set of possible rational zeros of $P(x)$,
   (B) determine the set of rational zeros of $P(x)$.

In the preceding chapter we restricted our discussion to polynomials with real coefficients. In this section we restrict our discussion to polynomials with rational coefficients in an effort to locate the rational zeros of this restricted class of polynomials.

---

586. Recall that a rational number r is said to be **reduced to lowest terms** or to be in **reduced form** if $r = $ ___ where b and c are integers with no common factors other than ± 1.

---

586. $\dfrac{b}{c}$

587. We shall need the following result from elementary number theory.

Let b and c be integers with no common factors other than ± 1 and a any integer. If c is a factor of $b \cdot a$, c must be a factor of a, since c is not a factor of b. Moreover, if c is a factor of $b^n \cdot a$, c must be a factor of a, since c is not a factor of b and hence not a factor of b^n.

---

587. Go on to the next frame.

588. Let $P(x) = a_n x^n + a_{n-1} x^{n-1} + \ldots + a_1 x + a_0$ be a polynomial whose coefficients are integers. If a rational number r is a zero of $P(x)$, then **(0)** $P(r) =$ _____

$=$ ___ .

588.
$a_n(r)^n + a_{n-1}(r)^{n-1} + \ldots + a_1(r) + a_0$;
0

589. If r is in reduced form, we can write $r =$ ____ , where

_____ .

---

589. $\dfrac{b}{c}$;

b and c are integers with no common factors other than ± 1

590. Since $r = \dfrac{b}{c}$, we can substitute in equation (0) of frame 588 and get

(1) _____ $= 0$.

590.
$a_n\left(\dfrac{b}{c}\right)^n + a_{n-1}\left(\dfrac{b}{c}\right)^{n-1} + \ldots + a_1\left(\dfrac{b}{c}\right) + a_0$

591. Multiplying both sides of equation (1) by c^n, we obtain

(2) _____ $=$ ___ .

591.
$a_n b^n + a_{n-1} b^{n-1} c + \overset{...}{\ldots} + a_1 b c^{n-1} + a_0 c^n$; 0
0

592. Hence

$a_n b^n = c\ ($ _____ $)$.

592.
$-a_{n-1} b^{n-1} - \ldots - a_0 c^{n-1}$

593. Thus c is a factor of $a_n b^n$. And, since c and b have no common factors, c must be a factor of ____ .

---

593. a_n

594. Thus we have shown that if $P(x) = a_n x^n + \ldots + a_0$ is a polynomial whose coefficients are integers, and $r = \dfrac{b}{c}$ is a rational number in reduced form, then if $r = \dfrac{b}{c}$ is a zero of $P(x)$, c is a factor of ___ .

---

594. a_n

595. We can also write equation

$$(2)\, a_n b^n + a_{n-1} b^{n-1} c + \ldots + a_1 b c^{n-1} + a_0 c^n = 0$$

as $a_0 c^n = b(\underline{\hspace{8cm}})$.

---

595. $-a_n b^{n-1} - \ldots - a_1 c^{n-1}$

596. Thus b is a factor of _____ .

---

596. $a_0 c^n$

597. And since b and c have no common factor, b must be

$\underline{\hspace{8cm}}$.

---

597. a factor of a_0

598. Thus we have shown that if $r = \dfrac{b}{c}$ is a zero of

$P(x) = a_n x^n + \ldots + a_0$, then $\underline{\hspace{6cm}}$.

---

598. b is a factor of a_0

599. We have proved the following result.

THEOREM 1. Let $P(x) = a_n x^n + \ldots + a_0$ be a polynomial whose coefficients are integers. If a rational number r is a zero of

$P(x)$ and $r = \dfrac{b}{c}$ is in reduced form, then

(i) c is $\underline{\hspace{4cm}}$,

(ii) b is $\underline{\hspace{4cm}}$.

---

599. a factor of a_n;
a factor of a_0

SUMMARY

Theorem 1

Let $P(x) = a_n x^n + \ldots + a_0$ be a polynomial whose coefficients are integers. If a rational number r is a zero of $P(x)$ and $r = \dfrac{b}{c}$ is in reduced form, then

      (i) c is a factor of a_n

and

      (ii) b is a factor of a_0.

Proof:

      (i) Since $r = \dfrac{b}{c}$ is a zero of $P(x)$,

$$(1) \quad a_n\left(\frac{b}{c}\right)^n + a_{n-1}\left(\frac{b}{c}\right)^{n-1} + \ldots + a_1\left(\frac{b}{c}\right) + a_0 = 0.$$

Multiplying both sides of equation (1) by c^n, we obtain

$$(2) \quad a_n b^n + a_{n-1} b^{n-1} c + \ldots + a_1 b c^{n-1} + a_0 c^n = 0.$$

Hence

$$a_n b^n = c(-a_{n-1} b^{n-1} - \ldots - a_0 c^{n-1}).$$

Thus c is a factor of $a_n b^n$. And, since c and b have no common factors, c must be a factor of a_n.

      (ii) We can also write equation (2) as

$$a_0 c^n = b(-a_n b^{n-1} - \ldots - a_1 c^{n-1}).$$

Thus b is a factor of $a_0 c^n$. And, since b and c have no common factors, b must be a factor of a_0.

---

600. Theorem 1 does not state that there are any rational zeros. It merely gives us a list of possible choices for rational zeros of a polynomial $P(x) = a_n x^n + \ldots + a_0$ whose coefficients are integers.

For, if $r = \dfrac{b}{c}$ is a zero of $P(x)$, then _____

and _____ .

---

600. c is a factor of a_n;
b is a factor of a_0

EXAMPLE 1

601. Thus if $a_n = 2$, $a_0 = 4$, and $r = \dfrac{b}{c}$ is a zero of $P(x)$, then

c can be $\pm$ ___ or $\pm$ ___ ; and b can be ___ , ___ , or ___ .

---

601. $1, 2$;
$\pm 1, \pm 2, \pm 4$

602. And r must equal one of the following numbers, $\pm$ **(a)** ___ ,

$\pm$ **(b)** ___ , $\pm$ **(c)** ___ , $\pm$ **(d)** ___ , which we derive by forming all

possible fractions $\dfrac{b}{c}$ with $c = \pm 2$ or ± 1, and $b = \pm 4, \pm 2$, or ± 1.

602.
(a) 1, **(b)** 2, **(c)** 4, **(d)** $\frac{1}{2}$

603. That is, the only possible rational zeros of a polynomial $P(x)$

with $a_n = 2$ and $a_0 = 4$ are _____ .

603.
$1, -1, 2, -2, 4, -4, \frac{1}{2}, -\frac{1}{2}$

EXAMPLE 2

604. Use the first and last coefficients of $P(x) = 3x^4 - x^3 + 4x - 2$
to determine the set of possible rational zeros of $P(x)$.

$$\left\{ \rule{8cm}{0pt} \right\}$$

604.
$1, -1, 2, -2, \frac{1}{3}, -\frac{1}{3}, \frac{2}{3}, -\frac{2}{3}$.

If you had difficulty, go on to the
next frame. If not, skip to frame 609.

605. If $P(x) = 3x^4 - x^3 + 4x - 2$ has a rational zero $r = \dfrac{b}{c}$

in reduced form, then c must be a factor of ___ and b must be a

factor of ___ .

---

605. $3; -2$

606. Thus c can be ___ , ___ , ___ , or ___ and b can be ___ , ___ ,

___ , or ___ .

---

606. $1, -1, 3, -3$;
$1, -1, 2, -2$

607. Hence we can form the set of possible rational zeros by

forming all possible quotients $\dfrac{b}{c}$ with $c =$ _____

and $b =$ _____ .

---

607. $1, -1, 3, -3$;
$1, -1, 2, -2$

608. Thus the set of possible rational zeros is

$\{$ _____ $\}$.

608.
$1, -1, 2, -2, \frac{1}{3}, -\frac{1}{3}, \frac{2}{3}, -\frac{2}{3}$

609. It follows immediately from theorem 1 that if the leading coefficient, a_n, is 1, then any rational zero must have _____ for its denominator.

---

609. 1 or -1

610. That is, if the leading coefficient is 1, any rational zero must be _____ .

---

610. an integer

EXAMPLE 3

611. Find the set of possible rational zeros of $P(x) = x^4 - 3x^3 + 7x - 6$ is

$\{$ _____ $\}$

---

611. $1, -1, 2, -2, 3, -3, 6, -6$.

If you had difficulty, go on to the next frame. If not skip to frame 615.

612. If $P(x) = x^4 - 3x^3 + 7x - 6$ has a rational zero $r = \dfrac{b}{c}$ in reduced form, $c = $ _____ and

$b = $ _____ .

---

612. 1 or -1;
$1, -1, 2, -2, 3, -3, 6, -6$

613. Thus r must be an integer, and we can form the set of possible rational zeros by forming all possible quotients $\dfrac{b}{c}$ with $c = $ _____

and $b = $ _____ .

---

613. $1, -1$;
$1, -1, 2, -2, 3, -3, 6, -6$

614. Thus the set of possible rational zeros of $P(x) = x^4 - 3x^2 + 7x - 6$.

$\{$ _____ $\}$.

614.
$1, -1, 2, -2, 3, -3, 6, -6$

240

EXAMPLE 4

615. To actually determine the rational zeros (if any) of the polynomial $P(x) = x^3 - 3x^2 - x + 4$, we first use theorem 1 to find the set of _____ .

---

615. possible rational zeros

616. If $P(x)$ has a rational zero $r = \dfrac{b}{c}$, in reduced form, then c must be a factor of ___ and b must be a factor of ___ .

---

616. $1; 4$

617. That is, any rational zero of $P(x)$ must be an integer and the set of possible rational zeros is

$\{$ _____ $\}$.

---

617. $1, -1, 2, -2, 4, -4$

618. Clearly not all six integers can be zeros of $P(x) =$ $x^3 - 3x^2 - x + 4$, since $P(x)$ has exactly _____ zeros.

---

618. three
(since $P(x)$ is of degree 3)

619. But r will be a zero if and only if $P(r) =$ ___ .

---

619. 0

620. We can either calculate $P(1), P(-1)$, etc. directly or find these values by synthetic division to see which of the six integers (if any) are, in fact, zeros.

By direct calculation we see that $P(1) = $ **(a)** ___ ,

$P(-1) = $ **(b)** ___ , $P(2) = $ **(c)** ___ , $P(-2) = $ **(d)** _____ .

---

620. (a) 1, **(b)** 1, **(c)** -2, **(d)** -14

621. And by synthetic division

$$
\begin{array}{r|rrrr}
4 & 1 & -3 & -1 & 4 \\
  &   & 4 & 4 & 12 \\
\hline
  & 1 & 1 & 3 & 16
\end{array}
\qquad
\begin{array}{r|rrrr}
-4 & 1 & -3 & -1 & 4 \\
   &   & -4 & 28 & -108 \\
\hline
   & 1 & -7 & 27 & -104
\end{array}.
$$

Hence $P(4) =$ ___ and $P(-4) =$ _____ .

---

621. $16; -104$

622. Thus we see that of the possible zeros $\{\,1, -1, 2, -2, 4, -4\,\}$

_____ is/are, in fact, (a) zero(s).

---

622. none

623. Hence $P(x) = x^3 - 3x^2 - x + 4$ has no _____ zeros.

---

623. rational

EXAMPLE 5

624. Determine the rational zeros (if any) of the polynomial

$P(x) = x^4 - 4x^2 + 5x + 10$.

$r = $ _____ .

---

624. -2.

If you had difficulty, go on to the next frame. If not, skip to frame 631.

625. We first use theorem 1, to find the set of _____

_____ .

---

625. possible rational zeros

626. If $r = \dfrac{b}{c}$ is a rational zero of $P(x) = x^4 - 4x^2 + 5x + 10$,

then $c = $ _____ and $b = $ _____ .

---

626. $1, -1$;
$1, -1, 2, -2, 5, -5, 10, -10$

627. And the set of possible rational zeros is

$\{$ _____ $\}$.

---

627. $1, -1, 2, -2, 5, -5, 10, -10$

628. Clearly, not all eight integers can be zeros of

$P(x) = x^4 - 4x^2 + 5x + 10$, since $P(x)$ has _____ zeros.

---

628. four
(since $P(x)$ is of degree 4)

629. r will be a zero of $P(x)$ if and only if _____ .

---

629. $P(r) = 0$

630. Thus we must calculate $P(1), P(-1)$, etc. either directly or by synthetic division. We get

$$P(1) = 12 \qquad P(5) = 560$$
$$P(-1) = 2 \qquad P(-5) = 510$$
$$P(2) = 20 \qquad P(10) = 9660$$
$$P(-2) = 0 \qquad P(-10) = 9560$$

Hence we see that of the possible zeros

$\{1, -1, 2, -2, 5, -5, 10, -10\}$, _____ is/are, in fact, (a) zero(s).

---

630. -2

EXAMPLE 6

631. Determine the rational zeros (if any) of the polynomial

$P(x) = 2x^4 - x^2 + 5$.

$r =$ _____

---

631. There are no rational zeros.

If you had difficulty, see frames 615 to 630.

EXAMPLE 7

632. Theorem 1 applies only to polynomials whose coefficients are integers. However, it may be used to determine the set of possible rational zeros of a polynomial with rational coefficients. We can change a polynomial with rational coefficients into an equivalent one whose coefficients are integers.

If $P(x) = x^3 - \frac{1}{3}x^2 + x - 5$, we can multiply $P(x)$ by ____

and get an equivalent polynomial _____ .

---

632. 3;

$3x^3 - x^2 + 3x - 15$

633. Two polynomials are equivalent if and only if

_____ .

---

633. they have the same set of zeros

634. Since $3x^3 - x^2 + 3x - 15 = 3(x^3 - \frac{1}{3}x^2 + x - 5) = 3P(x)$,

$3x^3 - x^2 + 3x - 15$ (whose coefficients are integers), has

_____ as

$P(x) = x^3 - \frac{1}{3}x^2 + x - 5$.

---

634. the same set of zeros

635. Thus we can find the zeros of $P(x) = x^3 - \frac{1}{3}x^2 + x - 5$ by finding the zeros of _____ .

---

635. $3x^3 - x^2 + 3x - 15$

EXAMPLE 8

636. We can find the zeros of $P(x) = x^3 - \frac{1}{2}x^2 + \frac{1}{5}x - 2$ by finding the zeros of the equivalent polynomial

_____ .

---

636. $10x^3 - 5x^2 + 2x - 20$

637. To show this in general let $P(x) = a_n x^n + \ldots + a_0$ be any polynomial with rational coefficients and zeros $r_1, r_2, \ldots, r_n$. We can write **(1)** $P(x) = a_n(\text{_____}) \ldots (\text{_____})$.

---

637. $x - r_1 ; x - r_n$

638. If we multiply $P(x)$ by the product K of all the denominators of the coefficients, then $KP(x)$ is a polynomial whose coefficients are integers, and $KP(x) = $ _____ .

---

638. $Ka_n(x - r_1) \ldots (x - r_n)$

639. Hence _____ are the zeros of $KP(x)$. That is, $KP(x)$ has the same zeros as _____ .

---

639. $r_1, \ldots, r_n$; $P(x)$

640. Thus we can find the set of possible rational zeros for $P(x)$ by finding that set for _____ .

---

640. $KP(x)$

EXAMPLE 9

641. Determine the rational zeros (if any) of the polynomial $P(x) = x^4 - \frac{1}{6}x^3 - \frac{4}{3}x^2 + \frac{1}{6}x + \frac{1}{3}$.

$r = $ _____

---

641. $1, -1, -\frac{1}{2}, \frac{2}{3}$.

If you had difficulty, go on to the next frame. If not, skip to frame 648.

642. If we multiply $P(x)$ by ___ , we get $6P(x) =$

_____ , an

equivalent polynomial whose coefficients are integers.

---

642. 6;
$6x^4 - x^3 - 8x^2 + x + 2$

643. Since $P(x)$ and $6P(x) = 6x^4 - x^3 - 8x^2 + x + 2$ have the same set of zeros, we find the set of possible zeros of $6P(x)$.

If $6P(x) = 6x^4 - x^3 - 8x^2 + x + 2$ has a rational zero $r = \dfrac{b}{c}$

in reduced form, then $c =$ _____

and $b =$ _____ .

---

643. $1, -1, 2, -2, 3, -3, 6,$ or -6;
$1, -1, 2,$ or -2

644. Thus the set of possible rational zeros of $6P(x)$ is

_____ .

---

644. $\left\{ 1, -1, 2, -2, \frac{1}{2}, -\frac{1}{2}, \right.$

$\left. \frac{1}{3}, -\frac{1}{3}, \frac{2}{3}, -\frac{2}{3}, \frac{1}{6}, -\frac{1}{6} \right\}$

645. Not all 12 possible rational zeros can be zeros since

$6P(x) = 6x^4 - x^3 - 8x^2 + x + 2$ has _____ zeros.
$\underset{\text{(how many?)}}{}$

---

645. four

646. Checking directly or by synthetic division on $6P(1)$, $6P(-1)$,

etc. shows that _____ are in fact the
zeros of $6P(x)$.

---

646. $1, -1, -\frac{1}{2},$ and $\frac{2}{3}$.

If you had difficulty, see
frames 620 to 622.

647. And since $P(x)$ and $6P(x)$ are equivalent,

_____ are the rational zeros of

$P(x) = x^4 - \frac{1}{6}x^3 - \frac{4}{3}x^2 + \frac{1}{6}x + \frac{1}{3}$.

---

647. $1, -1, -\frac{1}{2}$ and $\frac{2}{3}$

648. In checking the set of possible rational zeros for the actual rational zeros, we can often use some of the previous results to reduce the work involved. Suppose, for example, that the set of possible zeros for a polynomial $P(x)$ is $\{1, -1, 2, -2, 3, -3, 5, -5, 10, -10\}$ and if on calculating $P(3)$ by synthetic division, we find that all the numbers in the third row

have the same sign, then 3 is _____

of the set of real zeros of $P(x)$.

---

648. An upper bound.

If you had difficulty, see
frames 424 to 429.

649. If 3 is an upper bound of the real zeros, then there is certainly no need to check _____ and _____ to see if they are zeros.

---

649. 5; 10

650. Similarly, if on checking $P(-1)$ by synthetic division the numbers in the third row _____ , then -1 will be a lower bound of the set of real zeros of $P(x)$.

---

650. alternate in sign.

If you had difficulty, see frames 449 to 454.

651. So there is no need to check _____ to see if they are zeros.

---

651. $-2, -3, -5,$ and -10

652. We can also use Descartes's rule of signs to determine the possible number of positive and negative real zeros. If, for example, $P(x)$ has one variation in sign, then $P(x)$ has _____ real zero.

---

652. one positive

653. Thus if $\{1, -1, 2, -2, 3, -3, 5, -5, 10, -10\}$ is the set of possible zeros, and we have already found that 2 is a rational zero, it is clear that _____ cannot be rational zeros, and we need not check them.

---

653. $3, 5,$ and 10

654. Similarly, if $P(-x)$ has no variations in sign, then we know that $P(x)$ has _____ negative real zeros.

---

654. no

655. And there is no need to check _____ to see if they are rational zeros.

---

655. $-1, -2, -3, -5,$ and -10

EXAMPLE 10
656. Determine the rational zeros (if any) of the polynomial $P(x) = 2x^5 - 4x^4 + 3x^3 + x^2 - 5x + 3$.

$r = $ _____

---

656. 1 and -1.

If you had difficulty, go on to the next frame. If not, skip to frame 675.

657. If $P(x)$ has a rational zero $r = \dfrac{b}{c}$ in reduced form, then

$c =$ _____ and $b =$ _____ .

---

657. $1, -1, 2,$ or -2; $1, -1, 3,$ or -3

658. Thus the set of possible rational zeros of $P(x)$ is

{_____}.

---

658. $1, -1, 3, -3, \frac{1}{2}, -\frac{1}{2}, \frac{3}{2}, -\frac{3}{2}$

659. Before checking all the possible zeros, let us use Descartes' rule of signs to find how many positive and negative real zeros are possible. $P(x) = 2x^5 - 4x^4 + 3x^3 + x^2 - 5x + 3$ has

_____ variation(s) in sign.

---

659. four

660. Thus, $P(x)$ has _____
positive real zeros.

---

660. four, two, or no

661. $P(-x) =$ _____

has _____ variation(s) in sign.

---

661. $-2x^5 - 4x^4 - 3x^3 + x^2 + 5x + 3$; one

662. Thus $P(x)$ will have _____ negative real zero(s).

---

662. one

663. Since there may be four positive real zeros, and since there are only five possible positive rational zeros, that will not help us

much. But, since there is/are only _____ negative real zero(s),

if we find _____ negative zero(s), we need not check any more.

---

663. one; one

664. We shall also be alert as we check $P(1), P(-1)$, etc., by synthetic division, to see if any of the possible zeros is an upper or a

lower bound. Thus, by synthetic division, we see that $P(1) =$ ___ ,
since

$$
\begin{array}{r|rrrrrr}
1 & 2 & -4 & 3 & 1 & -5 & 3 \\
  &   &   &   &   &   &   \\
\hline
  &   &   &   &   &   &
\end{array}
$$
.

---

664. 0;

$$
\begin{array}{rrrrrr}
2 & -2 & 1 & 2 & -3 & \\
2 \quad -2 & 1 & 2 & -3 & 0 &
\end{array}
$$

665. Thus 1 is a _____ of $P(x)$.

---

665. positive zero

666. By synthetic division, $P(3) =$ _____ since

$$3 \,\rfloor\; 2 \quad -4 \quad 3 \quad 1 \quad -5 \quad 3$$

_____ .

---

666. 240;

$$\begin{array}{ccccccc} & 6 & 6 & 27 & 84 & 237 \\ 2 & 2 & 9 & 28 & 79 & 240 \end{array}$$

667. Thus $P(3)$ _____ a zero of $P(x)$.
(is, is not)

---

667. is not

668. But the numbers in the third row of the synthetic division have the same sign, hence 3 is _____

_____ .

---

668. an upper bound of the set of real zeros

669. Checking the remaining two possible positive zeros, $\frac{1}{2}$ and $\frac{3}{2}$, we see that $P(\frac{1}{2}) =$ _____ and $P(\frac{3}{2}) =$ _____ , by synthetic division.

---

669. $\frac{15}{16}$, $\frac{45}{16}$

670. Thus ____ is/are the positive rational zero(s) of $P(x)$.

---

670. 1

671. Now we check the possible negative zeros. $P(-1) =$ _____ .

---

671. 0

672. Thus -1 is a _____ of $P(x)$.

---

672. zero

673. In fact, we found in frame 662 that
$P(x) = 2x^5 - 4x^4 + 3x^3 + x^2 - 5x + 3$ has _____ negative real zero.

---

673. one

674. Hence we need not check any more of the possible negative zeros. Thus the rational zeros of
$P(x) = 2x^5 - 4x^4 + 3x^3 + x^2 - 5x + 3$ are _____ .

---

674. 1 and -1

EXERCISE 1

675. Find the set of possible rational zeros of
$P(x) = x^4 + 2x^3 - 7x^2 - 8x + 12.$

{ _____ }

---

675. $1, -1, 2, -2, 3, -3, 4, -4, 6,$
$-6, 12, -12.$

If you had difficulty, see
frames 600 to 608.

EXERCISE 2

676. Determine the rational zeros (if any) of the polynomial
$P(x) = x^4 + 2x^3 - 7x^2 - 8x + 12$ found in the preceding frame.

$r =$ _____

---

676. $-3, -2, 1,$ and $2.$

If you had difficulty, see frames
615 to 630 and 648 to 674.

EXERCISE 3

677. Find the set of possible rational zeros of
$P(x) = x^3 - \frac{11}{6}x^2 - \frac{1}{2}x + \frac{1}{3}.$

{ _____ }

---

677. $1, -1, 2, -2, \frac{1}{2}, -\frac{1}{2}, \frac{1}{3}, -\frac{1}{3},$

$\frac{2}{3}, -\frac{2}{3}, \frac{1}{6}, -\frac{1}{6}.$

If you had difficulty, see
frames 632 to 640.

EXERCISE 4

678. Determine the rational zeros (if any) of the polynomial
$P(x) = x^3 - \frac{11}{6}x^2 - \frac{1}{2}x + \frac{1}{3}$ found in the preceding frame.

$r =$ _____

---

678. $-\frac{1}{2}, \frac{1}{3},$ and $2.$

If you had difficulty, see
frames 641 to 647.

PROBLEMS

1. Use the first and last coefficients to determine the set of possible rational zeros for each of the following polynomials.

   (a) $P(x) = x^5 + 4x^3 - 3x^2 + 3$

   (b) $P(x) = 2x^4 - 2x^3 - 3x - 4$

   (c) $P(x) = 3x^6 + 2x^3 - 5$

   (d) $P(x) = 4x^3 - 3x^2 + x - 6$

   (e) $P(x) = x^4 - \frac{1}{3}x^3 + x^2 + \frac{1}{2}$

   (f) $P(x) = \frac{1}{10}x^3 + \frac{1}{5}x^2 + \frac{1}{4}x + \frac{3}{20}$

2. Use Descartes' rule of signs to determine the largest possible number of positive and negative rational zeros for the polynomials in problem 1.

3. (i) Find an upper and a lower bound for the set of rational zeros for the polynomials in problem 1.

   (ii) Find the set of rational zeros for the polynomials in problem 1. (It may be the empty set.)

4. Find the set of rational zeros for the following polynomials. (The set of rational zeros may be empty.)

   (a) $P(x) = x^3 + 2x^2 - 5x - 6$

   (b) $P(x) = x^3 - 7x + 6$

   (c) $P(x) = x^3 - 2x^2 - 5x + 6$

   (d) $P(x) = x^3 - 6x^2 + 12x - 8$

   (e) $P(x) = 6x^3 - x^2 - 12x - 5$

   (f) $P(x) = 2x^3 - 5x^2 - 28x + 15$

   (g) $P(x) = 6x^3 + 7x^2 - 16x - 12$

   (h) $P(x) = 10x^3 + 19x^2 - 5x - 6$

   (i) $P(x) = 2x^4 - 11x^3 + 9x^2 + 14x - 8$

   (j) $P(x) = x^4 + x^3 - 7x^2 - x + 6$

5. Find all the zeros for the following polynomials.

   (a) $P(x) = x^3 - 4x^2 + 3x + 2$

   (b) $P(x) = x^3 - 2x^2 + x - 2$

   (c) $P(x) = x^3 - 5x^2 + 5x - 1$

   (d) $P(x) = x^3 - 7x^2 + 17x - 15$

   (e) $P(x) = x^3 - 5x^2 + 7x + 13$

   (f) $P(x) = 2x^3 - x^2 + 2x - 1$

   (g) $P(x) = 3x^3 - 2x^2 + 9x - 6$

(h) $P(x) = 4x^3 - 2x^2 + 1$

(i) $P(x) = 9x^3 - 33x^2 + 16x + 6$

(j) $P(x) = x^4 - 4x^3 + 4x^2 + 4x - 5$

(k) $P(x) = x^4 - 8x^2 + 16$

(l) $P(x) = 2x^4 - 5x^3 - 3x^2 + 4x + 2$

(m) $P(x) = 6x^4 - 11x^3 + 7x^2 - 22x + 24$

(n) $P(x) = x^5 - 5x^4 + 5x^3 + 15x^2 - 36x + 20$

Answers are at end of book.

QUIZ

If you cannot answer the following questions correctly, review the appropriate frames.

1. Given $P(x) = x^4 + 5x^3 - x^2 - 2x - 4$,

    (a) find the set of all possible rational zeros;

    (b) determine the rational zeros (if any) of $P(x)$.

2. Find the set of all possible rational zeros for $P(x) = x^4 + \frac{1}{3}x^3 - 4x^2 + 2x - \frac{1}{2}$.

Answers are at end of book.

16 Graphs of Polynomial Functions

Upon completing this chapter, you should be able to

I. Given a polynomial function $f(x)$ with rational zeros, find the x-intercepts and graph $f(x)$ by plotting a few additional points and connecting them by a smooth curve.

II. Given a polynomial function $f(x)$ with non-rational zeros, find the intervals that contain the non-rational zeros, and graph the polynomial function by plotting a few points and connecting them by a smooth curve.

---

679. If the rule of a function $f : R \rightarrow R$ is given by a polynomial, with real coefficients, $f(x) = a_n x^n + \cdots + a_0$, f is called a **polynomial function**. Which of the following are polynomial functions $f : R \rightarrow R$?

(a) $f(x) = 5x + 6$

(b) $f(x) = 7x^2 - \sqrt{3}\, x + 9$

(c) $f(x) = 4x^2 + ix - 2$

(d) $f(x) = 3x^{-3} + 6x^{-2} - 4x^{-1} + 2$

(e) $f(x) = 4x^7 - \frac{1}{2}x^5 + \sqrt{3}\, x^2 - 9$

---

679. (a), (b), and (e).
NOTE: $4x^2 + ix - 2$ is not a function from R to R, since the coefficient for x is not real.

680. As in the case of linear and quadratic functions, the zeros of the polynomial $P(x) = a_n x^n + \cdots + a_0$ are the _____ of the graph of $f(x) = a_n x^n + \cdots + a_0$.

---

680. x-intercepts

681. Thus if $f(x) = (x - 1)(x + 2)(x + 3)$, the x-intercepts

are _____ .

---

681. $1, -2,$ and -3

EXAMPLE 1

682. If we can find the zeros of the polynomial, then we can graph the function $f(x) = a_n x^n + \cdots + a_0$ by plotting the x-intercepts and a few other points and connecting them by a smooth curve.

For example, to graph the polynomial function $f(x) = x^3 - x^2 - 4x + 4$, we first find the zeros of $f(x)$. Factoring we get $f(x) = x^3 - x^2 - 4x + 4 = (x + 2)(x - 1)(x - 2)$.

Thus the zeros are _____ .

---

682. $-2, 1,$ and 2

683. Hence the x-intercepts are _____ .

That is, the points $(-2, \_\_)$, $(1, \_\_)$, and $(2, \_\_)$ are on the graph.

---

683. $-2, 1,$ and 2; $0; 0; 0$

684. If we plot the additional points whose x-coordinates are -3, $-1, 0, \frac{3}{2}$, and 3 and connect them by a smooth curve, we shall have a fairly accurate graph.

By direct computation, $f(-1) = \_\_$ and $f(0) = \_\_$.

---

684. 6; 4

685. And, by synthetic division,

$$
\begin{array}{r|rrrr}
-3 & 1 & -1 & -4 & 4 \\
   &   & -3 & 12 & -24 \\
\hline
   & 1 & -4 & 8 & -20 \\
\end{array}
$$

$$
\begin{array}{r|rrrr}
\frac{3}{2} & 1 & -1 & -4 & 4 \\
            &   & \frac{3}{2} & \frac{3}{4} & -\frac{39}{8} \\
\hline
            & 1 & \frac{1}{2} & -\frac{13}{4} & -\frac{7}{8} \\
\end{array}
$$

$$
\begin{array}{r|rrrr}
3 & 1 & -1 & -4 & 4 \\
  &   & 3 & 6 & 6 \\
\hline
  & 1 & 2 & 2 & 10 \\
\end{array}
$$

Hence **(a)** $f(-3) =$ _____ , **(b)** $f(\frac{3}{2}) =$ _____ , and

(c) $f(3) =$ _____ .

685. (a) -20

(b) $-\dfrac{7}{8}$

(c) 10

686. Thus we want to plot the points $(-3,$ _____ $)$,

$(-2,$ ____ $), (-1,$ ____ $), (0,$ ____ $), (1,$ ____ $), (\frac{3}{2},$ ____ $)$,

$(2,$ ____ $),$ and $(3,$ ____ $).$

686. $20; 0; 6; 4;$
$0; -\frac{7}{8}; 0; 10$

687. Plot the points in frame 686 and connect them by a smooth curve.

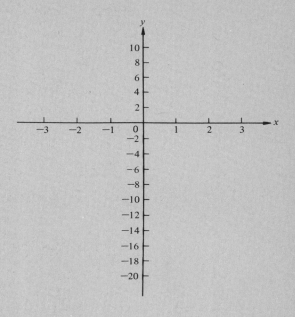

NOTE: We have used different scales for the *x*- and *y*-axes.

687.

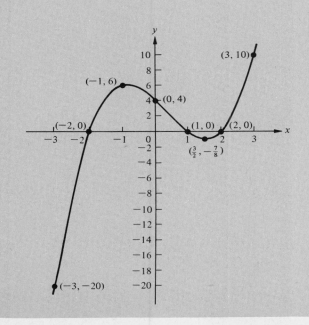

255

EXAMPLE 2

688. Graph the polynomial function $f(x) = (1 - x)(x^2 + 4x + 3)$.

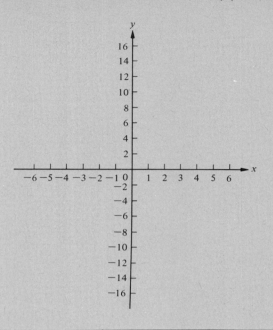

688.

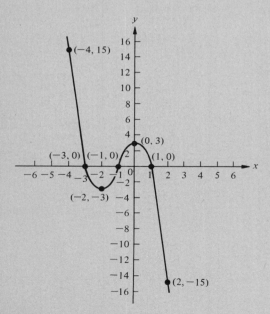

If you had difficulty, go on to the
next frame. If not, skip to frame 694.

689. We can find the x-intercepts of $f(x)$ by finding

_____ .

---

689. the zeros of $f(x)$

690. Since we can factor $x^2 + 4x + 3$ into

(_____), (_____), we get

$f(x) = $ _____ .

---

690. $(x + 1)(x + 3)$;
$(1 - x)(x + 1)(x + 3)$

691. Thus the x-intercepts are _____ .

---

691. $1, -1,$ and -3

692. We can get a fairly accurate graph by plotting the additional points whose x-coordinates are $-4, -2, 0,$ and 2. Note we have chosen an x-value on each side of each x-intercept.

(a) $f(-4) = $ ____   (b) $f(-2) = $ ____

(c) $f(0) \ = $ ____   (d) $f(2) \ = $ ____

---

692. (a) 15, (b) -3,
     (c) 3,   (d) -15

693. Thus plotting these points and connecting them by a smooth curve, we get the following graph.

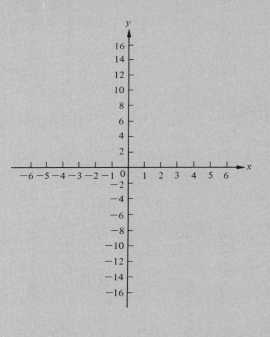

693.

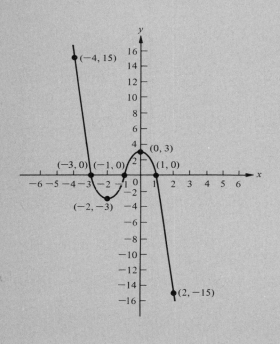

EXAMPLE 3

694. We have seen, however, in the previous chapters that it is, in general, very difficult to find all the zeros of a polynomial. In fact, many polynomials have no rational zeros. In this case we still can get a fairly good approximation to the graph of

$f(x) = a_n x^n + \ldots + a_0$, by plotting a few points and connecting them by a smooth curve.

For example, to graph $f(x) = x^4 - 4x^2 - x + 2$, we plot the points whose x-coordinates are $-3, -2, -1\frac{1}{2}, -1, 0, 1, 2,$ and 3.

$f(-3) = 50, f(-2) = 4, f(-1\frac{1}{2}) = -\frac{1}{2}$,

(a) $f(-1) = $ ___ , **(b)** $f(0) = $ ___ , **(c)** $f(1) = $ _____ , **(d)** $f(2) = $ ___ , and $f(3) = 44$.

---

694. (a) 0, **(b)** 2, **(c)** -2, **(d)** 0

695. Thus of the numbers $-3, -2, -1\frac{1}{2}, -1, 0, 1, 2,$ and 3 only

_____ is an/are x-intercept(s).

---

695. -1 and 2

696. Plotting the points $(-3, 50), (-2, 4), (-1\frac{1}{2}, -\frac{1}{2}) (-1, 0),$ $(0, 2), (1, -2), (2, 0), (3, 44)$ and connecting them by a smooth curve, we get the following graph.

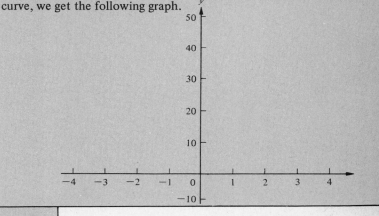

696.

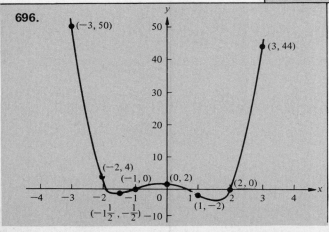

697. We found two zeros, **(a)** $x = $ _____ . And we see from the graph that $f(x)$ has a third zero between **(b)** _____ and $-1\frac{1}{2}$, and a fourth zero between **(c)** ___ and **(d)** ___ .

---

697. (a) -1 and 2,
(b) -2,
(c) 0, **(d)** 1

698. We conclude this from the fact that $f(-2)$ is positive and $f(-1\frac{1}{2})$ is _____ .

---

698. negative

699. Thus, by our assumption that the graph is a smooth unbroken curve, the function must be zero somewhere between _____ and _____ .

---

699. -2; $-1\frac{1}{2}$

700. Similarly, **(a)** $f(0)$ is _____ and **(b)** $f(1)$ is _____ . Thus the function must equal zero somewhere between **(c)** ___ and **(d)** ___ .

---

700. (a) positive,
(b) negative
(c) 0, **(d)** 1

701. It is true, in general, that if a and b are real numbers, and $f(a)$ and $f(b)$ have opposite signs, then $f(x)$ has a _____ between a and b.

---

701. zero (or x-intercept)

702. We state the following result without proof.

THEOREM 1. Let $P(x)$ be a polynomial with real coefficients. If a and b are real numbers such that $P(a)$ and $P(b)$ have opposite signs, then $P(x)$ has a _____ between a and b.

---

702. zero

703. That is, there is a number r between a and b such that $P(r) = $ ___ .

---

703. 0

704. Theorem 1 states that there is at least one zero between a and b. There may be more than one zero between a and b as shown by figure 1.

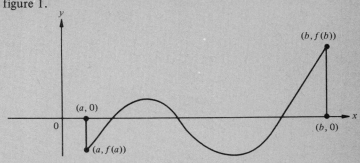

In figure 1, (a) $f(a)$ is _____ , (b) $f(b)$ is _____ ,

and there are (c) _____ zeros between a and b.
(how many?)

---

704. (a) negative,
(b) positive,
(c) three

705. Theorem 1 does not refer to the situation where $f(a)$ and $f(b)$ have the same sign. In figure 2, $f(a)$ and $f(b)$ are both

_____ and $f(x)$ has _____ zeros between a and b.
(how many?)

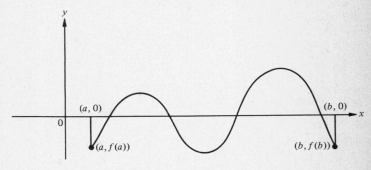

---

705. negative; four

706. On the other hand, in figure 3, $f(a)$ and $f(b)$ are both

_____ and $f(x)$ has _____ zeros between a and b.
(how many?)

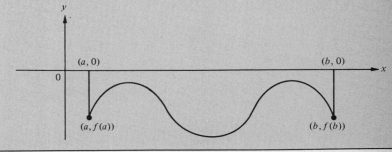

---

706. negative; no

707. Thus if $f(a)$ and $f(b)$ have the same sign, $f(x)$ may or may not have a _____ between a and b.

---

707. zero

708. On the other hand, if $f(a)$ and $f(b)$ have opposite signs, $f(x)$ _____ between a and b.

---

708. has at least one zero

EXAMPLE 4

709. Now let us find the intervals that contain the zeros of $P(x) = 2x^3 + 5x^2 - 2x - 2$. Since $P(x)$ is of degree ___ , it has at most _____ real zeros.

---

709. 3;
three

710. By synthetic division and the remainder theorem we have that $P(-3) = -5, P(-2) = 6, P(-1) = 3, P(0) = -2,$ and $P(1) = 3$. Thus the three zeros must occur in the intervals

(a) ___ $< x <$ (b) ___ , (c) ___ $< x <$ (d) ___ , and

(e) ___ $< x <$ (f) ___ .

---

710. (a) -3, (b) -2, (c) -1, (d) 0, (e) 0, (f) 1

EXAMPLE 5

711. The intervals that contain the zeros of

$P(x) = 2x^3 - 15x^2 + 22x + 21$ are _____

_____ .

---

711. $(-1, 0), (3, 4),$ and $(4, 5)$.

If you had difficulty, go on to the next frame. If not, skip to frame 713.

712. By synthetic division $P(-1) = -18, P(0) = 21, P(1) = 30,$ $P(2) = 21, P(3) = 6, P(4) = -3$ and $P(5) = 6$. Thus the three zeros are in the intervals (a) (_____ , _____) ,

(b) (___ , ___), (c) (___ , ___).

---

712. (a) $(-1, 0)$,
(b) $(3, 4)$,
(c) $(4, 5)$

EXAMPLE 6

713. The intervals that contain the zeros of

$P(x) = 2x^3 - 7x^2 - 4x + 14$ are _____ .

---

713. $(-2, -1), (1, 2),$ and $(3, 4)$.

If you had difficulty, see frames 697 to 712.

EXAMPLE 7

714. Graph the function $f(x) = (x + 3)(x + 1)(x - 1)(x - 3)$.

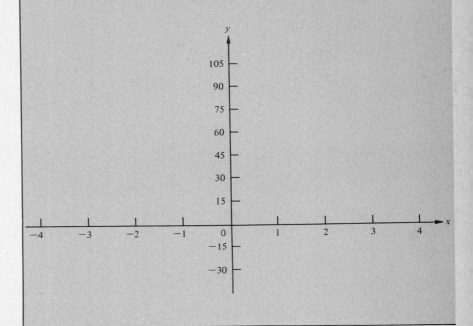

714.

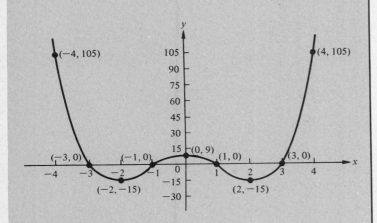

If you had difficulty, see frames 682 to 693.

EXERCISE 1

715. Find the intervals that contain the zeros of
$P(x) = 3x^3 - 5x^2 - 15x + 25$.

---

715. $(-3, -2), (1, 2),$ and $(2, 3)$.

If you had difficulty, see
frames 694 to 712.

EXERCISE 2

716. Graph the function $f(x) = 3x^3 - 5x^2 - 15x + 25$ found
in the preceding frame.

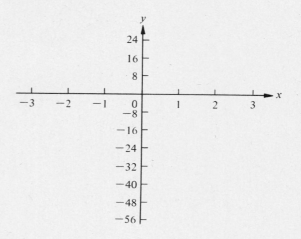

716.

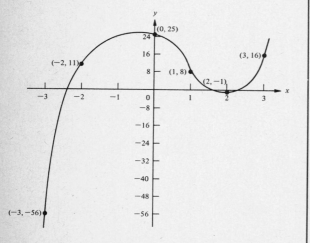

If you had difficulty, see
frames 694 to 712.

In Part II we have discussed the zeros of polynomials $P(x) = a_n x^n + \cdots + a_0$.
We have shown how to solve any polynomial of degree one or two, but we have not
shown how to find the zeros of a general polynomial of degree $\geqslant 3$.

We have restricted our discussion to polynomials with real coefficients, and even with
these polynomials we can be sure of finding only the rational zeros. Unfortunately, most
polynomials that arise in practical situations have irrational and complex zeros.

There are a number of methods available for approximating the irrational zeros of a
polynomial. However, these methods are often complicated, tedious, and, in this era
of high-speed computers, unnecessary, since it is possible to program computers to find
the zeros of polynomials.

For most purposes, it will be sufficient to find the rational zeros and the intervals that
contain any irrational zeros as we have done in this chapter.

PROBLEMS

1. Find the intervals that contain the zeros of the following polynomial functions.

   (a) $f(x) = x^3 - 9x^2 + 25x$

   (b) $f(x) = 3x^3 + 10x^2 - 2x - 4$

   (c) $f(x) = x^3 + 4x^2 + x - 5$

   (d) $f(x) = 2x^3 + 9x^2 - 2$

   (e) $f(x) = 2x^3 - 11x^2 + 10x + 3$

   (f) $f(x) = x^4 + 6x^3 + 9x^2 - 2$

   (g) $f(x) = x^4 - 4x^3 - 2x^2 + 12x + 8$

   (h) $f(x) = x^4 - 4x^3 - 4x^2 + 16x + 1$

   (i) $f(x) = x^4 + 8x^3 + 17x^2 + 4x - 2$

   (j) $f(x) = 3x^4 - 12x^3 - 9x^2 + 16x + 4$

2. Graph the polynomial functions in problem 1.

Answers are at end of book.

QUIZ

If you cannot answer the following questions correctly, review the appropriate frames.

1. Graph the function $f(x) = -(x + 2)(x - 1)(x - 3)$.

2. Find the intervals that contain the zeros of $f(x) = x^3 - 4x^2 - x + 5$ and graph the
function.

Answers at at end of book.

17 Rational Functions

Upon completing the chapter, you should be able to find the intercepts and asymptotes, check for symmetry, and graph rational functions $\dfrac{P(x)}{D(x)}$.

---

717. In Chapter 10, we saw that the sum, difference, and product of two polynomials _____ a polynomial.
(is, is not)

---

717. is

718. It was pointed out that, in general, the function obtained by dividing one polynomial $P(x)$ by another $D(x)$ _____ a polynomial.
(is, is not)

---

718. is not

719. We now return to a discussion of functions of the form $\dfrac{P(x)}{D(x)}$.

---

719. Go on to the next frame.

720. In the chapter on functions in Volume II we saw that if $f : A \rightarrow R$ and $g : A \rightarrow R$ are functions, then $\dfrac{f}{g} : A \rightarrow R$ is a function defined by $\dfrac{f}{g}(x) =$ _____ for all $x \in A$ for which

_____ .

---

720. $\dfrac{f(x)}{g(x)}$; $g(x) \neq 0$

721. In particular, if $P(x)$ and $D(x)$ are polynomial functions, then the function $\dfrac{P}{D}$ defined by $\dfrac{P}{D}(x) =$ _____ , for all $x \in R$ for which _____ is called a **rational function**.

---

721. $\dfrac{P(x)}{D(x)} ; D(x) \neq 0$

722. Which of the following expressions are **rational functions**?

(a) $\dfrac{3x^2 + 2x - 5}{2x + 6}$

(c) $\dfrac{2x + 3}{\sqrt{x^2 + 3x - 9}}$

(b) $\dfrac{3 \sin x}{5x - 9}$

(d) $\dfrac{x - 1}{x^4 - 3x - 5}$

---

722. (a) and (d)

723. We saw in Chapter 11 that polynomials of degree 2 are of the form _____ .

---

723. $ax^2 + bx + c$

724. Polynomials of degree 1 are of the form _____ .

---

724. $ax + b$

725. And polynomials of degree 0 are of the form ___ .

---

725. a

726. Thus any real or complex number may be thought of as a polynomial of degree ___ .

---

726. 0

727. Therefore, $D(x) = 1$ is a _____ .

---

727. polynomial of degree 0

728. Hence, if $P(x)$ is any polynomial, then $P(x) = \dfrac{P(x)}{1} = \dfrac{P(x)}{D(x)}$ may be thought of as a _____ function.

---

728. rational

729. The domain of $\dfrac{P(x)}{D(x)}$ does not contain those values of x for which _____ .

---

729. $D(x) = 0$ (since we cannot divide by 0)

	730. That is, the zeros of the polynomial $D(x)$ are not in the _____ of the rational function $\dfrac{P(x)}{D(x)}$.
730. domain	**731.** However, we have seen that a polynomial $D(x)$ of degree n has only ___ zeros.
731. n	**732.** Hence the rational function $\dfrac{P(x)}{D(x)}$ will be undefined for at most _____ numbers. (how many?)
732. n	**EXAMPLE 1** **733.** If $P(x) = x^4 - 3x^2 - 9$ and $D(x) = x^2 - 1$, then the rational function $\dfrac{P(x)}{D(x)}$ will be undefined for _____ numbers, $x =$ _____ .
733. two; 1 and -1	**EXAMPLE 2** **734.** If $P(x) = x^9 - 7x^4 + 12$ and $D(x) = x^2 - x - 6$, then the rational function $\dfrac{P(x)}{D(x)}$ will be undefined at $x =$ _____ .
734. 3 and -2	**735.** On the other hand, the rational function $\dfrac{P(x)}{D(x)}$ will equal 0 when _____ .
735. $P(x) = 0$	**EXAMPLE 3** **736.** Thus, if $P(x) = x - 9$ and $D(x) = x^3 - 3x^2 + 5$, then the rational function $\dfrac{P(x)}{D(x)} = 0$ at $x =$ ___ .
736. 9	**EXAMPLE 4** **737.** If $P(x) = x^2 + 3x - 4$ and $D(x) = x^5 + 1$, then $\dfrac{P(x)}{D(x)} = 0$ at $x =$ _____ .
737. 1 and -4	

738. We can use the concepts of the chapter on intercepts, symmetry, and asymptotes in Volume I to sketch the graphs of rational functions. The rational function $\dfrac{P(x)}{D(x)}$ will have as its x-intercepts the zeros of _____ , provided _____ does not also have a zero there.

---

738. $P(x)$; $D(x)$

739. And $\dfrac{P(x)}{D(x)}$ will have vertical asymptotes at the zeros of _____ , provided _____ does not also have a zero there.

---

739. $D(x)$; $P(x)$

EXAMPLE 5

740. To graph the rational function $y = \dfrac{x+2}{x^2-1}$, we **(i)** find the x- and y-intercepts, **(ii)** find the vertical and horizontal asymptotes, **(iii)** check for symmetry, **(iv)** sketch the graph by plotting a few additional points and connecting them by a smooth curve.

The x-intercepts occur when _____ .

---

740. $P(x) = x + 2 = 0$

741. Thus the only x-intercept is $x =$ _____ .

---

741. -2

742. We obtain the y-intercept by setting $x = 0$; we obtain

$y =$ _____ .

---

742. -2

743. The vertical asymptotes occur at the zeros of _____

_____ .

---

743. $D(x)$, the denominator

744. $D(x) = x^2 - 1 = $ **(a)** (_____) (_____) has two zeros

(b) $x =$ ___ and **(c)** $x =$ ___ .

---

744. **(a)** $x - 1$, $x + 1$,
(b) 1, **(c)** -1

745. Thus $y = \dfrac{x+2}{x^2-1}$ has vertical asymptotes at $x =$ _____ .

---

745. 1 and -1

746. A horizontal asymptote is the value that y approaches as x grows larger and larger. **(a)** If $x = 10$, $y =$ _____ , **(b)** if $x = 100$, $y =$ _____ , and **(c)** if $x = 1000$, $y =$ _____ .

---

746. **(a)** $\dfrac{12}{99} \approx \dfrac{1}{10}$,

(b) $\dfrac{102}{9999} \approx \dfrac{1}{100}$,

(c) $\dfrac{1002}{999,999} \approx \dfrac{1}{1000}$

747. Thus as x grows large in a positive direction, y approaches ___ .

---

747. 0

748. Similarly, **(a)** if $x = -10$, $y =$ _____ , **(b)** if $x = -100$, $y =$ _____ , and **(c)** if $x = -1000$, $y =$ _____ .

---

748. **(a)** $\dfrac{-8}{99} \approx -\dfrac{1}{10}$,

(b) $\dfrac{-98}{9999} \approx -\dfrac{1}{100}$,

(c) $\dfrac{-998}{999,999} \approx -\dfrac{1}{1000}$

749. Thus as x grows large in a negative direction, y approaches ___ .

---

749. 0

750. Hence the horizontal asymptote is $y =$ ___ .

---

750. 0

751. That is, the x-axis is the _____ .

---

751. horizontal asymptote

752. Recall that a curve is symmetric with respect to the x-axis if whenever a point (a, b) is on the curve, the point (___ , ___) is also on the curve.

---

752. $a, -b$

If you had difficulty, see frames 502 to 508 in Chapter 15 on intercepts, symmetry and asymptotes, in Volume I.

753. That is, two values are associated with a. They are ___ and

___ .

---

753. b; $-b$

754. Thus a *function f* can never be symmetric with respect to the x-axis, since for each element a in the domain of f there is assoicated

_____ element b in the range.

---

754. One and only one.

If you had difficulty, see
Volume II on sets and functions.

755. A curve is symmetric with respect to the y-axis if whenever

a point (a, b) is on the curve, the point (___ , ___) is also on
the curve.

---

755. $-a, b$

756. And to test for symmetry with respect to the y-axis, we have
the following rule: A curve is symmetric with respect to the y-axis

if its equation is unchanged when _____ .

---

756. x is replaced by $-x$.

If you had difficulty, see frames
519 to 521 of Chapter 15 on intercepts,
symmetry and asymptotes, in Volume I.

757. Thus replacing x by $-x$ in $y = \dfrac{x + 2}{x^2 - 1}$ we get

$y =$ _____ , which _____ the same as $y = \dfrac{x + 2}{x^2 - 1}$,
(is, is not)

---

757. $\dfrac{-x + 2}{x^2 - 1}$; is not

758. Hence $y = \dfrac{x + 2}{x^2 - 1}$ is not symmetric with respect to the ___

_____ .

---

758. y-axis

759. Finally, a curve is symmetric with respect to the origin if

whenever a point (a, b) is on the curve, the point (___ , ___)
is also on the curve.

---

759. $-a, -b$

760. And a curve is symmetric with respect to the origin if the

equation is unchanged when _____

_____ .

---

760. x is replaced by $-x$ and y is
replaced by $-y$.

If you had difficulty, see frames 528
to 531 of Chapter 15 on intercepts,
symmetry and asymptotes, in Volume I.

761. Thus replacing x by $-x$ and y by $-y$ in $y = \dfrac{x+2}{x^2-1}$ we get

_____ , which _____ the same
(is, is not)

as $y = \dfrac{x+2}{x^2-1}$.

---

761. $-y = \dfrac{-x+2}{x^2-1}$ or $y = \dfrac{x-2}{x^2-1}$;

is not

762. Hence $y = \dfrac{x+2}{x^2-1}$ is not symmetric with respect to

_____ .

---

762. the origin

763. In summary then $y = \dfrac{x+2}{x^2-1}$ has x-intercept, **(a)** $x = $ _____ ,

y-intercept, **(b)** $y = $ _____ , vertical asymptotes at **(c)** $x = $ _____ ,

and a horizontal asymptote at **(d)** $y = $ ____ . It is not symmetric with
with respect to the x-axis, the y-axis, or the origin.

---

763. **(a)** -2, **(b)** -2 **(c)** 1 and -1,
(d) 0.

If you had difficulty, see
frames 740 to 762.

764. To sketch the graph we first draw the asymptotes and the
x- and y-intercepts; we get the following.

764.

765. Now plot the additional

points $(-3, -\frac{1}{8})$, $(-\frac{3}{2}, \frac{2}{5})$, $(-\frac{1}{2}, -2)$,

$(\frac{1}{2}, -\frac{10}{3})$, and $(2, \frac{4}{3})$ and connect them by a smooth curve.

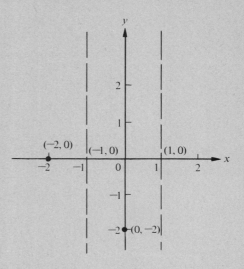

NOTE: We took a point on each side of each intercept and each vertical asymptote.

765.

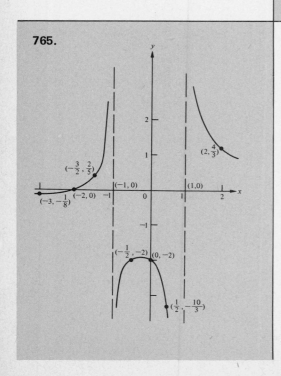

EXAMPLE 6

766. Given the rational function $y = \dfrac{5}{3x - 4}$, **(a)** find the intercepts, **(b)** find the asymptotes, **(c)** check for symmetry, and **(d)** sketch the graph.

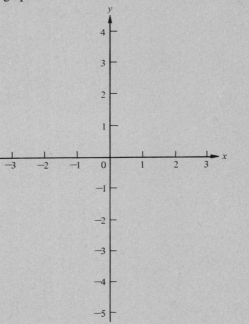

766.

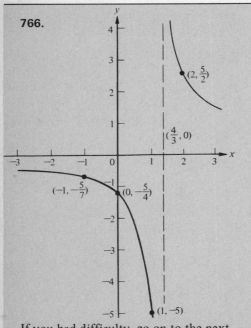

If you had difficulty, go on to the next frame. If not, skip to frame 780.

	767. $P(x) = 5$ has _____ zero(s), hence there is/are _____ x-intercept(s).
767. no; no	**768.** Setting $x = 0$, we get $y =$ _____ . Hence the y-intercept is _____ .
768. $\frac{5}{-4} = \frac{-5}{4}$; $-\frac{5}{4}$	**769.** The denominator $D(x) = 3x - 4$ has one zero , $x =$ _____ .
769. $\frac{4}{3}$	**770.** Thus $y = \dfrac{5}{3x - 4}$ has a _____ at $x = \frac{4}{3}$.
770. vertical asymptote	**771.** As x grows large (in either the positive or negative direction), the function $y = \dfrac{5}{3x - 4}$ appoaches _____ .
771. 0	**772.** Thus $y = 0$ is a _____ .
772. horizontal asymptote	**773.** Since $y = \dfrac{5}{3x - 4}$ is a function, the graph is not symmetric with respect to the _____ .
773. x-axis	**774.** Replacing x by $-x$ in $y = \dfrac{5}{3x - 4}$ gives _____ , which _____ the same as $y = \dfrac{5}{3x - 4}$. (is, is not)
774. $y = \dfrac{5}{-3x - 4}$; is not	**775.** Hence $y = \dfrac{5}{3x - 4}$ is not symmetric with respect to the _____ .
775. y-axis	

776. Finally, replacing x by $-x$ and y by $-y$ gives

_____ , which _____ the same as
(is, is not)

$$y = \frac{5}{3x - 4} \text{ .}$$

---

776. $-y = \dfrac{5}{-3x - 4}$ or $y = \dfrac{5}{3x + 4}$;

is not

777. Thus $y = \dfrac{5}{3x - 4}$ is not symmetric with respect to the

_____ .

---

777. origin

778. To sketch the graph, first draw the asymptotes and the y-intercept.

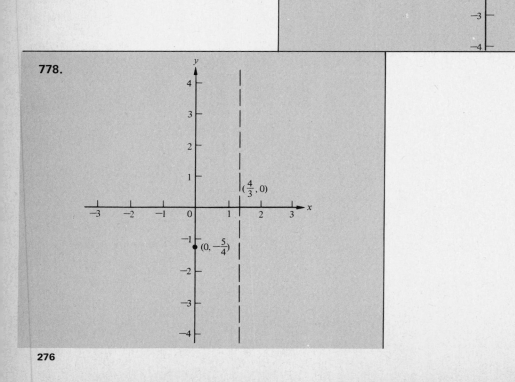

778.

779. In addition to the above information, plot the points $(-1, -\frac{5}{7})$, $(1, -5)$ and $(2, \frac{5}{2})$ and connect them by a smooth curve.

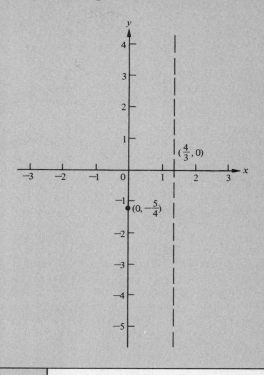

779.

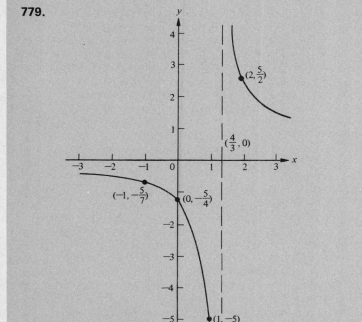

EXAMPLE 7

780. Given the rational function $y = \dfrac{2x}{x^2 - x - 2}$, **(a)** find the intercepts, **(b)** find the asymptotes, **(c)** check for symmetry, and **(d)** sketch the graph.

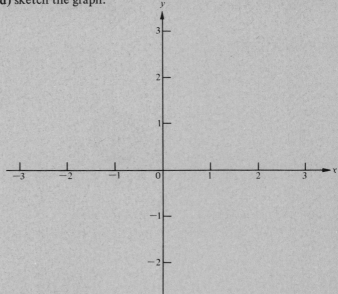

780.

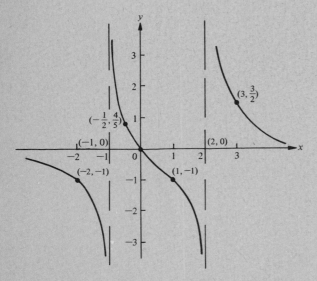

If you had difficulty,
see frames 740 to 779.

PROBLEMS

Find the intercepts and asymptotes, check for symmetry, with respect to the x-axis, the y-axis, and the origin, and graph the following rational functions.

1. $y = \dfrac{1}{x}$

2. $y = \dfrac{5}{x-2}$

3. $y = \dfrac{4}{3x}$

4. $y = \dfrac{4}{x+1}$

5. $y = \dfrac{3}{2x-5}$

6. $y = \dfrac{2x}{x-1}$

7. $y = \dfrac{x-2}{x}$

8. $y = \dfrac{x+1}{3x}$

9. $y = \dfrac{x-3}{x+4}$

10. $y = \dfrac{x+2}{3x-6}$

11. $y = \dfrac{5}{x^2-1}$

12. $y = \dfrac{2}{x^2+1}$

13. $y = \dfrac{3x}{x^2-4}$

14. $y = \dfrac{-4x}{x^2+4}$

15. $y = \dfrac{6x}{x^2+x-2}$

16. $y = \dfrac{2x}{x^2+x-6}$

17. $y = \dfrac{x^2-1}{x^2-x-6}$

18. $y = \dfrac{x^2-4}{x^2-3x-4}$

19. $y = \dfrac{x^2-1}{x^2+1}$

20. $y = \dfrac{x^2+1}{x^2-1}$

21. $y = \dfrac{x^3}{x-2}$

22. $y = \dfrac{x^3}{2x+4}$

Answers are at end of book.

If you cannot answer the following questions correctly, review the appropriate frames.

1. A rational function $R(x) = \dfrac{P(x)}{D(x)}$ will be zero when _____ = 0 and undefined

   when _____ .

2. Find the intercepts and asymptotes, check for symmetry, and sketch the graph of

   $$y = \frac{x-1}{x^2 - x - 2} .$$

Answers are at end of book.

Answers

Page 13

QUIZ

1. (a) a^{n+m}

   (b) $a^{m \cdot n}$

   (c) $a^n b^n$

   (d) $\dfrac{a^n}{b^n}$

   (e) a^{n-m}

2. $\dfrac{xz^5}{y^9}$

Page 26

QUIZ

1. (a) two

   (b) one

   (c) no (or 0)

2. (a) 27

   (b) $-\dfrac{1}{4}$

3. $19 + 6\sqrt{10}$

Page 42

QUIZ

1.

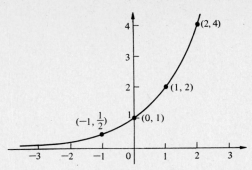

2. $y = a^x$ is a function; $y = a^x$ is positive for all x; $y = a^x$ increases as x increases; $a^x < 1$ if $x < 0$; $a^x = 1$ if $x = 0$; $a^x > 1$ if $x > 0$

3. ≈ 2.8

Page 55

QUIZ

1. (a) $\log_a a^x = x$ (b) $a^{\log_a x} = x$ (c) $y = a^x$; $\log_a y = x$
2. 3   3. $N = 125$ 4. $x = 37$ 5. $5^6 = 10^{6 \log_{10} 5}$

Page 74

PROBLEMS

1. (a) .6020   (d) .9542   (g) −.3680   (j) −.8451
   (b) .7781   (e) 1.000   (h) .2498   (k) 2.2831
   (c) .9030   (f) 0   (i) 1.505   (l) 1

2. (a) $\log_a \dfrac{xz^2}{y}$ (c) $\log_a \dfrac{x-3}{x+4}$

   (b) $\log_a \dfrac{y^2}{\sqrt{xz}}$ (d) $2(\log_a x - 1)$

3. (a) .8451   (d) $\dfrac{1.505}{.8451}$ (g) 0

   (b) $\dfrac{1}{.4771}$ (e) $-\dfrac{.8451}{.6990}$ (h) $\dfrac{1}{.4771}$

   (c) $\dfrac{.4771}{.3010}$ (f) $\dfrac{.2498}{.7781}$

1.

2. the set of positive real numbers R, the set of all real numbers
3. (a) not defined; (b) <0; (c) $=0$; (d) >0
4. (a) 1; (b) $\log_a M + \log_a N$; (c) $\log_a M - \log_a N$; (d) $P \cdot \log_a M$
5. (a) .1761; (b) 1.585

Page 90

PROBLEMS

1. (a) 3.75×10^1 (c) 5.92×10^{-1} (e) 8.13×10^3 (g) 1.38×10^2
   (b) 4.85×10^2 (d) 7.19×10^0 (f) 2.69×10^{-3} (h) 8.37×10^1
2. (a) 3.5490   (c) 1.5490   (e) $.5490 - 1$ (g) $.5490 - 3$
   (b) 2.5490   (d) 0.5490   (f) $.5490 - 2$ (h) $.5490 - 4$
3. (a) 2.3747   (c) 0.8627   (e) $.7889 - 2$ (g) .1720
   (b) 1.7657   (d) $.9248 - 1$ (f) $.6866 - 2$ (h) 2.5934
4. (a) 2.98   (c) 77,600   (e) .0278
   (b) 494   (d) .000527   (f) .00857
5. (a) 1.2041   (c) .1737   (e) -1.5327
   (b) 1.5977   (d) 7.8561   (f) -1.7924

QUIZ

1. 4.71×10^4 2. .6405   3. $.8785 - 2$
4. $.7292 + 2$ 5. 536   6. 6.9258

PROBLEMS

1. (a) 3.5979   (c) 1.8713   (e) .6034 − 1   (g) .8098 − 3
    (b) 2.7389   (d) 0.9599   (f) .7553 − 2   (h) 4.4415
2. (a) 1.923   (c) 4,575   (e) .003483
    (b) 34.68   (d) .0006457   (f) .9554

QUIZ

1. 3.6769   2. 3,985

PROBLEMS

1. 29.82   2. .2936   3. 1.336×10^{13} 4. 31,250   5. 6.496×10^{15}
6. 6.166×10^{13} 7. 20.42   8. 9.676   9. 4.15   10. .2123

QUIZ

1. (a) 1.888   (b) .04689

PROBLEMS

1. 1.404   2. 0.365   3. 1.138   4. .138   5. 3.875   6. 5.12
7. 3.082   8. 1.435   9. 238.3   10. 744,000   11. −7.757   12. 1.677
13. .9116   14. 4.321   15. $-\dfrac{201}{97}$ 16. 4   17. 11   18. $\dfrac{202}{99}$

Note: In the following, the last digit of your answer may differ from the one given depending on the way you solved the problem.
19. $x > .6611$ 20. $x < .5093$ 21. $x < .8618$ 22. $x > .6460$

QUIZ

1. (a) $x = 1.89$ (b) $x = 2.483$ (c) $x = \dfrac{13}{19}$

PROBLEMS

1. (a) yes   (b) no   (c) yes   (d) no
2. (a) 3   (b) 6   (c) 4   (d) 5
3.

	$P(x) + Q(x)$	$P(x) - Q(x)$	$P(x) \cdot Q(x)$
(a)	$2x^3 - 3x^2 + 1$	$2x^2 - 5x^2 - 11$	$2x^5 - 4x^4 + 12x^3 - 29x^2 - 30$
(b)	$5x^4 + 3x^2 + 3x + 4$	$5x^4 - 3x^2 - 5x + 6$	$15x^6 + 20x^5 - 5x^4 - 3x^3 + 11x^2$ $+ 21x - 5$
(c)	$x^3 + x + 3$	$-x^3 + 10x^2 + 3x + 3$	$5x^5 - 23x^4 - 12x^3 - 17x^2 - 3x$

4. (a) n (b) $\leqslant n$ (c) $n + m$
5.

	Quotient	Remainder
(a)	$x^2 - 2$	$3x + 6$
(b)	$2x^2 + 9x + 39$	160
(c)	$4x - 5$	$-11x + 12$
(d)	$\frac{1}{2}x^2 + x + \frac{7}{4}$	$6x + \frac{1}{4}$

6. (a) $2x^3 + 9x^2 + 2x - 1$ (b) $5x^3 + x^2 + 2x$
   (c) $11x^3 + 3x^2 + 14x + 4$ (d) $9x^6 + 6x^5 + 37x^4 + 24x^3 + 67x^2 + 42x + 7$
7. (a) -3 (b) 1   (c) 0   (d) -6
8. (a) $4 - 2i$ (b) 4   (c) 0   (d) 5

QUIZ

1. (a) and (d)   2. (a) 9   (b) 4   (c) 3
3. $4x^3 - 3x^2 - x + 8$; $4x^3 - 7x^2 + x + 6$
   $8x^5 - 14x^4 + 9x^3 + 9x^2 - 7x + 7$
4. $4x^2 + 8$; $-9x^2 + 16x - 30$
   $(x^3 - 2x + 3)(4x^2 + 8) + (-9x^2 + 16x - 30)$

PROBLEMS

1. (a) $x = 1, x = -2$ (b) $x = -1, x = 3$ (c) $x = -2, x = -6$

   (d) $x = 2, x = 4$ (e) $x = \frac{3}{2}, x = -2$ (f) $x = 1, x = -2$

2. (a) $x = -2 \pm \sqrt{5}$ (c) $x = -1 \pm \sqrt{3}i$

   (b) $x = 3 \pm \sqrt{14}$ (d) $x = \frac{1}{4} \pm \frac{\sqrt{15}}{4}i$

3. (a) $x = \frac{-3 \pm \sqrt{13}}{2}$ (b) $x = 2 \pm \sqrt{2}$ (c) $x = \frac{1 \pm \sqrt{31}i}{4}$

   (d) $x = 1$ (e) $x = -4$ (f) $x = \frac{-1 \pm \sqrt{5}i}{3}$

4. (a) $x = 2i, x = -i$ (b) $x = -2, x = i$ (c) $x = \frac{1}{i}, x = 3i$

   (d) $x = -\frac{i}{2}, x = -i$

5. (a) 2   (b) 1   (c) none   (d) 2

6. (a) $3; 5$ (b) $-2; -\dfrac{9}{2}$ (c) $-\dfrac{5}{3}; 4$ (d) $11; -17$

7. (a) $x = -\dfrac{1}{2}; x = 2$ (b) $x = -\dfrac{1}{3}, x = 1$ (c) $x = \dfrac{1}{3}, x = \dfrac{1}{4}$

(d) $x = i, x = -\dfrac{i}{2}$ (e) $x = 3 - i, x = 3 + i$ (f) $x = \dfrac{1}{2} - i, x = 2 + i$

9. (a) 9 and 10   (b) 29 and 30   **10.** (a) 18 and 20   (b) 14 and 16

8. (a)

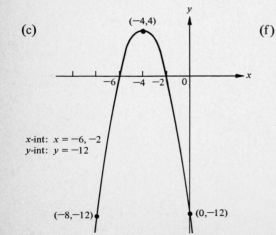

x-int: $x = -2, 1$
y-int: $y = -2$

$\left(-\dfrac{1}{2}, -\dfrac{9}{4}\right)$

(d)

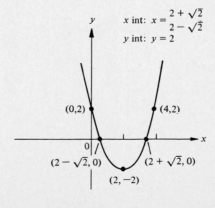

y-int: none
y-int: $y = 4$

$(2,10)$
$(-1,7)$
$(0,4)$
$\left(\dfrac{1}{4}, 3\dfrac{7}{8}\right)$

(b)

x-int: $x = 1$
y-int: $y = 1$

$(1,0)$ $(2,1)$
$(0, 1)$

(e)

$(-4,0)$

x-int: $x = -4$
y-int: $y = -16$

$(-8, -16)$ $(0, -16)$

(c)

$(-4,4)$

x-int: $x = -6, -2$
y-int: $y = -12$

$(-8,-12)$ $(0,-12)$

(f)

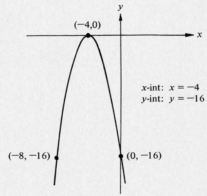

x int: $x = \dfrac{2 + \sqrt{2}}{2 - \sqrt{2}}$
y int: $y = 2$

$(0,2)$ $(4,2)$
$(2 - \sqrt{2}, 0)$ $(2 + \sqrt{2}, 0)$
$(2, -2)$

Page 170

QUIZ

1. (b) and (d)   **2.** 4   **3.** −3; 2; 6

4. (a) 2, −3   (b) $\dfrac{3+\sqrt{17}}{4}$, $\dfrac{3-\sqrt{17}}{4}$

5. (i) real and equal   (ii) real and distinct   (iii) complex conjugates
6. downward

3.

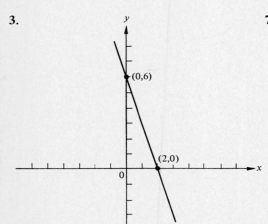

7.

Page 178

PROBLEMS

1. $\{\sqrt{2}i, -\sqrt{2}i, 2i, -2i\}$ **2.** $\{i, -i, \sqrt{3}, -\sqrt{3}\}$ **3.** $\{\dfrac{1}{\sqrt{3}}, -\dfrac{1}{\sqrt{3}}, \dfrac{1}{2}, -\dfrac{1}{2}\}$

4. $\{1, -1, \dfrac{1}{\sqrt{2}}, -\dfrac{1}{\sqrt{2}}\}$

5. $\{\dfrac{\pi}{2}\}$ **6.** $\{\dfrac{\pi}{3}, \dfrac{5\pi}{3}, \pi\}$ **7.** $\{27, -343\}$ **8.** $\{\dfrac{9}{4}, 4\}$

9. $\{-32, 1\}$ **10.** $\{\sqrt{128}, \sqrt{2187}\}$ **11.** $\{-2, \dfrac{1}{2}\}$ **12.** $\{\dfrac{1}{\sqrt{27}}i, 1\}$

13. $\{-2, 5\}$ **14.** $\{-1, 1\}$ **15.** $\{2\}$ **16.** $\{7\}$

QUIZ

1. 1, 32   **2.** 1, −1

PROBLEMS

1. (a) $(x+1)(5x^3 - 7x^2 + 3x - 6) + 10$ (b) $(x-1)(5x^3 + 3x^2 - x - 4) + 0$
   (c) $(x+2)(5x^3 - 12x^2 + 20x - 43) + 90$ (d) $(x-2)(5x^3 + 8x^2 + 12x + 21) + 46$
2. (a) $(x+1)(3x^3 + 2x^2 - 2x - 28) - 16$ (b) $(x-1)(3x^3 + 8x^2 + 8x - 22) - 66$
   (c) $(x+2)(3x^3 - x^2 + 2x - 34) + 24$ (d) $(x-2)(3x^3 + 11x^2 + 22x + 14) - 16$
3. (a) $(x + \frac{1}{2})(9x^3 - \frac{9}{2}x^2 - \frac{31}{4}x + \frac{31}{8}) - \frac{15}{16}$ (b) $(x + \frac{1}{3})(9x^3 - 3x^2 - 9x + 3) + 0$

   (c) $(x - \frac{1}{3})(9x^3 + 3x^2 - 9x - 3) + 0$ (d) $(x - \frac{1}{2})(9x^3 + \frac{9}{2}x^2 - \frac{31}{4}x - \frac{31}{8}) - \frac{15}{16}$
4. (a) $(x+2)(x^3 - 6x^2 + 11x - 6) + 0$ (b) $(x+1)(x^3 - 5x^2 + 4x + 12) - 24$

   (c) $(x - \frac{1}{2})(x^3 - \frac{7}{2}x^2 - \frac{11}{4}x + \frac{117}{8}) - \frac{75}{16}$ (d) $(x-3)(x^3 - x^2 - 4x + 4) + 0$
5. (a) $P(-3) = 12$ (b) $P(-1) = 2$ (c) $P(1) = 0$ (d) $P(2) = 17$
6. (a) $P(-2) = 7$ (b) $P(-1) = -13$ (c) $P(1) = -5$ (d) $P(2) = 23$
7. (a) $P(-\frac{1}{2}) = 12\frac{1}{4}$ (b) $P(-\frac{1}{3}) = 12\frac{23}{243}$ (c) $P(\frac{1}{3}) = 11\frac{220}{243}$ (d) $P(\frac{1}{2}) = 11\frac{3}{4}$

10. $5, 0$ 11. $5, -2$
12. (a) no   (b) yes   (c) yes   (d) yes   (e) no   (f) yes
18. (a) $P(x) = (x-1)(x-2)(x+4)$ (b) $P(x) = (x+1)(x+2)(x-2)$

   (c) $P(x) = (x+1)(x - \frac{1}{2})(x-3)$ (d) $P(x) = (x+3)(x+1)(x-1)(x-2)$

   (e) $P(x) = (x-1)(x-i)(x+2i)$ (f) $P(x) = [x-(1-i)][x-(1+i)](x+1)(x-4)$
19. (a) $P(x) = (x-1)^2(x-2)$ (b) $P(x) = (x+2)^3(x-1)(x-3)$

   (c) $P(x) = (x-2)^4(x+1)^2(x-3)$ (d) $P(x) = (x - \frac{1}{3})^2(x + \frac{1}{2})^2(x+1)$

20. (a) 3 (double), -2 (triple)   (b) $-\frac{1}{2}$ (multiplicity 4), 2

   (c) $-\frac{1}{3}$ (triple), 1 (double)   (d) $\frac{3}{2}$ (double), $1, -2$

   (e) 1 (double), $-\frac{1}{2}, 2$ (f) $-\frac{1}{2}, 2, 4$

   (g) $-1, 2, 4$ (b) 2 (double), $\frac{1}{2}$
21. (a) 3 (b) -3 (c) $-3, -2, -1$, and 3
22. (a) 4 (b) -3 (c) $-3, -1, 2$, and 4

16. (a)

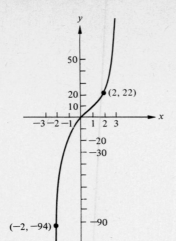

(b)

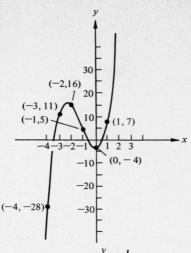

(c)

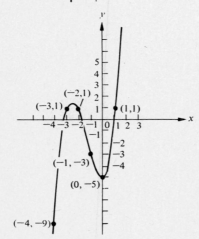

(d)

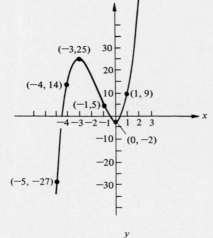

(e)

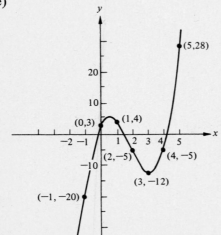

(f)

(g)

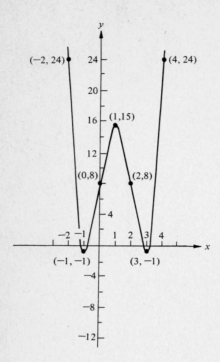

(h)

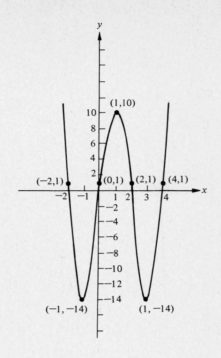

(i)

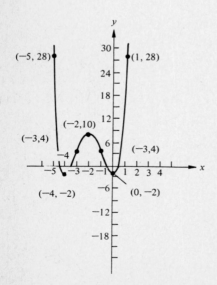

(j)

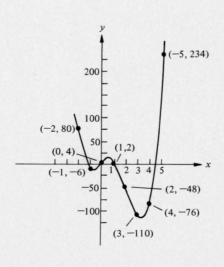

Page 215

QUIZ

1. -2 **2.** $(x-4)(x+6)(x-2i)$
3. $-i, 4, -2$ **4.** (a) $x^3 + 5x^2 - 2x - 4$ -9 (b) 11 (c) 2

Page 233

PROBLEMS

1. (a) $P(x) = (x-1)(x^2+1)(x^2-4x+5)$ (b) $P(x) = (x-3)(x+5)(x^2-6x+11)$
(c) $P(x) = (x^2-6x+10)(x^2+16)$ (d) $P(x) = (x-2)(x^2-4x+6)(x^2-2\sqrt{2}x+3)$
2. (a) $P(x) = (x^2+1)(x-1)(x+2)$ (b) $P(x) = (x^2+3)(x+1)(x-3)$
(c) $P(x) = (x^2-4x+6)(x+2)$ (d) $P(x) = (x^2-6x+10)(x+5)$
(e) $P(x) = (x^2-8x+17)(x^2+4x-1)$
3. (a) $\{i, -i, 1, -2\}$ (b) $\{\sqrt{3}i, -\sqrt{3}i, -1, 3\}$ (c) $\{2-\sqrt{2}i, 2+\sqrt{2}i, -2\}$
(d) $\{3+i, 3-i, -3\}$ (e) $\{4-i, 4+i, -2+\sqrt{5}, -2-\sqrt{5}\}$

4.

	Positive Zeros	Negative Zeros	Pairs of Complex Conjugates
(a)	3	1	none
or	1	1	1
(b)	1	1	1
(c)	1	2	1
or	1	none	2
(d)	3	2	none
	1	2	1
	3	none	1
or	1	none	2
(e)	3	none	none
or	1	none	1
(f)	3	1	1
or	1	1	2

QUIZ

1. $2-i, -1$ **2.** $(x+1)(x^2-4x+5)$
3. (i) 1 positive real zero, 3 negative real zeros, and no pairs of complex conjugates or
(ii) 1 positive real zero, 1 negative real zero, and one pair of complex conjugates

Page 250

PROBLEMS

1. (a) $\{1, -1, 3, -3\}$ (b) $\{1, -1, 2 -2, 4, -4, \frac{1}{2}, -\frac{1}{2}\}$ (c) $\{1, -1, 5, -5, \frac{1}{3},$
$-\frac{1}{3}, \frac{5}{3}, -\frac{5}{3}\}$

(d) $\{1, -1, 2, -2, 3, -3, 6, -6, \frac{1}{2}, -\frac{1}{2}, \frac{3}{2}, -\frac{3}{2}, \frac{1}{4}, -\frac{1}{4}, \frac{3}{4}, -\frac{3}{4}\}$

(e) $\{1, -1, 3, -3, \frac{1}{2}, -\frac{1}{2}, \frac{3}{2}, -\frac{3}{2}, \frac{1}{3}, -\frac{1}{3}, \frac{1}{6}, -\frac{1}{6}\}$

(f) $\{1, -1, 3, -3, \frac{1}{2}, -\frac{1}{2}, \frac{3}{2}, -\frac{3}{2}$

2. (a) 2 pos, 1 neg   (b) 1 pos, 1 neg   (c) 1 pos, 1 neg   (d) 3 pos, 0 neg
   (f) 0 pos, 3 neg

3. (i) (a) $1, -1$ (b) $2, -1$ (c) $1, -\frac{5}{3}$ (d) $\frac{3}{a}, 0$ (e) $\frac{1}{3}, 0$ (f) $0, -2$

   (ii) (a) ϕ (b) ϕ (c) $\{1\}$ (d) ϕ (e) ϕ (f) $\{-1\}$

4. (a) $\{-3, -1, 2\}$ (b) $\{1, 2, -3\}$ (c) $\{-2, 1, 3\}$ (d) $\{2\}$; 2 is a triple zero

   (e) $\{-1, -\frac{1}{2}, \frac{5}{3}\}$ (f) $\{-3, \frac{1}{2}, 5\}$ (g) $\{-2, -\frac{2}{3}, \frac{3}{2}\}$

   (h) $\{-2, -\frac{1}{2}, \frac{3}{5}\}$ (i) $\{-1, \frac{1}{2}, 2, 4\}$ (j) $\{-3, -1, 1, 2\}$

5. (a) $\{2, 1 + \sqrt{2}, 1 - \sqrt{2}\}$ (b) $\{2, i, -i\}$ (c) $\{1, 2 + \sqrt{3}, 2 - \sqrt{3}\}$
   (d) $\{3, 2 + i, 2 - i\}$

   (e) $\{-1, 3 + 2i, 3 - 2i\}$ (f) $\{\frac{1}{2}, i, -i\}$ (g) $\{\frac{2}{3}, \sqrt{3}i, -\sqrt{3}i\}$

   (h) $\{-\frac{1}{2}, \frac{1+i}{2}, \frac{1-i}{2}\}$

   (i) $\{3, \frac{1 + \sqrt{3}}{3}, \frac{1 - \sqrt{3}}{3}\}$ (j) $\{1, -1, 2 + i, 2 - i\}$ (k) $\{2, -2\}$; 2 and -2
      are double zeros

   (l) $\{-\frac{1}{2}, 1, 1 + \sqrt{3}, 1 - \sqrt{3}\}$ (m) $\{\frac{4}{3}, \frac{3}{2}, \frac{-1 + \sqrt{7}i}{2}, \frac{-1 - \sqrt{7}i}{2}\}$

   (n) $\{-2, 1, 2, 2 + i, 2 - i\}$

QUIZ

1. (a) $\{1, -1, 2, -2, 4, -4\}$ (b) no rational zeros

2. $\{\frac{1}{3}, -\frac{1}{3}, \frac{2}{3}, -\frac{2}{3}, 1, -1, 2, -2, 3, -3, 6, -6\}$

Page 265

PROBLEMS

1. (a) 0 is the only zero   (b) $(-4, -3), (-1, 0), (0, 1)$ (c) $(-4, -3), (-2, -1), (0, 1)$
   (d) $(-5, -4), (-1, 0), (0, 1)$ (e) $(-1, 0), (1, 2), (4, 5)$ (f) $(-4, -3), (-3, -2)$,
      $(-1, 0), (0, 1)$
   (g) $(-2, -1), (-1, 0), (2, 3), (3, 4)$ (h) $(-2, -1), (-1, 0), (2, 3), (3, 4)$
   (i) $(-5, -4), (-4, -3), (-1, 0), (0, 1)$ (j) $(-2, -1), (-1, 0), (1, 2), (4, 5)$

QUIZ

1.

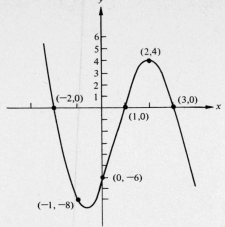

2. $(-2, -1), (1, 2), (3, 4)$

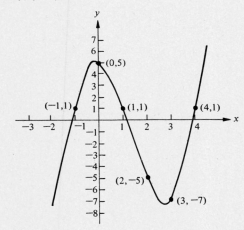

Page 279

PROBLEMS

	Intercepts	Symmetry	Horizontal Asymptotes	Vertical Asymptotes
1.	none, none	none	x-axis	y-axis
2.	none, $y = \dfrac{5}{2}$	none	x-axis	$x = 2$
3.	none, none	origin	x-axis	y-axis
4.	none, $y = 4$	none	x-axis	$x = -1$
5.	none, $y = -\dfrac{3}{5}$	none	x-axis	$x = \dfrac{5}{2}$
6.	$x = 0, y = 0$	none	$y = 2$	$x = 1$
7.	$x = 2$, none	none	$y = 1$	y-axis
8.	$x = -1$, none	none	$y = \dfrac{1}{3}$	y-axis

	Intercepts	Symmetry	Horizontal Asymptotes	Vertical Asymptotes
9.	$x = 3, y = -\dfrac{3}{4}$	none	$y = 1$	$x = -4$
10.	$x = -2, y = -\dfrac{1}{3}$	none	$y = \dfrac{1}{3}$	$x = 2$
11.	none, $y = -5$	y-axis	x-axis	$x = \pm 1$
12.	none, $y = 2$	y-axis	x-axis	none
13.	$x = 0, y = 0$	origin	x-axis	$x = \pm 2$
14.	$x = 0, y = 0$	origin	x-axis	none
15.	$x = 0, y = 0$	none	x-axis	$x = -2, x = 1$
16.	$x = 0, y = 0$	none	x-axis	$x = -3, x = 2$
17.	$x = \pm 1, y = \dfrac{1}{6}$	none	$y = 1$	$x = -2, x = 3$
18.	$x = \pm 2, y = -1$	none	$y = 1$	$x = -1, x = 4$
19.	$x = \pm 1, y = -1$	y-axis	$y = 1$	none
20.	none, $y = -1$	y-axis	$y = 1$	$x = \pm 1$
21.	$x = 0, y = 0$	none	none	$x = 2$
22.	$x = 0, y = 0$	none	none	$x = -2$

1.

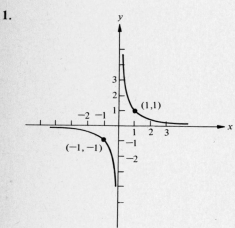

2.

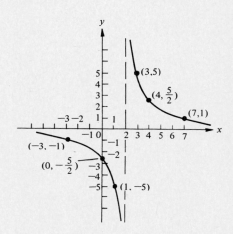

3.

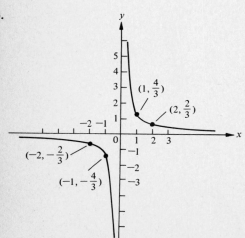

4.

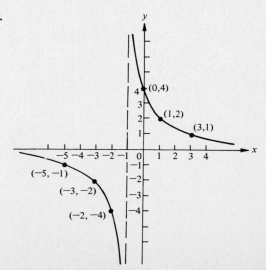

5.

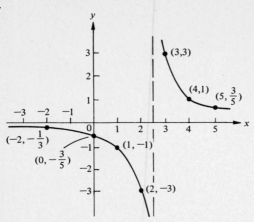

6.

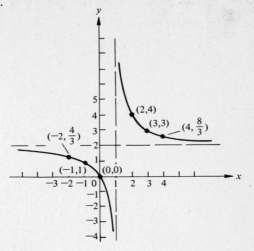

7.

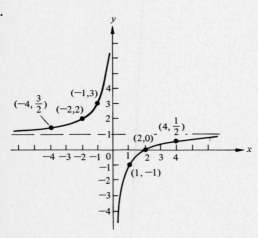

8.

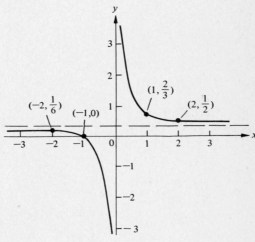

9.

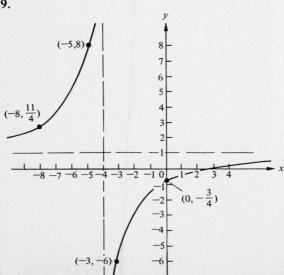

10.

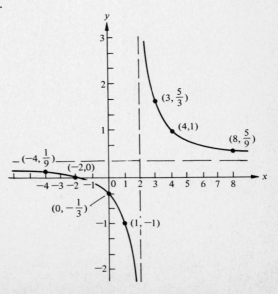

11.

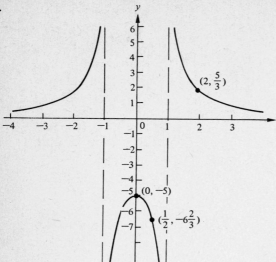

12.

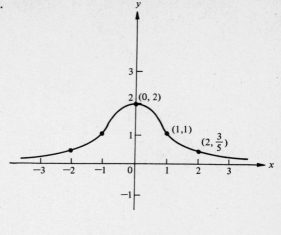

13.

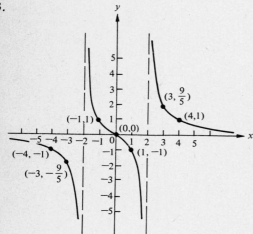

14.

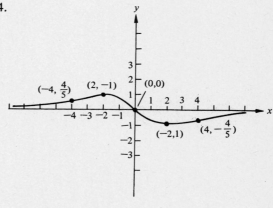

15.

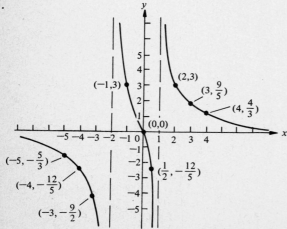

16.

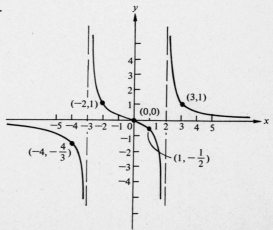

17.

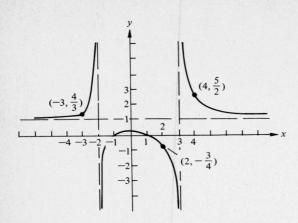

18.

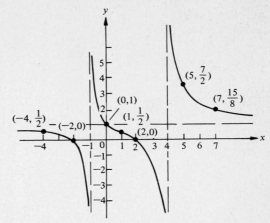

19.

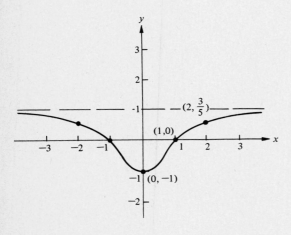

20.

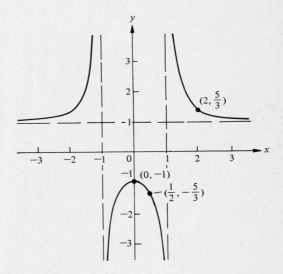

21.

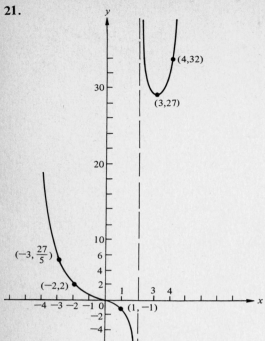

22.

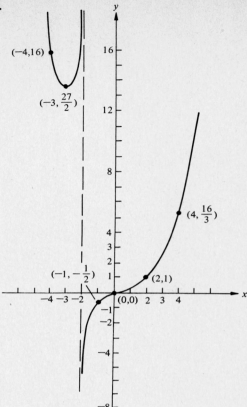

QUIZ

1. $P(x), D(x) = 0$
2.   1

        $\frac{1}{2}$

         $y = 0$

    $x = -1, x = 2$

    no symmetry

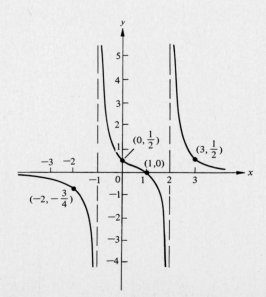

TABLE OF COMMON LOGARITHMS

TABLE OF COMMON LOGARITHMS

N	0	1	2	3	4	5	6	7	8	9
1.0	0000	0043	0086	0128	0170	0212	0253	0294	0334	0374
1.1	0414	0453	0492	0531	0569	0607	0645	0682	0719	0755
1.2	0792	0828	0864	0899	0934	0969	1004	1038	1072	1106
1.3	1139	1173	1206	1239	1271	1303	1335	1367	1399	1430
1.4	1461	1492	1523	1553	1584	1614	1644	1673	1703	1732
1.5	1761	1790	1818	1847	1875	1903	1931	1959	1987	2014
1.6	2041	2068	2095	2122	2148	2175	2201	2227	2253	2279
1.7	2304	2330	2355	2380	2405	2430	2455	2480	2504	2529
1.8	2553	2577	2601	2625	2648	2672	2695	2718	2742	2765
1.9	2788	2810	2833	2856	2878	2900	2923	2945	2967	2989
2.0	3010	3032	3054	3075	3096	3118	3139	3160	3181	3201
2.1	3222	3243	3263	3284	3304	3324	3345	3365	3385	3404
2.2	3424	3444	3464	3483	3502	3522	3541	3560	3579	3598
2.3	3617	3636	3655	3674	3692	3711	3729	3747	3766	3784
2.4	3802	3820	3838	3856	3874	3892	3909	3927	3945	3962
2.5	3979	3997	4014	4031	4048	4065	4082	4099	4116	4133
2.6	4150	4166	4183	4200	4216	4232	4249	4265	4281	4298
2.7	4314	4330	4346	4362	4378	4393	4409	4425	4440	4456
2.8	4472	4487	4502	4518	4533	4548	4564	4579	4594	4609
2.9	4624	4639	4654	4669	4683	4698	4713	4728	4742	4757
3.0	4771	4786	4800	4814	4829	4843	4857	4871	4886	4900
3.1	4914	4928	4942	4955	4969	4983	4997	5011	5024	5038
3.2	5051	5065	5079	5092	5105	5119	5132	5145	5159	5172
3.3	5185	5198	5211	5224	5237	5250	5263	5276	5289	5302
3.4	5315	5328	5340	5353	5366	5378	5391	5403	5416	5428
3.5	5441	5453	5465	5478	5490	5502	5514	5527	5539	5551
3.6	5563	5575	5587	5599	5611	5623	5635	5647	5658	5670
3.7	5682	5694	5705	5717	5729	5740	5752	5763	5775	5786
3.8	5798	5809	5821	5832	5843	5855	5866	5877	5888	5899
3.9	5911	5922	5933	5944	5955	5966	5977	5988	5999	6010
4.0	6021	6031	6042	6053	6064	6075	6085	6096	6107	6117
4.1	6128	6138	6149	6160	6170	6180	6191	6201	6212	6222
4.2	6232	6243	6253	6263	6274	6284	6294	6304	6314	6325
4.3	6335	6345	6355	6365	6375	6385	6395	6405	6415	6425
4.4	6435	6444	6454	6464	6474	6484	6493	6503	6513	6522
4.5	6532	6542	6551	6561	6571	6580	6590	6599	6609	6618
4.6	6628	6637	6646	6656	6665	6675	6684	6693	6702	6712
4.7	6721	6730	6739	6749	6758	6767	6776	6785	6794	6803
4.8	6812	6821	6830	6839	6848	6857	6866	6875	6884	6893
4.9	6902	6911	6920	6928	6937	6946	6955	6964	6972	6981
5.0	6990	6998	7007	7016	7024	7033	7042	7050	7059	7067
5.1	7076	7084	7093	7101	7110	7118	7126	7135	7143	7152
5.2	7160	7168	7177	7185	7193	7202	7210	7218	7226	7235
5.3	7243	7251	7259	7267	7275	7284	7292	7300	7308	7316
5.4	7324	7332	7340	7348	7356	7364	7372	7380	7388	7396

TABLE OF COMMON LOGARITHMS

N	0	1	2	3	4	5	6	7	8	9
5.5	7404	7412	7419	7427	7435	7443	7451	7459	7466	7474
5.6	7482	7490	7497	7505	7513	7520	7528	7536	7543	7551
5.7	7559	7566	7574	7582	7589	7597	7604	7612	7619	7627
5.8	7634	7642	7649	7657	7664	7672	7679	7686	7694	7701
5.9	7709	7716	7723	7731	7738	7745	7752	7760	7767	7774
6.0	7782	7789	7796	7803	7810	7818	7825	7832	7839	7846
6.1	7853	7860	7868	7875	7882	7889	7896	7903	7910	7917
6.2	7924	7931	7938	7945	7952	7959	7966	7973	7980	7987
6.3	7993	8000	8007	8014	8021	8028	8035	8041	8048	8055
6.4	8062	8069	8075	8082	8089	8096	8102	8109	8116	8122
6.5	8129	8136	8142	8149	8156	8162	8169	8176	8182	8189
6.6	8195	8202	8209	8215	8222	8228	8235	8241	8248	8254
6.7	8261	8267	8274	8280	8287	8293	8299	8306	8312	8319
6.8	8325	8331	8338	8344	8351	8357	8363	8370	8376	8382
6.9	8388	8395	8401	8407	8414	8420	8426	8432	8439	8445
7.0	8451	8457	8463	8470	8476	8482	8488	8494	8500	8506
7.1	8513	8519	8525	8531	8537	8543	8549	8555	8561	8567
7.2	8573	8579	8585	8591	8597	8603	8609	8615	8621	8627
7.3	8633	8639	8645	8651	8657	8663	8669	8675	8681	8686
7.4	8692	8698	8704	8710	8716	8722	8727	8733	8739	8745
7.5	8751	8756	8762	8768	8774	8779	8785	8791	8797	8802
7.6	8808	8814	8820	8825	8831	8837	8842	8848	8854	8859
7.7	8865	8871	8876	8882	8887	8893	8899	8904	8910	8915
7.8	8921	8927	8932	8938	8943	8949	8954	8960	8965	8971
7.9	8976	8982	8987	8993	8998	9004	9009	9015	9020	9025
8.0	9031	9036	9042	9047	9053	9058	9063	9069	9074	9079
8.1	9085	9090	9096	9101	9106	9112	9117	9122	9128	9133
8.2	9138	9143	9149	9154	9159	9165	9170	9175	9180	9186
8.3	9191	9196	9201	9206	9212	9217	9222	9227	9232	9238
8.4	9243	9248	9253	9258	9263	9269	9274	9279	9284	9289
8.5	9294	9299	9304	9309	9315	9320	9325	9330	9335	9340
8.6	9345	9350	9355	9360	9365	9370	9375	9380	9385	9390
8.7	9395	9400	9405	9410	9415	9420	9425	9430	9435	9440
8.8	9445	9450	9455	9460	9465	9469	9474	9479	9484	9489
8.9	9494	9499	9504	9509	9513	9518	9523	9528	9533	9538
9.0	9542	9547	9552	9557	9562	9566	9571	9576	9581	9586
9.1	9590	9595	9600	9605	9609	9614	9619	9624	9628	9633
9.2	9638	9643	9647	9652	9657	9661	9666	9671	9675	9680
9.3	9685	9689	9694	9699	9703	9708	9713	9717	9722	9727
9.4	9731	9736	9741	9745	9750	9754	9759	9763	9768	9773
9.5	9777	9782	9786	9791	9795	9800	9805	9809	9814	9818
9.6	9823	9827	9832	9836	9841	9845	9850	9854	9859	9863
9.7	9868	9872	9877	9881	9886	9890	9894	9899	9903	9908
9.8	9912	9917	9921	9926	9930	9934	9939	9943	9948	9952
9.9	9956	9961	9965	9969	9974	9978	9983	9987	9991	9996

Index